Prentice Hall Brief Review

Chemistry:
The Physical Setting

Patrick Kavanah

SAVVAS
LEARNING COMPANY

About the Author

Patrick Kavanah graduated from the University of Notre Dame with a Bachelor of Science degree in 1957, and pursued graduate work at Georgetown University and Columbia Teachers' College, earning a Master's Degree in Science Education at the University of Northern Iowa in 1964. He taught at Mahopac High School in Mahopac, NY, at Lago High School in Aruba, Netherlands Antilles, and for 31 years at Monroe-Woodbury High School in Central Valley, NY, where he was a Chemistry teacher and Chairman of the Science Department.

Dedication

The creative, technical and editorial staff at Savvas Learning Company wish to dedicate this text and its future revisions to the memory of Patrick Kavanah. Mr. Kavanah was an outstanding educator and mentor, and his vision and guidance have greatly influenced the direction of Chemistry Core content in New York State. It will remain the goal of the *Chemistry Science Brief Review* team to modify this text as necessary to reflect the most up-to-date NYS Curriculum while maintaining the clarity and style of Mr. Kavanah's original manuscript.

ISBN-13: 978-1-4188-3590-3
ISBN-10: 1-4188-3590-0

1 22

Brief Review in
Chemistry: The Physical Setting

New York Standards

Standard | Key Idea

4.2.1

Major Understanding

4.3.1a	4.3.1k	4.PS3.1i
4.3.1b	4.3.1l	4.PS3.1ii
4.3.1c	4.3.1m	4.PS3.1iii
4.3.1d	4.3.1n	4.PS3.1iv
4.3.1e	4.3.1q	4.PS3.1v
4.3.1f	4.3.1r	4.PS3.1vi
4.3.1g	4.3.1s	4.PS3.1x
4.3.1h	4.3.1t	4.PS3.1xi
4.3.1i	4.3.1u	4.PS3.1xii
4.3.1j	4.3.1cc	4.PS3.1xxii

4.3	4.3.2b	4.PS3.2ii
4.3.1w	4.3.3a	4.PS3.2iii
4.3.1x	4.3.3d	4.PS3.2v
4.3.1cc	4.4.1b	4.PS3.3i
4.3.1dd	4.5	4.PS3.3ii
4.3.1ee	4.5.2g	4.PS3.3iii
4.3.2a	4PS3.2i	

4.3.1ee	4.3.3d	4.PS3.3vii
4.3.3c	4.PS3.3iv	4.PS3.3viii
4.3.3e	4.PS3.3v	4.PS3.3ix
4.3.3f	4.PS3.3vi	4.PS3.4vii

4.3.1s	4.4.2a	4.PS4.2ii
4.3.1w	4.4.2b	4.PS4.2iii
4.3.1dd	4.4.2c	4.PS4.2iv
4.3.1jj	4.PS3.1xviii	
4.3.1kk	4.PS3.1xxii	
4.3.1nn	4.PS3.1xxiv	
4.3.4a	4.PS3.4i	
4.3.4b	4.PS3.4ii	
4.3.4c	4.PS3.4iii	
4.4	4.PS4.2i	

4.3.1g	4.3.1z	4.PS3.1xiii
4.3.1v	4.3.1aa	4.PS3.1xiv
4.3.1w	4.3.1bb	4.PS3.1xv
4.3.1x	4.5.2f	4.PS3.1xvi
4.3.1y	4.PS3.1x	4.PS3.1xviii

New York Standards

4.5.2a	4.5.2i	4.PS3.1viii
4.5.2b	4.5.2j	4.PS3.2xix
4.5.2c	4.5.2k	4.PS5.2i
4.5.2d	4.5.2l	4.PS5.2ii
4.5.2e	4.5.2m	4.PS5.2iv
4.5.2h	4.5.2n	4.PS5.2v

4.3.1nn	4.PS3.1xxvi
4.3.1oo	4.PS3.1xxiv
4.3.1pp	4.PS3.1xxviii
4.3.1qq	4.PS3.1xxx
4.PS3.1xxiv	
4.PS3.1xxv	

4.3.1ll	4.3.4g	4.PS3.1xxiii
4.3.1mm	4.3.4h	4.PS3.4v
4.3.4a	4.3.4i	4.PS3.4vi
4.3.4b	4.3.4j	4.PS3.4vii
4.3.4c	4.4.1c	4.PS4.1i
4.3.4d	4.4.1d	4.PS4.1ii
4.3.4f	4.PS3.1iv	

4.3.1ll	4.3.4g	4.PS3.1xxiii
4.3.1mm	4.3.4h	4.PS3.4v
4.3.4a	4.3.4i	4.PS3.4vi
4.3.4b	4.3.4j	4.PS3.4vii
4.3.4c	4.4.1c	4.PS4.1i
4.3.4d	4.4.1d	4.PS4.1ii
4.3.4f	4.PS3.1iv	

4.3.1rr	4.3.1zz
4.3.1ss	4.PS3.1xxxi
4.3.1tt	4.PS3.1xxxii
4.3.1uu	4.PS3.1xxxiii
4.3.1vv	4.PS3.1xxxiv
4.3.1ww	4.PS3.1xxxv
4.3.1xx	

About This Book

This book is designed to enhance review of the concepts, skills, and application of the Physical Science/Chemistry Core Curriculum that may be tested on the Regents Examination for The Physical Setting: Chemistry. Students can use the book in any order as each topic is independent except for the introduction of vocabulary words.

Features

Content Review

The presentation features aids for accessing the basic content that will be tested on the Regents Examination. Some material that will not be tested has been added to a few topics to enhance understanding, but that material is not assessed in the Practice Questions.

Illustrations Graphics visualize the concepts and vocabulary of chemistry as well as the types of drawings students will be required to interpret on the exam.

Vocabulary Many exam questions require an understanding of the language of chemistry.

Bold Words Vocabulary listed at the beginning of a topic and defined within that topic.

Underlined Words Terms that appear as bold in other topics or describe basic chemistry concepts.

Sample Problems Step-by-step detailed solutions guide the problem-solving process, reinforce content knowledge, and provide examples of problems found on the exam.

Sidebars

Memory Jogger Recalls relevant information covered elsewhere in this book or previous science courses.

Digging Deeper Provides specific examples of some concepts or expands core content.

Review Questions Questions similar to those on the exam, totaling more than 900, clarify and reinforce understanding.

Practice Questions for the Exam

More than 500 Practice Questions are written and organized to mimic the Regents exam.

Part A Multiple-choice questions test knowledge.

Part B-1 Multiple-choice questions that test skills and understandings.

Parts B-2 and C Questions often require an extended constructed response with a more detailed answer supported by applications or examples.

Reference and Support

Strategies for Answering Test Questions give support to help you interpret and answer the range of exam questions.

Appendix 1, The *Reference Tables for Physical Setting/Chemistry*, is integral to this content review and are annotated with an Ⓡ. Review and Practice Questions refer you to them.
Appendix 2, *Graphing and Math Skills*, provides a review of basic math and graphic skills, which are an integral part of some exam questions.
Appendix 3, *Using the Reference Tables*, provides an explanation of each table along with questions for practice. **Appendix 4,** *Topical Summary of Regents Chemistry*, is a list of commonly-tested concepts for review with page numbers for easy reference.

The **Glossary** defines all bold vocabulary words and underlined words. The **Index** cross-references concepts in the topics.

Regents Examinations

The most recent released Regents Examinations are reproduced at the end of this book to provide practice in taking actual Regents Examinations.

Answer Key with Diagnostic Tests

A separate Answer Key includes all answers to the Review and Practice Questions along with topic-by-topic Diagnostic Tests to help determine which concepts require more intense review.

Strategies for
Answering Test Questions

This section provides strategies to help you answer various types of questions on the Regents Examination for The Physical Setting/Chemistry. Strategies are provided for answering multiple-choice and constructed-response questions as well as for questions based on diagrams, data tables, and graphs and questions that use the *Reference Tables for Physical Setting/Chemistry*, which are reproduced in the Appendix.

Strategies for Multiple-Choice Questions

Multiple-choice questions will likely account for more than 50% of the Regents Examination for The Physical Setting/Chemistry. Part A is comprised totally of multiple-choice questions, whereas Part B contains some, but not all, multiple-choice questions. Therefore, it is important to be good at deciphering multiple-choice questions. Here are a few helpful strategies. For any one question, not all strategies will need to be used. The numbers are provided for reference, not to specify an order (except for Strategies 1 and 2).

1. Always read the entire question, but wait to read the choices. (See Strategy 4.)

2. Carefully examine any data tables, diagrams, photographs, or relevant part(s) of the *Reference Tables for Physical Setting/Chemistry* associated with the question.

3. Underline key words and phrases in the question that signal what you should be looking for in the answer. This will make you read the question more carefully. This strategy applies mostly to questions with a long introduction.

4. Try to think of an answer to the question before looking at the choices given. If you think you know the answer, write it on a separate piece of paper before reading the choices. Next, read all of the choices and compare them to your answer before making a decision. Do not select the first answer that seems correct. If your answer matches one of the choices, and you are quite sure of your response, you are probably correct.

Even if your answer matches one of the choices, carefully consider all of the answers because the obvious choice is not always the correct one. If there are no exact matches, re-read the question and look for the choice that is most similar to your answer.

5. Eliminate any choices that you know are incorrect. Lightly cross out the numbers for those choices on the exam paper. Each choice you can eliminate increases your chances of selecting the correct answer.

6. If the question makes no sense after reading through it several times, leave it for later. After completing the rest of the exam, return to the question. Something you read on the other parts of the exam may give you some ideas about how to answer this question. If you are still unsure, go with your best guess. There is no penalty for guessing, but answers left blank will be counted as wrong. If you employ your best test-taking strategies, you just may select the correct answer.

Strategies for Constructed-Response Questions

Some questions in Part B and all questions in Part C of the Regents Examination for Physical Setting/Chemistry require a constructed response. Some of these questions may require you to write one or two sentences. No matter which type of answer is requested, the following strategies will help you write constructed responses.

1. Always read through the entire question.

2. Underline key words and phrases in the question that signal what you should be looking for in the answer. This will make you read the question more carefully.

3. Look over the *Reference Tables for Physical Setting/Chemistry* for any helpful information related to the question.

4. Write a brief outline, or at least a few notes to yourself, about what should be included in the answer.

5. Pay attention to key words that indicate how to answer the question and what you

need to say in your answer. Several of these words are very common. For example, you might be asked to discuss, describe, explain, define, compare, contrast, or design. The table below lists key words and directions for your answers.

6. When you write your answer, don't be so general that you are not really saying anything. Be very specific. You should use the correct terms and clearly explain the processes and relationships. Be sure to provide details, such as the names of processes, names of structures, and, if it is appropriate, how they are related. If only one example or term is required, do not give two or more. If one is correct and the other is wrong, your answer will be marked wrong.

7. If a question has two or three parts, answer each part in a separate sentence or paragraph. This will make it easy for the person scoring your paper to find all of the information. When writing your answer, don't shortchange one part of the question by spending too much time on another part.

8. If sentences are called for in the answer, be sure that you write sentences. A sentence should always have a subject and a verb,

and it should not start with the word *because*. Note that you will not lose points for incorrect grammar, spelling, punctuation, or poor penmanship. However, such errors and poor penmanship could impair your ability to make your answer clear to the person scoring your paper. If that person cannot understand what you are trying to say, you will not receive the maximum number of points.

9. When the question calls for you to write the answer in paragraphs, do not write a "standard" essay such as you would write for social studies. Do not spend time writing an introduction, several short paragraphs, and a conclusion. Write your outline, and then answer the question directly.

Strategies for Questions Based on Diagrams

Both multiple-choice and extended-response question frequently include diagrams or pictures. Usually the diagrams provide information needed to answer the question. The diagrams may be realistic, or they may be schematic. Schematic drawings show the relationships among parts and sometimes the sequence in a system. Follow these strategies:

Using Key Words to Direct Your Answers	
Key Word	**What Direction Your Answer Should Take**
Analyze	• Break the idea, concept, or situation into parts, and explain how they relate. • Carefully explain relationships, such as cause and effect.
Discuss	• Make observations about the topic or situation using facts. • Thoroughly write about various aspects of the topic or situation.
Describe	• Illustrate the subject using words. • Provide a thorough account of the topic. • Give complete answers.
Explain	• Clarify the topic of the question by spelling it out completely. • Make the topic understandable. • Provide reasons for the outcome.
Define	• State the exact meaning of the topic or word. • Explain what something is or what it means.
Compare	• Relate two or more topics with an emphasis on how they are alike. • State the similarities between two or more examples.
Contrast	• Relate two or more topics with an emphasis on how they are different. • State the differences between two or more examples.
Design	• Plan an experiment or component of an experiment. Map out your proposal being sure to provide information about all of the required parts.
State	• Express or tell in words. • Explain or describe using at least one fact, term, or relationship.

1. First study the diagram and think about what the diagram shows you. Be sure to read any information, such as titles or labels, that go with the diagram.
2. Read the question. Follow the strategies for either multiple-choice or constructed-response questions listed previously.

Strategies for Questions Based on Data Tables

Most data tables contain information that summarizes a topic. A table uses rows and columns to condense information and to present it in an organized way. Rows are the horizontal divisions going from left to right across the table, while columns are vertical divisions going from top to bottom. Column headings name the type of information included in a table. Sometimes different categories of information are listed down the left-hand column of the table. When answering a question with a data table, use the following strategies.

1. Find the title of the table. It is usually located across the top.
2. Determine the number of columns in the table and their purpose.
3. Determine the number of rows and their purpose.
4. Read across the rows and down the columns to determine what the relationships are.
5. Now you are ready to read the question with the data table. Answer the question by using the suggested strategies for multiple-choice or constructed-response questions listed previously.

Strategies for Questions Based on Graphs

Graphs represent relationships in a visual form that is easy to read. Three different types of graphs commonly used on science Regents Examinations are line graphs, bar graphs, and circle graphs. Line graphs are the most common, and they show the relationship between two changing quantities, or variables. When a question is based on any of the three types of graphs, the information you need to correctly answer the question can usually be found on the graph.

When answering a question that includes a graph, first ask yourself these questions:

- What information does the graph provide?
- What are the variables?
- What seems to happen to one variable as the other changes?

After a careful analysis of the graph, use the appropriate strategies for multiple-choice or constructed-response questions.

Strategies for Questions Based on Readings

Some questions in Part C of the Regents Examination will require the reading of a chemistry-related passage. The answers to the questions will be based upon the article's content and your knowledge of chemistry. The key to doing well on these questions is a thorough reading and comprehension of the article and a strong overall knowledge of chemistry. To help prepare for this portion of the Regents Examination, read the following sample reading passages and answer the related questions.

Base your answers to questions 1 through 3 on the information below, the *Reference Tables for Physical Setting/Chemistry,* and your knowledge of chemistry.

Radioactivity and radioactive isotopes have the potential for both benefiting and harming living organisms. One use of radioactive isotopes is in radiation therapy as a treatment for cancer. cesium-137 is sometimes used in radiation therapy.

A sample of cesium-137 was left in an abandoned clinic in Brazil in 1987. Cesium-137 gives off a blue glow because of its radioactivity. The people who discovered the sample were attracted by the blue glow and had no idea of any danger. Hundreds of people were treated for overexposure to radiation, and four people died.

1. Using Reference Table N, complete the equation below for the radioactive decay of Cs-137. Include both atomic number and mass number for each particle. [1]

$$^{137}_{55}Cs \rightarrow {}^{0}_{-1}e + {}^{137}_{56}Ba$$

2. If 12.5 grams of the original sample of cesium-137 remained after 90.69 years, what was the mass of the original sample? [1]

3. Suppose a 40-gram sample of iodine-131 and a 40-gram sample of cesium-137 were both abandoned in the clinic in 1987. Explain why the sample of iodine-131 would not pose as great a radiation risk to people today as the sample of cesium-137 would. [1]

Base your answers to questions 4 through 6 on the information below.

A glass tube is filled with hydrogen gas at low pressure. An electric current is passed through the gas causing it to emit light. This light is passed through a prism to separate the light into the bright, colored lines of hydrogen's visible spectrum. Each colored line corresponds to a particular wavelength of light. One of hydrogen's spectral lines is a red light with a wavelength of 656 nanometers.

Tubes filled with other gases produce different bright-line spectra that are characteristic of each kind of gas. These spectra have been observed and recorded.

4. Explain, in terms of electron energy states and energy changes, how hydrogen's bright-line spectrum is produced. [1]

5. Explain how the elements present on the surface of a star can be identified using bright-line spectra. [1]

6. A student measured the wavelength of hydrogen's visible red spectral line to be 647 nanometers. Show a correct numerical setup for calculating the student's percent error. [1]

Base your answers to questions 7 through 10 on the information below.

Propane is a fuel that is sold in rigid, pressurized cylinders. Most of the propane in a cylinder is liquid, with gas in the space about the liquid level. When propane is released from the cylinder, the propane leaves the cylinder as a gas. Propane gas is used as a fuel by mixing it with oxygen in the air and igniting the mixture, which is represented by the balanced equation below.

$$C_3H_8(g) + 5O_2(g) \rightarrow 3CO_2(g) + 4H_2O(\ell) + 2219.2 \text{ kJ}$$

A small amount of methanethiol, which has a distinct odor, is added to the propane to help consumers detect a propane leak. In methanethiol, the odor is caused by the thiol functional group (-SH). Methanethiol, CH_3SH, has a structure very similar to the structure of methanol.

7. Draw a particle diagram to represent propane in a pressurized cylinder. Your response must include at least six molecules of propane in the liquid phase and six molecules of propane in the gaseous phase. [1]

8. Draw a potential energy diagram for this reaction. [1]

9. Determine the total amount of energy released when 2.50 moles of propane is completely reacted with oxygen. [1]

10. Draw a structural formula for a molecule of methanethiol. [1]

Use of Reference Tables for Physical Setting/Chemistry to Help Answer Questions

In recent Regents Examinations between 20% and 35% of the questions have involved the use of the *Reference Tables for Physical Setting/ Chemistry*. You should become thoroughly familiar with all details of these tables. Sometimes the questions will specifically refer you to the reference tables, but most often you will be expected to know what information is included within the reference tables.

The text helps you become more familiar with the content of the reference tables by referring to the tables within the text presentation. These references are indicated by an Ⓡ on the page.

The Atom

How Scientists View Atomic Composition

? *Look at your desk. What do you think it is made of?* ?

You might say wood, metal, or plastic. If you were living in Greece 2500 years ago, you would have said "earth." At that time, the Greek philosopher Empedocles claimed that all matter was composed of fire, air, water, and earth.

Empedocles also described two other components—love and discord. It was love that held the other components together in matter and discord that kept them apart. In that way, an object, substance, or organism could be described as a ratio of fire, air, water, earth, love, and discord.

These components were considered eternal and could not be explained. Yet about 2000 years later, scientists did begin to explain them and the nature of matter itself.

The Atom

Vocabulary

atom	excited state	neutron
atomic mass	ground state	nucleus
atomic mass unit	heterogeneous	orbital
atomic number	homogeneous	proton
compound	isotope	pure substance
electron	mass number	valence
element	mixture	wave-mechanical model

Topic Overview

Chemistry is the study of <u>matter,</u> which is anything that has mass and volume. The desk that you are sitting at, the air around you, and your body are all made up of matter. <u>Chemistry</u> deals with the composition of matter and the changes that matter may undergo.

Scientists have long sought the answers to solve the question, "What are we, the earth, and the stars made of?" Our present answer is that there are only about 100 different building blocks that explain the composition of the entire visible universe. Our present model has been the result of the thinking and experiments of scientists over a few thousand years. Today's model adequately explains how so many different objects can be made from such a few fundamental building blocks. These fundamental particles, called atoms, are themselves made of even smaller parts.

Early Studies of Atoms

The Greeks' view of the nature of matter as being composed of fire, air, water, and earth lasted until the 1600s when Robert Boyle identified gold and silver as themselves being elemental; that is, they are not themselves made of fire, air, earth, or water. As Boyle's ideas were slowly accepted, additional elements were discovered, and the Greek concept of what makes up matter faded.

Dalton's Atomic Theory

The work of Boyle led John Dalton to propose his revolutionary theory in the 1700s. He theorized that the basic unit of matter is a tiny particle called an **atom.**

Dalton's theory of the atom can be summarized by the following points.

- All elements are composed of indivisible atoms.
- All atoms of a given element are identical.

- Atoms of different elements are different; that is, they have different masses.
- Compounds are formed by the combination of atoms of different elements.

Although we now know that some of Dalton's theory was not correct, it laid the important groundwork for the current concept of the atom.

Structure of the Atom

Experimental studies of the atom soon showed that it was not indivisible but was made up of even smaller parts.

Electrons J. J. Thomson used a cathode ray tube to show one of these smaller units that make up an atom. Because the ray produced in the tube was deflected a certain way by an electrical or magnetic field, he concluded that the ray was formed by particles and that the particles were negatively charged. The only source available for the particles was the atoms present. Thus, Thomson theorized that an atom contains small, negatively charged particles, which he named **electrons.**

A concept of the atom developed in which these negatively charged particles were visualized as being embedded in atoms, just as we might find raisins in bread. This model was called the "plum pudding" model. In this model, the mass of the rest of the atom was evenly distributed and positively charged, taking up all of the space not occupied by the electrons.

The Nucleus If electrons are present in atoms, what makes up the rest of the atom? One scientist who studied this question was Ernest Rutherford. A group of scientists that included Rutherford conducted the following experiment, with surprising results. Look at Figure 1-1A. They directed <u>alpha particles,</u> which are positively charged particles that are much smaller than an atom, at a thin piece of gold foil. If the plum pudding model of the atom were correct, all of the alpha particles would pass through the foil with just a few being slightly deflected.

As the scientists expected, most of the particles passed straight through the foil, and a few were slightly deflected. But to their amazement, some of the alpha particles were greatly deflected, and some even bounced back, as shown in Figure 1-1B. From this experiment, Rutherford concluded that atoms have a dense central core, called a **nucleus,** while the remainder of the atom is essentially empty space. Because alpha particles are positively charged and

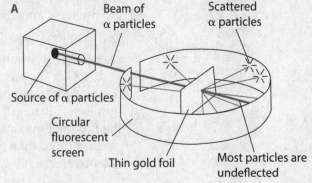

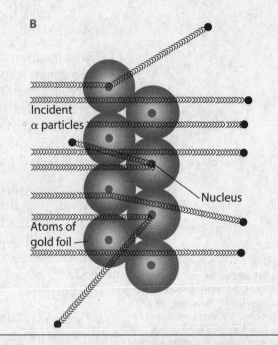

Figure 1-1. The Rutherford gold-foil experiment:
(A) Scattering of alpha particles (B) The deflections of the alpha particles showed that atoms have a dense, positively charged center. Experimental results showed that only about one alpha particle out of each 10,000 was dramatically deflected.

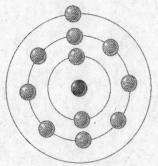

Figure 1-2. The Bohr model of the atom: Protons and neutrons are in the dense central nucleus with electrons orbiting in valence shells.

were repelled by the nucleus, the nucleus must also be positively charged because like charges repel each other.

Protons and Neutrons Since atoms are electrically neutral, scientists reasoned that there must be positive charges to offset the negatively charged electrons, and these charges must be located in the nucleus. These positively charged particles are called **protons.** In addition to protons it was later discovered that there are additional particles in the nucleus that do not have either a positive or negative charge. These neutral particles are called **neutrons.**

Modern Atomic Theory

Scientists used the information derived from this and other experiments to further describe atomic structure.

The Bohr Model of the Atom In the early 20th century the common model of the atom was the Bohr or "planetary" model. The model showed a center, the nucleus, and rings of orbiting electrons.

Normally, composition of the nucleus shows the number of positively charged protons and the number of neutral neutrons present as shown in Figure 1-2. The electrons are shown in concentric circles or shells around the nucleus, designated by the letters K, L, M, N, O, P, and Q or the numbers 1 through 7. The K shell can hold a maximum of 2 electrons, the L shell a maximum of 8. The outermost shell of an atom may not contain more than 8 electrons. These outermost electrons are called **valence** electrons.

When a valence shell is filled, the element is a noble gas. When a shell is filled, the next element begins to fill the next higher energy valence shell.

The same information can be shown in a linear form. The symbol of the element is followed by showing the number of electrons in each succeeding shell. Thus Na-2-8-1 represents the sodium atom. The "Na" represents the nucleus and the 2-8-1 shows the electron arrangement in the K, L, and M shells. The electron structure of each element is shown on the Periodic Table of the Elements in the *Reference Tables for Physical Setting/Chemistry.* (R)

The Wave-Mechanical Model Advances in the study of energy aided in modifying the atomic model. Energy had been viewed as being waves, and matter as particles. By the 1900s, energy and matter were both viewed as acting as both waves and particles. The wave aspect of nature was expanded, and it was also proposed that energy was made up of tiny packets called quanta. These energy packets acted like particles.

When it was later determined that the electron not only has properties of mass but also has wavelike properties, this concept of a dual nature was incorporated into the current model of the atom, the **wave-mechanical model.** This modern model of the atom pictures the atom as having a dense, positively charged nucleus as proposed in the planetary model. The major difference between the wave-mechanical model and the Bohr model is found in the manner in which the electrons are pictured. Instead

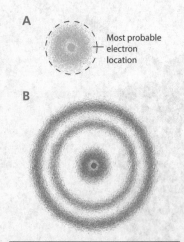

A

Most probable electron location

B

Figure 1-3. Electron cloud model of the atom: The modern model of the atom shows a dense nucleus. (A) In this diagram of hydrogen, each dot represents a possible location for the electron. The ring shows the most probable location of an electron. (B) In this model of a cross-section of a multielectron atom, the dots represent probable locations of electrons. Each of the darker circles represents an orbital.

of moving in definite, fixed orbits around the nucleus as suggested in the Bohr model, the wave-mechanical model portrays electrons with distinct amounts of energy moving in areas called orbitals. An **orbital** is described as a region in which an electron of a particular amount of energy is most likely to be located. Models of orbitals are shown in Figure 1-3.

Thus, the modern model of the atom is not the invention of a single scientist, but rather one that has evolved over a long period of time. Figure 1-4 summarizes some of the atomic models involved in the evolution of the current atomic model.

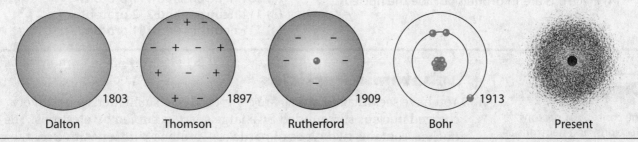

Figure 1-4. Changing views of atomic structure over time: The representations show the cannonball, plum pudding, nuclear, planetary, and wave-mechanical atomic models.

Review Questions

Set 1.1

1. The concept that matter is composed of tiny, discrete particles is generally attributed to the

   (1) Greeks
   (2) Romans
   (3) English
   (4) Germans

2. The first subatomic particle discovered was the

   (1) proton   (3) electron
   (2) neutron   (4) photon

3. Which statement describes the distribution of charge in an atom?

   (1) A positively charged nucleus is surrounded by one or more negatively charged electrons.
   (2) A positively charged nucleus is surrounded by one or more positively charged electrons.
   (3) A neutral nucleus is surrounded by one or more negatively charged electrons.
   (4) A neutral nucleus is surrounded by one or more positively charged electrons.

4. In the wave-mechanical model of the atom, an orbital is the most probable location of

   (1) a proton.   (3) a neutron.
   (2) a positron.   (4) an electron.

5. The model of the atom that pictured the atom with electrons stuck randomly throughout the mass of the atom was called the

   (1) cannonball model
   (2) plum pudding model
   (3) planetary model
   (4) wave-mechanical model

6. After bombarding a gold foil sheet with alpha particles, scientists concluded that atoms mainly consist of

   (1) electrons   (3) protons
   (2) empty space   (4) neutrons

7. Experimental evidence indicates that the nucleus of an atom

   (1) contains most of the mass of the atom
   (2) contains a small percentage of the mass of the atom
   (3) has no charge
   (4) has a negative charge

8. Which particle has no charge?

   (1) electron   (3) neutron
   (2) positron   (4) proton

9. Modern theory pictures an electron as
   (1) a particle only
   (2) a wave only
   (3) both a particle and a wave
   (4) neither a particle nor a wave

10. Which statement describes a concept included in the wave-mechanical model of the atom?
   (1) Positrons are in shells outside the nucleus.
   (2) Neutrons are in shells outside the nucleus.
   (3) Protons are in orbitals outside the nucleus.
   (4) Electrons are in orbitals outside the nucleus.

11. An atom of nickel has a mass of 64 amu. This atom has
   (1) 28 protons in its nucleus.
   (2) 64 protons in its nucleus.
   (3) 28 protons orbiting its nucleus.
   (4) 64 protons orbiting its nucleus.

12. Element number 111 is called roentgenium. Which best describes the nucleus of an atom of this element having a mass of 272 amu?
   (1) 272 protons and 111 neutrons
   (2) 161 neutrons and 111 protons
   (3) 111 neutrons and 272 protons
   (4) 111 neutrons and 161 protons

Digging Deeper

The concept of protons, electrons, and neutrons as fundamental particles can be used to explain most of the chemical behavior of an atom. However, recent research has shown that protons and neutrons are themselves made of smaller particles called quarks. Each quark has a fractional charge of either $\frac{2}{3}+$ or $\frac{1}{3}-$. Each proton and neutron is composed of three quarks. Because it has a total 1+ charge, a proton must be composed of two quarks each with a charge of $\frac{2}{3}+$ and one quark with a charge of $\frac{1}{3}-$. A neutron has no charge, so it must be composed of one quark with a charge of $\frac{2}{3}+$ and two quarks each with a charge of $\frac{1}{3}-$.

Subatomic Particles

You have seen that all atoms are composed of a small, dense, positively charged nucleus surrounded by a large space occupied by electrons. The nucleus contains two types of particles—protons with a positive charge, and neutrons with no charge.

Protons have a mass of only 1.67×10^{-24} g. Because the mass of a proton is so small, it is more convenient to use a different scale whose units are called **atomic mass units** to represent its mass. A proton is assigned 1.0 atomic mass unit (amu). A neutron has approximately the same mass as a proton.

Each atom of a specific element must contain the same number of protons as every other atom of that element. The number of protons in the nucleus of an atom is the **atomic number** of that element. For example, chlorine has an atomic number of 17. Each chlorine atom contains 17 protons in its nucleus.

Electrons occupy the space of an atom outside the nucleus and have a charge equal to, but opposite of, a proton. Electrons are much less massive than either the proton or neutron, having a mass of only 1/1836 amu. Table 1-1 summarizes information about each of the particles that make up an atom.

It has been mentioned that the mass of an atom is extremely small. The atomic mass scale replaces grams as the unit used to describe the masses of atoms. The nucleus of a carbon atom containing 6 protons and 6 neutrons is taken as the standard mass, and the mass of any atom is a ratio between its mass and that of the carbon nucleus. The sum of the numbers of protons and neutrons in the nucleus is called the **mass number** of the nucleus. Thus, a nucleus with 7 protons and 7 neutrons has a mass number of 14. When determining the mass of an atom, the mass of the electrons is so small it is not considered in the calculation.

Table 1-1. Some Subatomic Particles				
Particle	Charge	Mass	Location	Symbol
Proton	1+	1 amu	nucleus	$_1^1H$ or p
Neutron	0	1 amu	nucleus	$_0^1n$
Electron	1−	1/1836 amu	outside	$_{-1}^{0}e$

Table 1-2. Isotopes of Hydrogen

Particle	Protons	Neutrons	Mass Number	Symbol
Protium	1	0	1 amu	$_1^1H$
Deuterium	1	1	2 amu	$_1^2H$
Tritium	1	2	3 amu	$_1^3H$

Isotopes Although all the atoms of a given element must contain the same number of protons, the number of neutrons may vary. Most atoms of hydrogen contain only a proton. Remembering that the mass number of an atom is the sum of its protons and neutrons, this atom of hydrogen has a mass of 1 amu. In addition to this atom with a mass of 1 amu, there are some atoms of hydrogen that have a nucleus with both a proton and a neutron. While this is still an atom of hydrogen, it has a mass number of 2. There is still another type of hydrogen with a nucleus containing two neutrons in addition to a proton; this atom has a mass number of 3. These different forms of an atom are called isotopes. **Isotopes** are atoms of the same element that have different numbers of neutrons, and hence have different mass numbers. Table 1-2 describes the isotopes of the element hydrogen.

Isotope Symbols Isotopes can be identified by using a symbol that indicates both the element and its mass number. Thus, C-12 represents a carbon atom with a mass number of 12. The mass number represents the sum of the protons and neutrons. The difference between the atomic number of an atom and its mass number is the number of neutrons. Because the atomic number (number of protons) of C-12 is 6, the number of neutrons will also be 6. Different ways to symbolize carbon-14 isotopes are shown in Figure 1-5.

C-14	^{14}C
Carbon-14	$_6^{14}C$

Figure 1-5. Some symbols of isotopes: Common isotopic notations of carbon atoms that contain six protons and eight neutrons

Atomic Masses

You have seen that the mass number of a given nucleus must be an integer because it is the sum of the numbers of protons and neutrons in the nucleus. However, when you examine the periodic table of the elements, you will notice that most of the elements have masses that are fractional values. These masses are called the **atomic masses** of the elements, and they are the average mass of all the isotopes in a sample of the element.

SAMPLE PROBLEM

Find the number of neutrons in an atom of $_{34}^{79}Se$.

SOLUTION: Identify the known and unknown values.

Known
atomic number = 34
mass number = 79

Unknown
number of neutrons = ?

1. Write the relationship for number of neutrons, atomic number, and atomic mass.

Neutrons = Mass number − Atomic number

2. Substitute the known values and solve for the number of neutrons.

Neutrons = 79 − 34 = 45

Atomic mass can be calculated from the mass and the abundance of naturally occurring isotopes. Carbon has two naturally occurring stable isotopes. Most carbon atoms—98.89%—are C-12, while the remaining 1.108% are C-13. What is the atomic mass of carbon?

SOLUTION: Identify the known and unknown values.

Known
98.89% C-12
1.108% C-13

Unknown
atomic mass = ? amu

1. Convert the percentages to decimal numbers, and multiply the mass of each isotope by its decimal abundance.

$$12 \text{ amu} \times 0.9889 = 11.87 \text{ amu}$$
$$13 \text{ amu} \times 0.01108 = 0.1440 \text{ amu}$$

2. Add these masses of isotopes.

$$11.87 \text{ amu} + 0.1440 \text{ amu} = 12.01 \text{ amu}$$

How can chlorine have an atomic mass of 35.454 amu? The answer is found in the relative numbers of the isotopes of chlorine. There are two major isotopes of chlorine, Cl-35 and Cl-37. The atomic mass of chlorine is the average of the two isotopes. But the average of Cl-35 and Cl-37 would seem to give chlorine an average mass of 36 amu. That would be true if Cl-35 and Cl-37 were equally abundant in nature, but such is not the case.

If you had four test grades, 90%, 90%, 90% and 80%, you would not have an average test grade of 85%. Your average would be 87.5%. In the same way, if there are many more atoms of Cl-35 than Cl-37, the average mass would be closer to 35 amu. Consult either the periodic table or a table of properties of the elements for average atomic masses.

Location of Electrons

Remember that electrons are found in the space of the atom around the nucleus. Experiments have shown that the electrons are not found just anywhere around the nucleus; they are found in orbitals. An orbital is a region where an electron can most probably be found.

Energy Levels The orbitals in an atom form a series of energy levels in which electrons may be found. Each electron in an atom has its own distinct amount of energy that corresponds to the energy level that it occupies. Electrons can gain and lose energy and move to different energy levels, but they do so in a unique way. Instead of being able to absorb any amount of energy, an electron can only absorb a discrete, or fixed amount of energy that would allow it to move to a higher energy level. While this concept is difficult for us to understand, an analogy may help. When we climb up or down a set of stairs, we must exert enough energy to move from one step to another. We can't stop at a half a step. In a like manner, if an electron moves from one energy level to a different energy level, it must give off or absorb the energy difference between those two levels.

Ground and Excited States When the electrons occupy the lowest available orbitals, the atom is said to be in the **ground state.** The electrons in a ground state atom have filled the available spaces from the lowest energy level to higher levels until all the electrons are accounted for. The linear symbol Na-2-8-1 shows the electron arrangement for a ground state sodium atom.

When electrons are subjected to stimuli such as heat, light, or electricity, an electron may absorb energy and temporarily move to a higher energy level. This unstable condition is called an **excited state.** Na-2-7-2 is one of the many possible arrangements for an excited atom of sodium. An excited-state electron quickly returns to a lower available level, emitting the same amount of energy it absorbed to go to the higher energy level.

The energy emitted may be in the form of infrared, ultraviolet, or visible light. The light given off from a fluorescent or a neon light is caused by excited electrons returning to lower energy levels. While the light appears as one color to our eyes, it is actually composed of many different wavelengths, each of which is seen as a different line when viewed through an instrument called a spectroscope.

Unlike a continuous spectrum produced by holding a prism in sunlight, the visible light produced by electrons is confined to narrow lines of color called bright line spectra. Each atom has its own distinct pattern of emission lines (or bright line spectrum), and these spectra are used to identify elements.

SAMPLE PROBLEM

What element is represented by the following line spectrum?

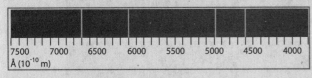

Bright-line spectrum of an element

SOLUTION: Identify the known and unknown values.

Known
Spectra of several elements

Unknown
Identity of the element = ?

1. Compare the lines on the spectrum of the element shown above to those in Figure 1-6.

2. Notice that the first line shown for the unknown element is at 4600. Two elements on the reference table have spectral lines at that frequency, Li and Sr. The second line of the unknown is at 4960. Both elements have lines approximately at this reading, but Sr has two lines between 4600 and 4960 that are not in the unknown. The unknown is Li. Check for accuracy by noting that Li has a line at 6090, while Sr does not.

Spectra

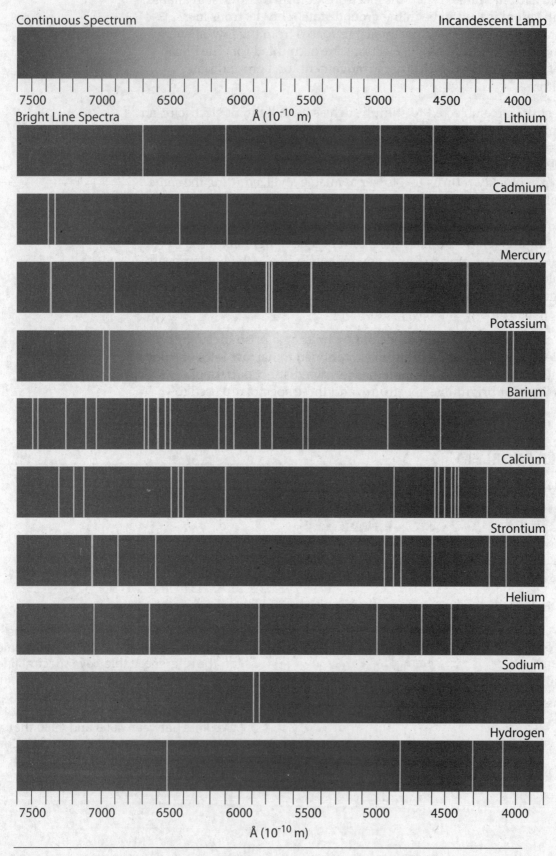

Figure 1-6. Emission spectra: The bright lines are emission lines and are unique to each type of atom.

13. The atomic mass of an element is defined as the weighted average mass of that element's

    (1) most abundant isotope
    (2) least abundant isotope
    (3) naturally occurring isotopes
    (4) radioactive isotopes

14. Element X has two isotopes. If 72.0% of the element has an isotopic mass of 84.9 amu and 28.0% has an isotopic mass of 87.0 amu, the average atomic mass of element X is numerically equal to

    (1) $(72.0 + 98.9)(28.0 + 87.0)$
    (2) $(72.0 - 84.9)(28.0 - 87.0)$
    (3) $(0.720)(84.9) + (0.280)(87.0)$
    (4) $(72.0)(84.9) + (28.0)(87.0)$

15. A neutral atom with 6 electrons and 8 neutrons is an isotope of

    (1) carbon   (3) nitrogen
    (2) silicon   (4) oxygen

16. The average isotopic mass of chlorine is 35.5 amu. Which mixture of isotopes (shown as percents) produces this mass?

    (1) 50% C-12 and 50% C-13
    (2) 50% Cl-35 and 50% Cl-37
    (3) 75% Cl-35 and 25% Cl-37
    (4) 75% C-12 and 25% C-13

17. The major portion of an atom's mass consists of

    (1) electrons and protons
    (2) electrons and neutrons
    (3) neutrons and positrons
    (4) neutrons and protons

18. Which atoms have the same number of neutrons?

    (1) H-1 and He-3   (3) H-3 and He-3
    (2) H-2 and He-4   (4) H-3 and He-4

19. Atoms of ^{16}O, ^{17}O and ^{18}O have the same number of

    (1) neutrons but a different number of protons
    (2) protons but a different number of neutrons
    (3) protons but a different number of electrons
    (4) electrons but a different number of protons

20. A neutron has approximately the same mass as

    (1) an alpha particle   (3) an electron
    (2) a beta particle   (4) a proton

21. The total number of protons and neutrons in the nuclide $^{35}_{17}Cl$ is

    (1) 52   (2) 35   (3) 18   (4) 17

22. The nuclides $^{14}_{6}C$ and $^{14}_{7}N$ are similar in that they both have the same

    (1) mass number
    (2) atomic number
    (3) number of neutrons
    (4) nuclear charge

23. What is the nuclear charge of an atom with a mass of 23 and an atomic number of 11?

    (1) 11+   (2) 12+   (3) 23+   (4) 34+

24. Compared to the charge and mass of a proton, an electron has

    (1) the same charge and a smaller mass
    (2) the same charge and the same mass
    (3) an opposite charge and a smaller mass
    (4) an opposite charge and the same mass

25. Which of the following statements is correct?

    (1) A proton is positively charged; a neutron is negatively charged.
    (2) A proton is negatively charged; a neutron is positively charged.
    (3) A proton is positively charged; an electron is negatively charged.
    (4) A proton is negatively charged; an electron is positively charged.

26. Which symbols represent atoms that are isotopes of each other?

    (1) ^{14}C and ^{14}N (3) ^{131}I and ^{131}I
    (2) ^{16}O and ^{18}O (4) ^{222}Rn and ^{222}Ra

27. When electrons in an excited state fall to lower energy levels, energy is

    (1) absorbed
    (2) released
    (3) neither absorbed nor released
    (4) both released and absorbed

28. The characteristic bright-line spectrum of an atom is produced when

    (1) nuclei undergo fission
    (2) nuclei undergo fusion
    (3) electrons move from higher to lower energy levels
    (4) electrons move from lower to higher energy levels

Electron Arrangement

Although the electrons in an atom contribute little to the mass of an atom, their arrangement determines its chemical properties. The chemical properties of an element are based on the number of electrons in the outer energy level of its atoms. These outer electrons are called <u>valence electrons.</u> How can you determine how the electrons are arranged in an atom and, therefore, how many valence electrons an atom has?

Quantum Numbers

Remember that the first energy level in an atom can contain two electrons and the second can contain eight. We can't see the electron arrangement in an atom. How were these numbers determined? A theory, called the <u>quantum theory</u>, was developed to explain the chemical behavior of atoms.

Electrons can be described by a set of four numbers called <u>quantum numbers</u>. The first number describes the major energy level of the electron and is called the principal quantum number. The principal quantum number is the same as the number of the energy level that contains the electron. If an electron has a principal quantum number of 2, it is in the second energy level from the nucleus.

Each energy level has one or more sublevels associated with it. Each energy level contains as many sublevels as the number of the level. For example, energy level three has three sublevels.

The first sublevel of any energy level is designated the s sublevel. If a second sublevel is present, it is p. The third is d, and the fourth is f. Sublevels are described by using the number of the principal energy level together with the letter designation of each sublevel. For example, $3s$ describes the first sublevel of the third energy level.

The third quantum number relates to the orbitals in the sublevels and their orientations. Remember that an orbital is a location inside the atom where an electron is most likely to be found.

Electrons that are in s sublevels are found in orbitals with spherical shapes without sharp edges surrounding the nucleus. There is only one way a sphere can be arranged, so there is only one orbital in an s sublevel.

The p orbital is somewhat dumbbell in shape. There are three of these orbitals at each principal energy level higher than energy level one. The p orbitals are arranged at right angles to each other and can be designated as p_x, p_y, and p_z. Thus, each p sublevel contains three orbitals. Figure 1-7 shows the shapes of s and p orbitals.

At levels three and higher, there is another type of sublevel, the d sublevel containing five orbitals. From principal level four and higher, f sublevels with seven orbitals are found. The shapes of the orbitals in both the d and f sublevels are complex, so only s and p orbitals are shown.

The fourth quantum number relates to the spin of an electron. This number indicates that each orbital can contain two electrons spinning in opposite directions.

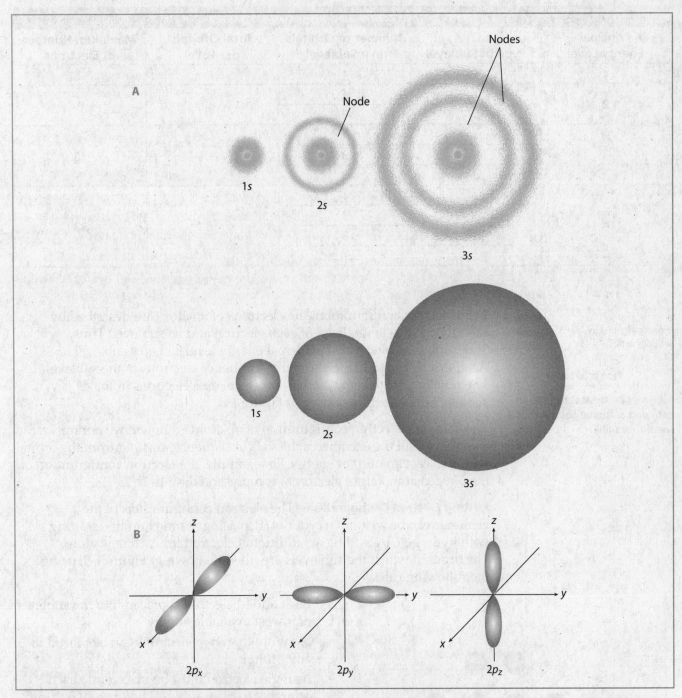

Figure 1-7. Shape and relative sizes of orbitals: (A) Look at the shape and relative sizes of 1s, 2s, and 3s orbitals. The upper diagrams are cross sections of the diagrams beneath. The dark areas show where electrons are most probably located. Notice that there are areas, called nodes, where it is unlikely to find an electron. (B) Shapes and orientations of *p* orbitals

Table 1-3 summarizes how the maximum number of electrons per energy level is determined using these four quantum numbers.

Electron Configurations

Quantum numbers describe the distribution of the electrons in an atom when you remember that electrons will occupy the lowest sublevel possible. This distribution of the electrons in an atom is called its <u>electron configuration</u>.

Table 1-3. Orbitals and Electron Capacity

Principal Energy Level	Type of Sublevel	Number of Orbitals in a Sublevel	Total Orbitals per Level	Maximum Number of Electrons
1	s	1	1	2
2	s	1	4	8
	p	3		
3	s	1	9	18
	p	3		
	d	5		
4	s	1	16	32
	p	3		
	d	5		
	f	7		

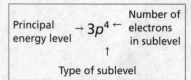

Principal energy level → $3p^4$ ← Number of electrons in sublevel

↑

Type of sublevel

Figure 1-8. Orbital notation: Each part of orbital notation has a specific meaning.

In an electron configuration, the electrons of an atom are described by identifying the energy level of each electron and its sublevel. Thus, $3s$ describes an electron at principal energy level 3 in an s sublevel. A superscript is added to show the number of electrons in the sublevel. The notation $4p^5$ tells the reader that there are 5 electrons in the $4p$ sublevel. Look at the example in Figure 1-8.

The complete electron configuration of an atom is shown by writing symbols for all the occupied sublevels in sequence, starting from the orbital with the least amount of energy. For example, the electron configuration of the oxygen atom (eight electrons) is represented by $1s^2 2s^2 2p^4$.

Writing Electron Configurations The electron configurations of the elements can be written in order of increasing atomic number, starting with hydrogen, by adding an additional electron for each new atom. The order in which the sublevels are filled is shown in Figure 1-9, using the following rules.

- Each added electron is placed into the sublevel of lowest available energy.
- No more than two electrons can be placed in any orbital.
- A single electron must be placed into each orbital of a given sublevel before any pairing takes place. (Hund's Rule)
- The outermost principal energy level can only contain electrons in s and p orbitals.

Order of Electron Fill While there are many locations that electrons might fill in an atom, the most stable condition exists when they fill the lowest available energy orbitals. This simply means that the first energy level, which is less energetic than any other, is filled first. In level two, the s orbital, then the p orbitals, are filled. Next, the s and p orbitals of the third level are

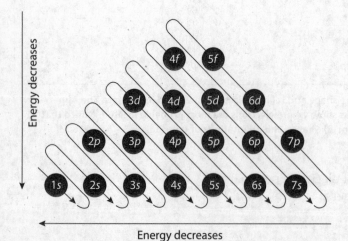

Figure 1-9. Electron configurations: To find the electron configuration of an atom, simply begin adding electrons to the 1s sublevel and continue adding them in the order shown.

filled, but the 3d level is not filled next. Instead, the 4s sublevel is filled, followed by the 3d. Why does this change in order occur? As the number of sublevels per energy level increases, the space taken up by the sublevels increases and the energy levels begin to overlap.

Orbital Notation While electron configuration notation is useful, it does not show how electrons are distributed in each sublevel. Figure 1-10 shows two ways of illustrating the distribution of electrons in an atom. A circle or square can be used to represent an orbital. An electron is represented either by a line or an arrow. When two lines are drawn in an orbital they represent an orbital pair with opposite spins. If arrows are used to represent the electrons, two arrows pointed in opposite directions represent a pair of electrons with opposite spin.

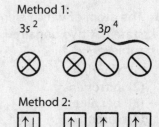

Figure 1-10. Two methods of showing orbital notation: The arrows in an orbital are drawn in opposite directions to indicate that the electrons have opposite spins.

SAMPLE PROBLEM

A phosphorus atom has an electron configuration of $1s^22s^22p^63s^13p^4$. Is the atom in its ground state, or is it in an excited state?

SOLUTION: Identify the known and unknown values.

Known
electron configuration of $1s^22s^22p^63s^13p^4$

Unknown
excited or ground state

1. Look at Figure 1-10 for order of filling of orbitals.

2. If the order is changed, or if a sublevel other than the last one is unfilled, the atom is probably in an excited state. The ground state configuration of a phosphorus atom would be $1s^22s^22p^63s^23p^3$. In the known configuration, one electron is in a higher sublevel than it would be in its ground state, so the atom is excited.

Review Questions

Set 1.3

29. Which is the electron configuration of an atom in the excited state?

   (1) $1s^22s^22p^2$
   (2) $1s^22s^22p^1$
   (3) $1s^22s^22p^53s^2$
   (4) $1s^22s^22p^63s^1$

30. Which atom in the ground state contains only one completely filled p orbital?

   (1) Ne   (3) He
   (2) O   (4) Be

31. What is the total number of electrons in the second principal energy level of a calcium atom in the ground state?

   (1) 6   (3) 8
   (2) 2   (4) 18

32. Which is the correct orbital notation of a lithium atom in the ground state?

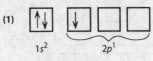

33. The atom of which element in the ground state has two unpaired electrons in the 2p sublevel?

    (1) fluorine
    (2) nitrogen
    (3) beryllium
    (4) carbon

34. What is the total number of occupied s orbitals in an atom of nickel in the ground state?

    (1) 1   (2) 2   (3) 3   (4) 4

35. Which atom in the ground state has only three electrons in the 3p sublevel?

    (1) phosphorus   (3) argon
    (2) potassium   (4) aluminum

36. What is the total number of occupied principal energy levels in a neutral atom of neon in the ground state?

    (1) 1   (2) 2   (3) 3   (4) 4

37. Which is the electron configuration of an atom in the excited state?

    (1) $1s^12s^1$
    (2) $1s^22s^1$
    (3) $1s^22s^22p^1$
    (4) $1s^22s^22p^2$

38. Which orbital notation correctly represents the outermost principal energy level of a nitrogen atom in the ground state?

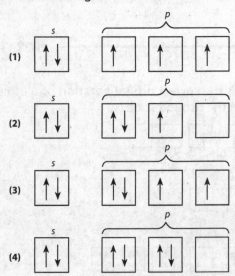

39. Which electron configuration represents a potassium atom in the excited state?

    (1) $1s^22s^22p^63s^23p^3$
    (2) $1s^22s^22p^63s^13p^4$
    (3) $1s^22s^22p^63s^23p^64s^1$
    (4) $1s^22s^22p^63s^23p^54s^2$

40. In an atom of lithium in the ground state, what is the total number of orbitals that contain only one electron?

    (1) 1   (2) 2   (3) 3   (4) 4

41. What is the total number of completely filled principal energy levels in an atom of argon in the ground state?

    (1) 1   (2) 2   (3) 3   (4) 4

42. What is the total number of electrons needed to completely fill all the orbitals in an atom's second principal energy level?

    (1) 16   (2) 2   (3) 8   (4) 4

43. An atom in the excited state can have an electron configuration of

    (1) $1s^22s^2$
    (2) $1s^22p^1$
    (3) $1s^22s^22p^5$
    (4) $1s^22s^22p^6$

44. What is the total number of sublevels in the fourth principal energy level?

    (1) 1   (2) 2   (3) 3   (4) 4

45. Which electron configuration represents an atom in the excited state?

    (1) $1s^22s^22p^63s^2$
    (2) $1s^22s^22p^63s^1$
    (3) $1s^22s^22p^6$
    (4) $1s^22s^22p^53s^2$

46. Which element has atoms in the ground state with a sublevel that is only half filled?

    (1) helium   (3) nitrogen
    (2) beryllium   (4) neon

47. Which sublevel contains a total of five orbitals?

    (1) s   (2) p   (3) d   (4) f

48. What is the maximum number of electrons that can occupy the fourth principal energy level of an atom?

    (1) 6   (2) 8   (3) 18   (4) 32

49. What is the total number of unpaired electrons in an atom of oxygen in the ground state?

    (1) 6   (2) 2   (3) 8   (4) 4

50. Which of the following sublevels has the highest energy?

    (1) 2p   (2) 2s   (3) 3p   (4) 3s

51. What is the maximum number of electrons in an orbital of any atom?

    (1) 1   (2) 2   (3) 6   (4) 10

52. What is the electron configuration of a Mn atom in the ground state?

(1) $1s^22s^22p^63s^2$
(2) $1s^22s^22p^63s^23p^6s3d^54s^2$
(3) $1s^22s^22p^63s^23p^63d^54s^14p^1$
(4) $1s^22s^22p^63s^23p^63d^7$

53. Which orbital notation correctly represents a noble gas in the ground state?

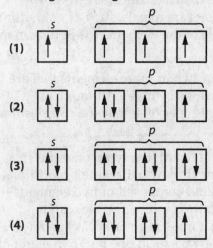

54. Which atom in the ground state has three half-filled orbitals?

(1) P   (3) Al
(2) Si   (4) Li

55. What is the total number of completely filled sublevels found in an atom of krypton in the ground state?

(1) 10   (3) 8
(2) 2   (4) 4

56. Assuming that the orbitals of nickel fill in the order described in Figure 1-10, what is the total number of sublevels that contain electrons in the third principal energy level of a nickel atom in the ground state?

(1) 1   (3) 3
(2) 2   (4) 4

57. An atom has an electron configuration $1s^22s^22p^63s^23p^5$. How many valence electrons are represented in this configuration?.

(1) 2   (3) 5
(2) 3   (4) 7

Types of Matter

The world is composed of millions of different materials, and they are all combinations of atoms. As we look at the world around us, two categories of matter can be distinguished.

Homogeneous and Heterogeneous Matter

Some matter looks uniform and doesn't seem to be made up of parts. A sample of pure water does not have distinguishable parts and has the same composition throughout. When a material has uniform composition throughout, the sample is said to be **homogeneous.** Homogeneous matter can contain more than one type of particle, but particles are uniformly distributed. Sugar dissolved in water is an example of matter that contains both sugar and water but is homogeneous because the smallest particles that make up sugar and water are uniformly distributed.

Other materials are obviously made up of parts. A chocolate chip cookie has pieces of chocolate embedded in the cookie dough. When you examine a piece of concrete, you can see tiny pebbles and pieces of sand embedded in the cement. Such materials, which have varying composition, are said to be **heterogeneous.** Heterogeneous materials are made up of parts with different chemical and physical properties. These parts are not uniformly mixed or dispersed.

Matter can be divided into the major categories of pure substances and mixtures. Pure substances are homogeneous; mixtures can be either heterogeneous or homogeneous.

Pure Substances

A sample of matter is a **pure substance** if its composition is the same throughout the sample. The two types of pure substances are elements and compounds. Oxygen gas, an element, and water, a compound, are examples of pure substances.

Elements **Elements** are substances that cannot be broken down or decomposed into simpler substances by chemical means. There are 91 elements that occur naturally, and more than a dozen elements are synthesized in laboratories. Most elements are metals, such as gold, iron, and aluminum. Examine a periodic table of the elements to see how many different elements you recognize.

Compounds **Compounds** are composed of two or more elements that are chemically combined in definite proportions by mass. Although all compounds contain at least two different types of atoms, the composition of a compound is the same throughout.

The law of definite proportions is the statement that types of atoms in a compound exist in a fixed ratio. Examine the law of definite proportions as shown in Figure 1-11. Water is a compound composed of two elements—hydrogen and oxygen—that are chemically combined. Water can be decomposed into these two elements in a mass ratio of 1:8. When any sample of water is decomposed it will always yield one part by weight of hydrogen for each eight parts of oxygen. When 9 g of water are decomposed they will always produce 1 g of hydrogen and 8 g of oxygen. If 36 g of water decomposed, how many grams of oxygen would be produced? Because the proportions remain the same, 32 g of oxygen would be produced.

Pure substances have a constant composition, both within a given sample and from one sample to another. There is another type of matter that does not have a constant composition.

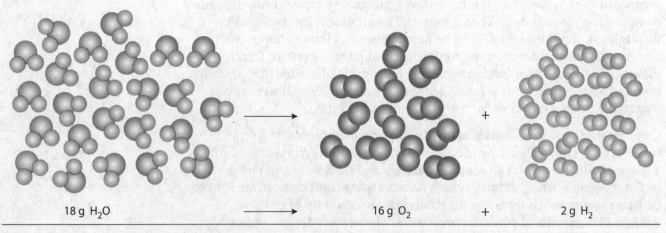

18 g H_2O 16 g O_2 +   2 g H_2

Figure 1-11. The law of definite proportions: This diagram is a model of the decomposition of water. Notice that for every 18 g of water, 16 g of oxygen and 2 g of hydrogen form.

Mixtures

Mixtures are combinations of two or more pure substances that can be separated by physical means. Mixtures are different from compounds because their composition is not definite or "fixed," and the parts can be separated by physical means. For example, different amounts of sugar can be dissolved in a liter of water, and each result would be a water solution of sugar. Even though the sugar seems to disappear and become part of the water, it really doesn't. If the water evaporates, the sugar is left behind; the water and sugar separate.

Some mixtures are homogeneous, and some are heterogeneous. Solutions are mixtures that are homogeneous. Most mixtures are heterogeneous. Soil and concrete are good examples of heterogeneous mixtures. The different parts of each can be easily seen.

Distinguishing Between Mixtures and Compounds

Look at Figure 1-12. Both mixtures and compounds contain two or more different elements. However, the two categories are quite different when one considers their composition and properties.

In a mixture, elements such as iron and sulfur can be present in different ratios. Each substance that makes up the mixture retains its properties. Iron is magnetic and can be separated from a mixture of iron and sulfur with a magnet. Sulfur retains its elemental yellow color in the mixture.

However, if these two elements chemically react, they combine in a mass ratio of 1.74 parts of iron to 1.00 part of sulfur. In the compound the iron is no longer magnetic, and the sulfur loses its yellow color. The compound has its own properties. For example, iron sulfide has a different melting point than either elemental sulfur or iron.

In a later topic, you will learn about different methods that can be used to separate the parts of a mixture.

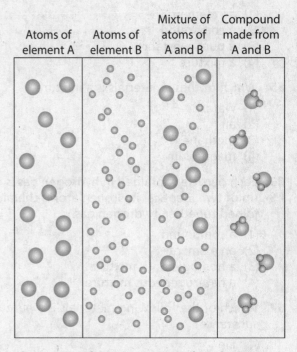

Figure 1-12. Elements, compounds and mixtures: Study the models and notice the differences among elements, compounds, and mixtures.

Review
Questions

Set 1.4

58. Which of the following cannot be decomposed by chemical means?

(1) sodium
(2) ethanol
(3) sucrose
(4) water

59. A compound differs from an element in that a compound

(1) is homogeneous
(2) has a definite composition
(3) has a definite melting point
(4) can be decomposed by a chemical reaction

60. A compound differs from a mixture in that a compound always has a

(1) homogeneous composition
(2) maximum of two elements
(3) minimum of three elements
(4) heterogeneous composition

61. Most elements are

(1) metals
(2) nonmetals
(3) gases
(4) made in a laboratory

62. A pure substance that is composed only of identical atoms is classified as

(1) a compound
(2) an element
(3) a heterogeneous mixture
(4) a homogeneous mixture

63. Which is characteristic of all mixtures?

(1) They are homogeneous.
(2) They are heterogeneous.
(3) Their compositions are in a definite ratio.
(4) Their compositions may vary.

64. A heterogeneous material may be

(1) an element
(2) a compound
(3) a pure substance
(4) a mixture

65. Which of these materials is a mixture?

(1) water
(2) air
(3) methane
(4) magnesium

66. Each particle contained in hydrogen gas is made up of two identical hydrogen atoms chemically joined together. Hydrogen gas is

(1) a compound
(2) an element
(3) a homogeneous mixture
(4) a heterogeneous mixture

67. Which of the following materials is a pure substance?

(1) air
(2) water
(3) fire
(4) earth

68. Which statement is an identifying characteristic of a mixture?

(1) A mixture can consist of a single element.
(2) A mixture can be separated by physical means.
(3) A mixture must have a definite composition by weight.
(4) A mixture must be homogeneous.

69. Which substance can be decomposed by a chemical change?

(1) ammonia   (3) magnesium
(2) aluminum   (4) manganese

Answer the following questions using complete sentences.

70. A sample of a material is passed through a filter paper. A white deposit remains on the paper, and a clear liquid passes through. The clear liquid is then evaporated, leaving a white residue. What can you determine about the nature of the sample?

71. A substance is found to contain only calcium and sulfur. How would you determine whether the substance is a compound or a mixture?

72. Using ⬭ to represent a hydrogen molecule and ⬤ to represent an oxygen molecule, draw a picture of a mixture of hydrogen and oxygen gases.

73. What are some of the differences between a mixture of iron and oxygen and a compound composed of iron and oxygen?

74. Is a pepperoni pizza homogeneous or heterogeneous? Explain your answer.

75. Examine the contents of the four containers shown below. Use complete sentences to identify each as containing only elements, only compounds or a mixture of these. Explain each of your answers.

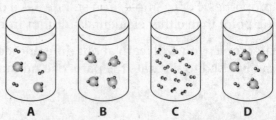

A   B   C   D

76. Are the contents of Container D in question 75 homogeneous or heterogeneous? Explain your answer.

77. A chemist receives two samples. Analysis of one sample shows it to be 88.88% oxygen by mass and 11.12% hydrogen. Analysis of the other sample shows it to be 94.12% oxygen and 5.88% hydrogen. Are these samples of the same material? Explain your answer.

Directions

Review the Test-Taking Strategies section of this book. Then answer the following questions. Read each question carefully and answer with a correct choice or response.

Part A

1 The model of the atom that pictured the atom with electrons traveling in circular orbits was called the
   (1) planetary model
   (2) cannonball model
   (3) wave-mechanical model
   (4) plum pudding model

2 Which sequence represents a correct order of historical developments leading to the modern model of the atom?
   (1) the atom is a hard sphere → most of the atom is empty space → electrons exist in orbitals outside the nucleus
   (2) the atom is a hard sphere → electrons exist in orbitals outside the nucleus → most of the atom is empty space
   (3) most of the atom is empty space → electrons exist in orbitals outside the nucleus → the atom is a hard sphere
   (4) most of the atom is empty space → the atom is a hard sphere → electrons exist in orbitals outside the nucleus

3 Compared to the entire atom, the nucleus of the atom is
   (1) smaller and contains most of the atom's mass
   (2) smaller and contains little of the atom's mass
   (3) large and contains most of the atom's mass
   (4) large and contains little of the atom's mass

4 In a famous experiment, positively charged particles were aimed at a thin sheet of gold foil. The results of this experiment were that
   (1) most of the particles failed to pass through the foil
   (2) most of the particles were repelled, showing that gold has a negative core
   (3) a few of the particles were repelled, showing that the gold has a positive core
   (4) a few of the particles were repelled, showing that the gold was neutral

5 Neutral atoms must contain equal numbers of
   (1) protons and electrons
   (2) protons and neutrons
   (3) protons, neutrons, and electrons
   (4) neutrons and electrons

6 Which of the following is true of a compound but not a mixture?
   (1) A compound contains more than one element.
   (2) All the nuclei in a compound contain the same number of protons.
   (3) A compound may be heterogeneous.
   (4) The composition of a compound does not vary.

7 Compared with an electron, a proton has
   (1) more mass and the same charge
   (2) more mass and an opposite charge
   (3) equal mass and the same charge
   (4) equal mass and an opposite charge

8 The total number of electrons in a neutral atom of any element is always equal to the atom's
   (1) mass number
   (2) number of neutrons
   (3) number of protons
   (4) number of nucleons

9 All isotopes of neutral atoms of sodium have
   (1) 11 protons and 12 neutrons
   (2) 12 protons and 11 neutrons
   (3) 11 protons and 11 electrons
   (4) 12 protons and 12 electrons

10 There are three isotopes of hydrogen, H-1, H-2, and H-3. All of these isotopes have
   (1) a mass of 2 amu
   (2) an atomic number of 1
   (3) 1, 2, or 3 neutrons
   (4) 1, 2, or 3 protons

11 An atom in the excited state contains
   (1) more electrons than an atom in the ground state
   (2) more protons than an atom in the ground state
   (3) more potential energy than an atom in the ground state
   (4) more mass than an atom in the ground state

12 As an electron moves from the excited state to the ground state, the potential energy of the electron
(1) decreases
(2) increases
(3) remains the same
(4) becomes zero

13 Which of the following particles has the smallest mass?
(1) neutron
(2) electron
(3) proton
(4) hydrogen atom

14 An element occurs as a mixture of isotopes. The atomic mass of the element is based upon
(1) the mass of the individual isotopes, only
(2) the relative abundances of the isotopes, only
(3) both the masses and the relative abundances of the individual isotopes
(4) neither the masses nor the relative abundances of the individual isotopes

Part B–1

15 100 g of a clear liquid is evaporated and a few grams of white crystals remain. The original liquid was a
(1) heterogeneous compound
(2) heterogeneous mixture
(3) homogeneous compound
(4) homogeneous mixture

16 Two samples of bronze, a uniform material, are analyzed and found to contain different percentages of tin. Based on this information, bronze is likely a
(1) homogeneous compound
(2) heterogeneous compound
(3) homogeneous mixture
(4) heterogeneous mixture

17 In the electron cloud model of the atom, an orbital is defined as the most probable
(1) location of an electron.
(2) charge of an electron.
(3) conductivity of an electron.
(4) mass of an electron.

18 There are three isotopes of oxygen: O-16, O-17, and O-18. These neutral atoms contain
(1) equal numbers of protons, neutrons, and electrons
(2) equal numbers of protons and neutrons, but different numbers of electrons
(3) equal numbers of protons and electrons, but different numbers of neutrons
(4) different numbers of protons, neutrons, and electrons

19 What is the charge on a particle that contains 9 protons, 10 neutrons, and 9 electrons?
(1) It is neutral.
(2) It has a net charge of 1+.
(3) It has a net charge of 1−.
(4) It has a net charge of 28+.

20 An element has two isotopes. 90% of the isotopes have a mass number of 20 amu, while 10% have a mass number of 22 amu. The atomic mass of the element
(1) cannot be determined without knowing the atomic number
(2) is 21 amu
(3) is closer to 20 amu than to 22 amu
(4) is closer to 22 amu than to 20 amu

21 If the atomic number of a neutral element is 35, and its nucleus contains 40 neutrons, which of the following is correct?
(1) The atom is bromine, and it has 35 electrons.
(2) The atom is bromine, and it has a mass number of 40.
(3) The atom is zirconium, and it has a mass number of 75.
(4) The atom is zirconium, and it has 40 electrons.

22 Examine the diagram of the atom. What element does it represent?

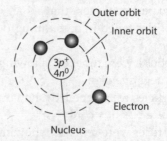

(1) hydrogen
(2) helium
(3) lithium
(4) carbon

23 An atom of Cl-35 contains
  (1) 17 protons, 17 neutrons, and 18 electrons
  (2) 17 protons, 18 neutrons, and 17 electrons
  (3) 18 protons, 17 neutrons, and 17 electrons
  (4) 18 protons, 18 neutrons, and 18 electrons

24 Which must be a mixture of substances?
  (1) solid
  (2) liquid
  (3) gas
  (4) solution

25 What is the number of electrons in a completely filled second shell of an atom?
  (1) 32
  (2) 2
  (3) 18
  (4) 8

Parts B–2 and C

26 Explain, in terms of protons and neutrons, why U-235 and U-238 are different isotopes of the element uranium.

Base your answers to questions 27–29 on the information below.

The bright-line spectra for three elements and a mixture of elements are shown below.

Bright-Line Spectra

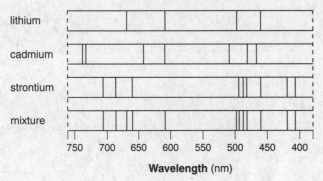

Wavelength (nm)

27 Explain, in terms of *both* electrons and energy, how the bright line spectrum of an element is produced.

28 Identify *all* the elements in the mixture.

29 State the total number of electrons that would be found in a neutral atom of cadmium.

Base your answers to questions 30–32 on the information below.

Atomic Diagrams of Magnesium and Aluminum

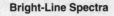

30 Explain, in terms of protons and electrons, why both of these diagrams depict atoms that are considered neutral.

31 Determine the mass number of the magnesium atom represented by the electron-shell diagram.

32 The linear symbol for the ground-state electron configuration of aluminum is Al-2-8-3. Construct a linear symbol for an excited-state configuration of the aluminum atom.

Base your answers to questions 33 through 35 on the data table, which shows three isotopes of neon.

Some Isotopes of Neon		
Isotope	**Atomic Mass** (atomic mass units)	**Percent Natural Abundance**
Ne-20	19.99	90.9%
Ne-21	20.99	0.3%
Ne-22	21.99	8.8%

33 In terms of atomic particles, state one difference between these three isotopes of neon.

34 Based on the atomic masses and the natural abundances shown in the data table, show a correct numerical setup for calculating the average atomic mass of neon.

35 Based on the natural abundances, the average atomic mass of neon is closest to which whole number?

Base your answers to questions 36 and 37 on the information below.

Naturally occurring elemental carbon is a mixture of isotopes. The percent composition of the two most abundant isotopes is listed below.

- 98.93% of the carbon atoms have a mass of 12.00 amu.
- 1.07% of the carbon atoms have a mass of 13.00 amu.

36 Show a correct numerical setup for calculating the average atomic mass of carbon.

37 Describe, in terms of subatomic particles found in the nucleus, one difference and one similarity in the nuclei of the two isotopes. The response must include both isotopes.

Formulas and Equations

TOPIC 2

How Scientists Communicate With Symbols

? *Which "water" would all scientists around the world understand?* **?**

l'eau

wasser

acqua

agua

H_2O

ماء

물

水

вода

ύδωρ

water

Find the answer in this topic.

25

2 Formulas and Equations

Vocabulary

analysis	exothermic	qualitative
chemical change	formula	quantitative
coefficient	molecular formula	reactant
decomposition	molecule	single replacement
diatomic molecule	physical change	subscript
double replacement	polyatomic ion	symbol
empirical formula	product	synthesis
endothermic		

Topic Overview

Chemists in every country of the world speak many different languages. Despite their language differences, it is necessary for them to communicate with each other in a clear and concise manner. Chemists have agreed to a universal language of symbols to identify the elements of the earth, and a system of formulas and equations to explain how the elements interact. In this topic you will explore how the symbols are used to identify the different elements and how they can be combined into formulas representing the millions of different compounds. Then you will learn how these formulas can be combined into chemical equations to show the quantitative and qualitative aspects of chemical reactions.

Chemical Symbols and Formulas

While the names of the elements are often different in various languages of the world, it is important that a person in any country can quickly and accurately determine which element is being referred to.

Chemical Symbols

A system for a universal shorthand to identify the elements has been agreed upon. Each element has been assigned a unique one-, two-, or three-letter **symbol** for its identification. The first letter of a symbol is always capitalized. If there are any other letters in the symbol, they are lower case.

Some of the more common elements have a single letter symbol, such as O for oxygen and H for hydrogen. Other elements have symbols with two letters. Only recently discovered elements that don't yet have permanent names are given three-letter symbols. These elements are given systematic names that represent their atomic number until a name can be agreed upon by the International Union of Pure and Applied Chemists (IUPAC).

Symbols are usually easy to remember, as the letters in the symbol often relate to the English name of the element, such as He for helium and Al for aluminum. Sometimes the letters of the symbol do not correspond to the common English element name but relate instead to the Latin or Greek name, such as K (Latin *kalium*) for potassium, and Na (Latin *natrium*) for sodium. Table 2-1 shows the names and symbols of elements with atomic numbers 1–20.

Table 2-1. Names and Symbols for the First 20 Elements

Atomic Number	Name	Symbol	Atomic Number	Name	Symbol
1	hydrogen	H	11	sodium	Na
2	helium	He	12	magnesium	Mg
3	lithium	Li	13	aluminum	Al
4	beryllium	Be	14	silicon	Si
5	boron	B	15	phosphorus	P
6	carbon	C	16	sulfur	S
7	nitrogen	N	17	chlorine	Cl
8	oxygen	O	18	argon	Ar
9	fluorine	F	19	potassium	K
10	neon	Ne	20	calcium	Ca

Diatomic Molecules When writing the symbols of uncombined elements, almost all are written as monatomic, that is, without a subscript. A **subscript** is a number to the right and slightly below a symbol that tells the number of atoms present. A subscript is not written if only one atom is present. Therefore, the symbol for iron is Fe, neon is Ne, and carbon is C.

There are, however, several important exceptions. Some elements exist in nature as two identical atoms covalently bonded into a **diatomic molecule.** Oxygen normally exists as O_2, a diatomic molecule. Other elements that exist as diatomic molecules are hydrogen (H_2), nitrogen (N_2), and the elements of Group 17 of the periodic table (F_2, Cl_2, Br_2, and I_2). Be sure that whenever you write the formulas for any of these uncombined elements, that you write them as diatomic molecules.

Chemical Formulas

Compounds are composed of combinations of elements chemically combined in definite proportions by weight (mass). **Formulas** use chemical symbols and numbers to show both qualitative and quantitative information about a substance. **Qualitative** information relates to things that cannot be counted or measured, such as what elements are in the compound. **Quantitative** information deals with things that can be either counted or measured, such as the number of atoms of each element present in a unit of the compound.

In a formula of a compound, the symbols for the elements supply the qualitative information. The formula CO tells the reader that the compound consists of carbon and oxygen. Notice the difference between CO and Co. The first is a combination of two elements in a compound, carbon monoxide, while the second is the symbol for an element, cobalt.

Carbon monoxide

CO
one carbon atom,
one oxygen atom

Carbon dioxide

CO$_2$
one carbon atom,
two oxygen atoms

Figure 2-1. Subscripts in a formula: The use of subscripts shows the relative number of atoms of each type in a compound. No subscript is written if only one atom of an element is present.

Recall that the numbers to the right and slightly below a symbol, called subscripts, supply quantitative information, telling us the number of atoms of those elements in a unit of the compound. For example, the symbols in the formula H_2SO_4 give us the qualitative information that the compound contains hydrogen, sulfur, and oxygen. The subscript 2 after the H indicates that there are two atoms of hydrogen present. No subscript is written after the S, so there is one sulfur atom. The 4 after O informs the reader that there are four atoms of oxygen present. Figure 2-1 shows the use of subscripts for the two compounds of carbon and oxygen. Table 2-2 shows some formulas for elements and compounds. Notice that the formula for a monatomic element is just its symbol.

Table 2-2. Formulas for Some Elements and Compounds			
Name	**Formula**	**Name**	**Formula**
neon	Ne	calcium hydroxide	$Ca(OH)_2$
sulfuric acid	H_2SO_4	magnesium nitrate	$Mg(NO_3)_2$
glucose	$C_6H_{12}O_6$	sodium chloride	NaCl
uranium	U	gold	Au
chlorine	Cl_2	dihydrogen oxide	H_2O
ammonia	NH_3	hydrochloric acid	HCl
methane	CH_4	sodium hydroxide	NaOH
iron	Fe	benzene	C_6H_6
ammonium phosphate	$(NH_4)_3PO_4$	silver nitrate	$AgNO_3$

Types of Formulas Two basic types of formulas provide different types of information about a compound. Empirical formulas include all types of compounds. Molecular formulas are important when considering compounds formed from atoms sharing electrons.

Empirical Formulas An **empirical formula** represents the simplest integer ratio in which atoms combine to form a compound. Ionic substances do not form discrete units or molecules, but rather an array of ions (charged particles). Ionic formulas indicate the ratio of the ions in a compound. The formula $MgCl_2$ tells us that for every magnesium ion in the compound there are two chloride ions. Formulas of ionic substances are empirical formulas.

Molecular Formulas Covalently bonded substances form discrete units called **molecules.** In some cases, such as H_2O, the empirical formula not only represents the simplest ratio, but it also represents the actual ratio of the atoms in a molecule of water. In other cases, the **molecular formula** may be a multiple of the empirical formula. For example the molecular formula of glucose is $C_6H_{12}O_6$, which is six times the empirical formula CH_2O.

Atoms, Compounds, and Ions

It's easy to interpret a formula for an element or a compound, but it's a bit more complicated to write the formula for a compound. How do you know what elements form the compound and in what proportion? To understand how elements form compounds, an understanding of atoms and ions is essential.

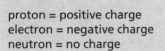
Memory Jogger

proton = positive charge
electron = negative charge
neutron = no charge

Atoms and compounds are electrically neutral; that is, they do not have a net charge. Both atoms and compounds contain positively charged protons and negatively charged electrons, but there are equal numbers of positive and negative charges, producing a neutral atom or compound.

Ions, however, are not neutral and may be either positively or negatively charged. An ion that contains more protons than electrons will be positively charged, while an ion with more electrons than protons will have a negative charge. Positively charged ions attract negatively charged ions in a ratio that produces a neutral compound.

Ionic Charges

The charge of an ion is indicated by a superscript following the symbol of the ion. When the ion has a charge of either $1+$ or $1-$, the number 1 is omitted, and only the sign of the charge is shown. Thus the sodium ion with a charge of $1+$ is written as Na^+, and chlorine with a charge of $1-$ is Cl^-. The symbols of all other ions show both the size and sign of the charge. An aluminum ion is written as Al^{3+}, and an oxygen ion is shown as O^{2-}.

Polyatomic Ions A **polyatomic ion** is a group of atoms covalently bonded together, possessing a charge. Selected Polyatomic Ions in the *Reference Tables for Physical Setting/Chemistry* is a list of common polyatomic ions and their charges.

On Table 2-2 you will notice that three of the formulas contain symbols enclosed in parentheses. Parentheses are used to enclose polyatomic ions when there is more than one of the ions in a unit of a compound. The subscript written after the parentheses tells the reader how many of the ions are present in the compound. The subscript refers to each of the elements in the ion. For example, $(NH_4)_3PO_4$ tells the reader that there are three NH_4^+ ions, each containing one nitrogen atom and four hydrogen atoms, for a total of three nitrogen atoms and 12 hydrogen atoms. NH_4^+ is a polyatomic ion called the ammonium ion and has a charge of $1+$. The second part of the formula, PO_4^{3-}, is the formula of one phosphate ion that contains one phosphorus atom and four oxygen atoms. Like the ammonium ion, it has a charge, but it is $3-$. Figure 2-2 shows formulas, names, and models of some common polyatomic ions.

Forming a Compound Compounds can form in several different ways. One way is by the attraction of oppositely charged ions. Monatomic or polyatomic ions attract each other in a ratio that produces a neutral compound. Many of the compounds listed in Table 2-2 are formed in this manner.

Coefficients

You know what information a subscript provides in a chemical formula. However, sometimes there is a number called a **coefficient** written in front of a formula. The coefficient tells how many units of the formula are present, and it applies to the entire formula. To determine the number of atoms present, consider the formula without the coefficient, and then multiply each value by the coefficient to find the total of each type of atom. For example, $2H_2O$ means that there are two molecules of water. These two molecules contain four hydrogen atoms and two oxygen atoms.

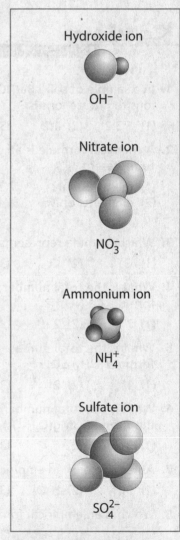

Hydroxide ion

OH^-

Nitrate ion

NO_3^-

Ammonium ion

NH_4^+

Sulfate ion

SO_4^{2-}

Figure 2-2. Polyatomic ions: Names, formulas, and models show the relationship of atoms in these polyatomic ions.

Table 2-3. Atoms in Calcium Nitrate	
Formula	**Atoms**
$Ca(NO_3)_2$	1 calcium
	2 nitrogen
	6 oxygen
$3Ca(NO_3)_2$	3 calcium
	6 nitrogen
	18 oxygen

The expression $4Mg(NO_3)_2$ contains four magnesium atoms, eight nitrogen atoms, and 24 oxygen atoms. Additional examples are provided in Table 2-3.

Hydrates

When water from some ionic solutions evaporates, the solute forms a crystal lattice that binds water within the structure. Such a compound is called a <u>hydrate.</u> These crystals have a definite number of water molecules for each unit of the compound. Barium chloride ($BaCl_2$) traps two water molecules as shown by the formula of the hydrate, $BaCl_2 \cdot 2H_2O$. Copper sulfate ($CuSO_4$) has five water molecules and a formula of $CuSO_4 \cdot 5H_2O$. Alum ($NaAl(SO_4)_2$) has 12 water molecules attached, $NaAl(SO_4)_2 \cdot 12H_2O$. The anhydrous (not hydrated) compound can be obtained by heating the crystals to drive off the water.

In a chemical reaction, the water in a hydrate does not react. However, it adds mass to the compound. For example, 10.0 g of a truly dry crystal of copper(II) sulfate contains more $CuSO_4$ than 10.0 g of the hydrated crystal, which contains both $CuSO_4$ and H_2O. If a certain amount of a material is made from a hydrated crystal, the mass of water must be considered in determining how much of the compound must be used.

Review Questions
Set 2.1

1. In a sample of solid $Ba(NO_3)_2$ the ratio of barium ions to nitrate ions is
   (1) 1:3:2   (2) 1:2   (3) 2:1   (4) 1:6

2. A chemical formula is an expression used to represent
   (1) mixtures only   (3) compounds only
   (2) elements only   (4) elements and compounds

3. Which formula represents a compound?
   (1) Ca   (2) Cr   (3) CO   (4) Co

4. What is the total number of atoms in the formula $Ca(NO_3)_2$?
   (1) 7   (2) 2   (3) 3   (4) 9

5. What is the total number of sulfur atoms in the formula $(NH_4)_2SO_4$?
   (1) 1   (2) 2   (3) 3   (4) 4

6. What is the total number of hydrogen atoms in the formula $3Mg(C_2H_3O_2)_2$?
   (1) 3   (2) 6   (3) 12   (4) 18

7. An example of an empirical formula is
   (1) S_2H_2 (2) H_2O_2 (3) C_2Cl_2 (4) $CaCl_2$

8. Which is an empirical formula?
   (1) C_2H_2 (2) C_2H_4 (3) Al_2Cl_6 (4) K_2O

9. What is the empirical formula of a compound with the molecular formula $C_6H_{12}O_6$?
   (1) $C_4H_8O_4$ (2) $C_3H_6O_3$ (3) $C_2H_4O_2$ (4) CH_2O

10. Which compound has the same empirical and molecular formula?
    (1) H_2O_2 (2) NH_3 (3) C_2H_6 (4) Hg_2Cl_2

11. The empirical formula of a compound is CH_2. The molecular formula of this compound could be
    (1) CH_4 (2) C_2H_2 (3) C_2H_4 (4) C_3H_3

12. Which polyatomic ion is found in the compound $NaClO_2$?
    (1) acetate (2) chlorite (3) chlorate (4) oxalate

13. Which formula type is correctly paired with an example having the simplest whole-number ratio of atoms of the elements in the compound?
    (1) empirical formula – C_2H_5
    (2) empirical formula – C_4H_{10}
    (3) molecular formula – C_2H_6
    (4) molecular formula – C_4H_{10}

14. Which formula represents a compound with the fewest number of oxygen atoms?
    (1) K_3PO_4 (3) $Fe_2(SO_4)_3$
    (2) $Al(OH)_3$ (4) $BaCl_2 \bullet 2H_2O$

15. Which formula represents a compound having only one phosphate ion?
    (1) $Ca_3(PO_4)_2$ (2) AlP   (3) PH_3 (4) Na_3PO_4

Writing Formulas and Naming Compounds

All compounds must be electrically neutral, that is, the sum of the charges must equal zero. Common oxidation states for each element are listed in the upper right hand corner of each element's box in the periodic table. For many elements, the oxidation state is equal to the charge on the ion. Elements from Group 1 have an oxidation number of +1 and always have a charge of 1+ in compounds. All Group 2 elements have 2+ charges in compounds. Group 3 elements usually have a 3+ charge.

Equalizing Charges

Compounds achieve neutrality by having an equal number of positive and negative charges. When a sodium ion (Na^+) and a chloride ion (Cl^-) combine, they will do so in a 1:1 ratio. The resulting formula will be NaCl, as such a ratio produces a neutral compound. Figure 2-3 shows the formulas of three compounds in which the charges of the ions are equal, but opposite.

In the case of a combination of Mg^{2+} with Cl^-, a 1:1 ratio would not produce a neutral compound. To achieve neutrality there must be two Cl^- ions for each Mg^{2+}. The correct formula will be $MgCl_2$. When ions have unequal and opposite charges, a simple technique will produce the correct formula. Simply write the charge of one ion as the subscript of the other. Transfer the number only, not the sign. Notice that this procedure automatically balances the positive and negative charges, producing neutral formulas.

Polyatomic ions form compounds with oppositely charged ions in the same way as single ions. The formula for Na^+ combining with NO_3^- is simply $NaNO_3$. How would calcium (Ca^{2+}) combine with the nitrate ion (NO_3^-)? Because two nitrate ions are needed, enclose the nitrate ion in parentheses and write the subscript 2 after it, forming $Ca(NO_3)_2$.

Ion formula	Compound formula
$K^+ Cl^-$	KCl
$Mg^{2+} S^{2-}$	MgS
$Al^{3+} N^{3-}$	AlN

Figure 2-3. Examples of compounds with a 1:1 ion ratio: The three compounds shown are potassium chloride, magnesium sulfide, and aluminum nitride.

Naming Compounds

Compounds are named according to the types of elements that form them. Ionic compounds, whether they are binary (contain only two elements) or contain polyatomic ions, are named by one method. Covalent compounds that contain only nonmetals are named by a different method.

Binary Ionic Compounds The name of a binary ionic compound comes from the names of the elements in the compound. The positively charged particle, often a metallic ion, is placed first. The negatively charged ion will end the formula. A compound containing the sodium ion and the ion of chlorine will begin as *sodium*. The name of the negative ion is slightly changed from the element to end in -*ide*, making the negative ion of chlorine *chloride*. Hence, the compound containing the sodium and chloride ions is simply sodium chloride. Figure 2-5 summarizes naming binary compounds.

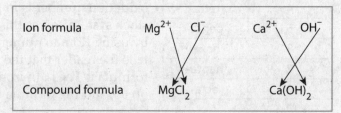

Figure 2-4. Examples of ions with unequal charges: To obtain the correct formula, write the absolute value of the ion charge as the subscript of the other ion.

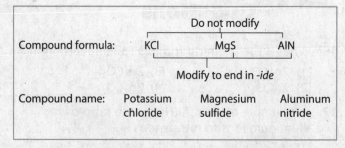

Figure 2-5. Naming binary compounds

Other Ionic Compounds Naming compounds containing polyatomic ions is simple. When the positive portion is a metal, use the unmodified metal name plus the name of the negative polyatomic ion. For example, the name of KNO_3 is potassium nitrate.

Most polyatomic ions are negatively charged. Ammonium (NH_4^+) is an important exception. In a compound containing the ammonium ion, if the negative ion is a nonmetal, the ending is *-ide*. If the ammonium ion is combined with another polyatomic ion, they each retain their names.

Examples:	NH_4Cl	ammonium chloride
	NH_4NO_3	ammonium nitrate

Binary Covalent Compounds If a binary compound contains two nonmetals rather than a metal and a nonmetal, it is a molecular substance not composed of ions. The order in which the elements are arranged in the formula can be determined by considering the electronegativity values of the elements (See the *Reference Tables for Physical Setting/Chemistry*). The element with the lower electronegativity value is written first. For example, consider a compound containing carbon and oxygen. Because carbon has an electronegativity value of 2.6 while oxygen has a value of 3.4, carbon is written first. As in other binary compounds, the name of the compound will end in *-ide*. Because these two elements often can form more than one compound, a prefix is used to tell the reader how many atoms of each element are present. CO is named carbon monoxide, while CO_2 is named carbon dioxide. If only one atom of the first element is present, the prefix *mono-* is not used. If the element name starts with a vowel, any final *a* or *o* in the prefix is not used. For example, NO is named nitrogen monoxide, while N_2O_4 is dinitrogen tetroxide. Table 2-4 shows common prefixes used to name these compounds.

Table 2-4. Common Prefixes

Number of Atoms	Prefix
1	mono-
2	di-
3	tri-
4	tetra-
5	penta-
6	hexa-
7	hepta-
8	octa-

The Stock System Some metals have more than one common oxidation state. For example, iron can have an oxidation number of either +2 or +3, which leads to a potential difficulty in naming compounds of iron. Which oxidation number is implied in the name iron chloride, the +2 or +3? The stock system solves this problem by simply stating the oxidation number by using Roman numerals after the name of the metal. Iron(II) chloride tells the reader that the iron has an oxidation number of +2, and the formula is $FeCl_2$. In iron(III) chloride, the iron has an oxidation number of +3, and the formula is $FeCl_3$.

Review Questions   Set 2.2

16. What is the chemical formula for zinc carbonate?

(1) Zn_2CO_3

(2) $ZnCO_3$

(3) $Zn(CO_3)_2$

(4) Zn_3CO_2

17. In a sample of solid $Al(NO_3)_3$, the ratio of aluminum ions to nitrate ions is

(1) 1:1   (2) 1:2   (3) 1:3   (4) 1:6

18. In a sample of solid calcium phosphate $Ca_3(PO_4)_2$, the ratio of calcium ions to phosphate ions is

(1) 1:1   (2) 2:3   (3) 3:2   (4) 3:4

19. What is the total number of atoms in $(NH_4)_2SO_4$?

(1) 10   (2) 11   (3) 14   (4) 15

20. What is the total number of oxygen atoms present in one unit of $Mg(ClO_3)_2$?

    (1) 5   (2) 2   (3) 3   (4) 6

21. What is the total number of atoms of oxygen in the formula $Al(ClO_3)_3 \cdot 6H_2O$?

    (1) 6   (2) 9   (3) 10   (4) 15

22. Write the correct formulas for the following binary ionic compounds.

    (a) lithium fluoride   (d) beryllium chloride
    (b) calcium oxide   (e) potassium iodide
    (c) aluminum nitride   (f) aluminum oxide

23. Write the correct formulas for the following binary molecular compounds.

    (a) carbon monoxide   (d) carbon dioxide
    (b) boron tribromide   (e) carbon tetrabromide
    (c) sulfur hexafluoride   (f) nitrogen dioxide

24. Write the correct formulas for the following compounds that contain polyatomic ions.

    (a) sodium hydroxide   (d) aluminum phosphate
    (b) potassium nitrate   (e) aluminum nitrate
    (c) magnesium sulfate   (f) ammonium nitrate

25. Name each of the following binary ionic compounds.

    (a) NaBr   (d) $MgCl_2$
    (b) MgS   (e) AlF_3
    (c) CaO   (f) CaI_2

26. Name each of the following binary molecular compounds.

    (a) O_2F_2 (d) SF_2
    (b) SiF_4 (e) H_2S
    (c) S_4N_4 (f) P_4O_{10}

27. Name each of the following compounds.

    (a) $Ca(NO_3)_2$ (d) Na_3PO_4
    (b) KOH   (e) $LiNO_3$
    (c) $MgCO_3$ (f) $Mg(C_2H_3O_2)_2$

28. Write formulas for each of the following compounds.

    (a) iron(II) oxide   (d) mercury(II) iodide
    (b) tin(II) sulfide   (e) lead(II) nitrate
    (c) copper(I) chloride   (f) iron(III) oxide

29. Write the names of each of the following using stock nomenclature.

    (a) CuCl   (d) $Pb(NO_3)_2$
    (b) FeS   (e) $Sn(OH)_2$
    (c) HgI_2 (f) Fe_2O_3

30. Which is the correct name for the compound Na_2SO_4?

    (1) sodium (II) sulfate   (3) sodium (IV) sulfate
    (2) sodium sulfate   (4) sodium sulfur oxide

31. Based on listed oxidation states, which formula would most likely result when sulfur and oxygen combine to form a compound?

    (1) OS_2 (2) OS_3 (3) SO_3 (4) SO_5

32. Which is named potassium chlorate?

    (1) $KClO_3$ (3) $KClO_4$
    (2) K_3ClO (4) KClO

33. Which formulas represent possible oxides of vanadium?

    (1) VO_3 and VO_5 (3) V_2O_3 and V_2O_5
    (2) V_3O_2 and V_5O_2 (4) V_3O and V_5O

34. The formula $Mg(OH)_2$ contains

    (1) 2 magnesium atoms   (3) 1 hydrogen atom
    (2) 1 oxygen atom   (4) 2 hydroxide ions

Chemical Reactions and Equations

The world around us is constantly changing. Some of these changes result from substances undergoing phase changes, such as ice melting or water boiling. In these cases, the **physical changes** that have taken place have not resulted in the formation of a new substance, but rather only a change in appearance of the starting material.

Other changes are more dramatic. When a substance is burned, whether it is a piece of paper or gasoline, the substances produced are quite different from the starting materials. These changes in which the identity of the products differs from the identity of the reactants are called **chemical changes.** In this section you will learn how to use chemical symbols to form equations that represent these chemical changes. A well-defined chemical change is called a <u>chemical reaction.</u>

Burning of Carbon Dioxide

carbon + oxygen $\longrightarrow$ carbon dioxide

$$C(s) + O_2(g) \longrightarrow CO_2(g)$$

Figure 2-6. Word equation and formulaic equation

Chemical Equations

A chemical equation shows what takes place during a chemical reaction. It is similar to an algebraic equation in that what is written on one side of the equation equals what is written on the other side. A plus sign is used to separate each of the reactants and each of the products. The arrow is read as "produces" or "yields."

A substance that enters into a reaction is called a **reactant** and is written to the left of the arrow. A substance that is produced by a reaction is called a **product** and is written to the right of the arrow.

In the equation shown in Figure 2-6, carbon and oxygen are reactants, and carbon dioxide is a product. Plus signs separate reactants and products. Notice that in the equation, the atoms of the reactants and products are the same, but the manner in which they are combined is different. This figure shows how using models of the reactants and products can be used in an equation.

Endothermic and Exothermic Processes

Chemical and physical changes involve the loss or gain of energy, most often expressed as heat. It takes heat to cook an egg. Heat is released when fuel is burned. Photosynthesis requires the energy of the sun in order to occur. When sodium hydroxide dissolves in water, the water warms up. Based on whether energy is absorbed or released, you can classify these energy changes into the two major groups as shown in Table 2-5. Because of this classification, energy is often included as either a reactant or a product in an equation.

Table 2-5. Summary of Endothermic and Exothermic Reactions				
Type of Reaction	Surrounding Temperature	Potential Energy of Reactants	Potential Energy of Products	Energy Change
Endothermic	decreases	less	more	positive
Exothermic	increases	more	less	negative

Endothermic Processes Processes that require energy in order to occur are called **endothermic** processes. The physical change of ice melting is endothermic. Chemical changes that occur as food cooks are endothermic. The energy required is absorbed from the surroundings, thus lowering the surrounding temperature. In endothermic processes, the reactants absorb energy as they become products. Hence, the products have more potential energy than the reactants.

$$H_2O(s) + energy \rightarrow H_2O(\ell)$$
$$6CO_2 + 6H_2O + energy \rightarrow C_6H_{12}O_6 + 6O_2$$

Exothermic Processes Processes that release thermal energy when they occur are **exothermic**. The burning of carbon in oxygen is an example of an exothermic reaction. Freezing of water is exothermic. The energy released from these processes is given off to the surroundings, thus raising the surrounding temperature. In exothermic reactions, the products have less potential energy than the reactants.

$$CH_4 + 3O_2 \rightarrow CO_2 + 2H_2O + energy$$
$$C_6H_{12}O_6 + 6O_2 \rightarrow 6CO_2 + 6H_2O + energy$$

Balancing Chemical Equations

You can see by examining a correctly written chemical equation that the number of each type of atom is the same on both sides of the equation. This observation confirms the <u>law of conservation of mass</u>, which states that matter is neither created nor destroyed in chemical reactions. In any chemical reaction, the numbers and kinds of atoms must remain unchanged in the reaction.

Look at Figure 2-7. In the first equation there is conservation of atoms. There is one carbon atom shown on both the reactant and product side and two atoms of oxygen on either side. This equation agrees with the law of conservation of mass and is called a balanced equation.

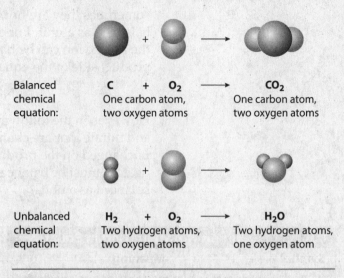

| Balanced chemical equation: | C + O_2 $\longrightarrow$ CO_2 |
| | One carbon atom, two oxygen atoms → One carbon atom, two oxygen atoms |

| Unbalanced chemical equation: | H_2 + O_2 $\longrightarrow$ H_2O |
| | Two hydrogen atoms, two oxygen atoms → Two hydrogen atoms, one oxygen atom |

Figure 2-7. A balanced and an unbalanced equation

The second equation is different. While there are two atoms of hydrogen on both sides of the arrow, there are two atoms of oxygen on the reactant side but only one atom of oxygen on the product side. This equation is not balanced. As it is written, one atom of oxygen has been lost, or not conserved.

The equation must be changed so that it is balanced. How is this done? Remember that subscripts show the ratio of different types of atoms, and subscripts cannot be changed in a correctly written formula. The formula of oxygen gas is O_2 and cannot be changed. The only way to balance an equation, once correct formulas have been written, is to change the coefficients in the equation. Remember that coefficients are the numbers written before a formula.

You may want to think of balancing an equation as being similar to balancing a seesaw. In the second example the unbalanced equation is heavy with oxygen atoms on the reactant side. Because none of the reactant oxygen atoms can be removed, the only way to correct the imbalance is to add more oxygen atoms to the product side. This is done by placing a coefficient of 2 in front of the formula of water.

$$H_2(g) + O_2(g) \rightarrow 2H_2O(g)$$

The coefficient applies to both the hydrogen and oxygen in water. The equation is now balanced in terms of oxygen atoms, as there are two on each side. The hydrogen atoms are now unbalanced because there are four hydrogen atoms on the product side but only two on the reactant side. This can be remedied by placing a 2 in front of the formula of hydrogen.

$$2H_2(g) + O_2(g) \rightarrow 2H_2O(g)$$

Inspection of the equation shows that there now is a conservation of atoms. Four atoms of hydrogen and two atoms of oxygen are now on each side of the equation. The equation is now balanced.

If you examine equations that involve polyatomic ions, you will notice that sometimes the ions are the same in the reactants and products, and sometimes they are not. If polyatomic ions remain the same, they can be balanced as a unit. For example, in the following unbalanced equation, the nitrate ion can be balanced as a unit because it stays a nitrate ion on the product side of the equation.

$$AgNO_3 + MgCl_2 \rightarrow Mg(NO_3)_2 + AgCl$$

However, in the following unbalanced equation, the phosphite (PO_3^{3-}) and nitrate ions are changed during the reaction. They do not appear unchanged on the product side of the equation. In such a case, each type of atom must be balanced separately, and the polyatomic ions cannot be balanced as a unit.

$$HNO_3 + H_3PO_3 \rightarrow NO + H_3PO_4 + H_2O$$

You may have noticed that some symbols have appeared in parentheses after the formulas. It is often important to indicate the physical state of the substances in an equation. The symbol (s) is used to show that the substance is a solid, (ℓ) indicates that it is a liquid, and (g) shows the substance to be a gas. In addition, (aq) means that the material is dissolved in water; that is, it is in an aqueous solution. Table 2-6 summarizes some common symbols used in equations.

Table 2-6. Common Notation Used in Equations

Symbol	Meaning
+	Separates two reactants or two products
→	Separates reactants from products; read as *yields* or *produces*
(s)	Identifies the substance as a solid
(ℓ)	Identifies the substance as a liquid
(g)	Identifies the substance as a gas
(aq)	Identifies the substance as being dissolved in aqueous (water) solution

Review Questions

Set 2.3

35. Consider the following unbalanced equation.

$$C_3H_8(g) + O_2(g) \rightarrow H_2O(g) + CO_2(g)$$

When the equation is completely balanced using smallest whole numbers, the coefficient of O_2 is

(1) 5　　　(2) 2　　　(3) 3　　　(4) 7

36. When the equation $Al(s) + O_2(g) \rightarrow Al_2O_3(s)$ is correctly balanced using smallest whole numbers, the sum of the coefficients will be

(1) 9　　　(2) 7　　　(3) 3　　　(4) 12

37. Consider the following unbalanced equation.

$$Ca(OH)_2 + (NH_4)_2SO_4 \rightarrow CaSO_4 + NH_3 + H_2O$$

What is the sum of the coefficients when the equation is completely balanced using the smallest whole-number coefficients?

(1) 5　　　(2) 7　　　(3) 9　　　(4) 11

38. When the equation $Al_2(SO_4)_3 + ZnCl_2 \rightarrow AlCl_3 + ZnSO_4$ is correctly balanced using smallest whole numbers, the sum of the coefficients is

(1) 9　　　(2) 8　　　(3) 5　　　(4) 4

39. Consider the following unbalanced equation.

$$C_8H_{16}(g) + O_2(g) \rightarrow H_2O(g) + CO_2(g)$$

When the equation is completely balanced using smallest whole numbers, the coefficient of O_2 is

(1) 8　　　(2) 12　　　(3) 14　　　(4) 16

40. Consider the following unbalanced equation.

$$FeCl_2 + Na_2CO_3 \rightarrow FeCO_3 + NaCl$$

When the equation is completely balanced using smallest whole numbers, the coefficient of NaCl is

(1) 6　　　(2) 2　　　(3) 3　　　(4) 4

41. Consider the following unbalanced equation.

$$Ag + H_2S \rightarrow Ag_2S + H_2$$

What is the sum of the coefficients when the equation is completely balanced using the smallest whole-number coefficients?

(1) 5　　　(2) 8　　　(3) 10　　　(4) 4

42. Consider the following incomplete equation:

$2NH_4Cl(aq) + CaO(s) \rightarrow$ _____ $+ H_2O(\ell) + CaCl_2(aq)$

Which expression completes the balanced equation?

(1) $HNO_3(aq)$ (3) $NH_3(aq)$

(2) $2HNO_3(aq)$ (4) $2NH_3(aq)$

43. Consider the following unbalanced equation.

$$N_2(g) + O_2(g) \rightarrow N_2O_5(g)$$

When the equation is completely balanced using smallest whole numbers, the coefficient of $N_2(g)$ is

(1) 1   (2) 2   (3) 5   (4) 4

Types of Reactions

While it would be difficult, if not impossible, to put all chemical reactions into distinct categories, there are four major types of reactions that you should know. It is important to be able to recognize these types and write equations to represent them.

Synthesis (Combination) Reactions When two or more reactants combine to form a single product, the reaction is a **synthesis,** or combination, reaction. The combination of hydrogen and oxygen to form water that was shown earlier is an example.

$$2H_2(g) + O_2(g) \rightarrow 2H_2O(g)$$

Many synthesis reactions are commonplace, such as the rusting of iron.

$$4Fe(s) + 3O_2(g) \rightarrow 2Fe_2O_3(s)$$

Synthesis reactions not only take place between elements, but they may also involve compounds.

$$CO_2(g) + H_2O(\ell) \rightarrow H_2CO_3(aq)$$

It is convenient to write this type of equation in a general form such as

$$A + B \rightarrow AB$$

A and B represent either elements or compounds, and AB represents a compound that is made of A and B. See Figure 2-8.

Decomposition (Analysis) Reactions A **decomposition,** or **analysis,** reaction is the reverse of a synthesis reaction in that a single compound is broken down (decomposed) into two or more simpler substances. All decomposition reactions begin with a single reactant.

$$H_2O(\ell) \rightarrow H_2(g) + O_2(g)$$

Although many decomposition reactions produce elements as the products, Figure 2-9 shows the breaking down of one compound into two compounds.

$$CaCO_3(s) \rightarrow CaO(s) + CO_2(g)$$

The general form of this reaction is the exact opposite of the equation for a synthesis reaction.

$$AB \rightarrow A + B$$

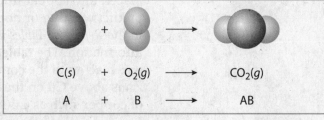

Figure 2-8. **Equation of a synthesis reaction:** In this example, two elements combine to form a compound.

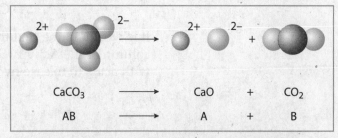

Figure 2-9. **Equation of a decomposition reaction:** The models for $CaCO_3$ and CaO show that the compounds are ionic and do not form molecules. They are compounds that exist as ions.

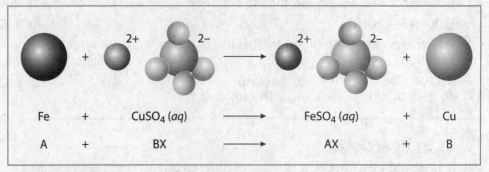

Fe   + $CuSO_4$ (*aq*) ⟶ $FeSO_4$ (*aq*)   +   Cu

A   +   BX ⟶ AX   +   B

Figure 2-10. Equation of a single replacement reaction: The copper and iron ions are part of the compounds that are in solution, but the iron and copper atoms are solid metals.

Single Replacement Reactions When a piece of copper wire is placed into a solution of silver nitrate, a chemical reaction takes place. In a short period of time shiny crystals form on the copper wire, and the solution gradually becomes blue. Analysis of the crystals shows them to be silver metal. The blue color is caused by copper ions in solution. In this reaction the copper metal has replaced silver ions in silver nitrate, producing silver metal and copper ions.

$$Cu(s) + 2AgNO_3(aq) \rightarrow Cu(NO_3)_2(aq) + 2Ag(s)$$

This type of reaction where one element replaces another element in a compound is called a **single replacement** reaction (Figure 2-10). This type of reaction always involves an element and a compound. The general formula for this type of reaction where a metal replaces another metal in a compound is

$$A + BX \rightarrow B + AX$$

Will the reverse reaction take place, that is, will silver metal react with copper nitrate to produce copper and silver nitrate? If silver is placed into copper nitrate solution, no copper is formed. How can we predict whether or not a reaction will take place? The Activity Series in the *Reference Tables for Physical Setting/Chemistry* will provide the information. The table is arranged so that a metal listed on the table will react with the compound of a metal that is below it. For example, Zn is above Cu on the table. Therefore, Zn will react with a compound of copper such as $Cu(NO_3)_2$.

$$Zn + Cu(NO_3)_2 \rightarrow Cu + Zn(NO_3)_2$$

Because Cu is below Zn, it will not react with compounds of Zn.

$$Cu + Zn(NO_3)_2 \rightarrow \text{no reaction.}$$

It is worth noting that there is one element that is not a metal in the left column of the Activity Series, H_2. All metals above hydrogen will react with acids to release hydrogen gas and produce a salt. For example,

$$Mg + 2HCl \rightarrow H_2 + MgCl_2$$

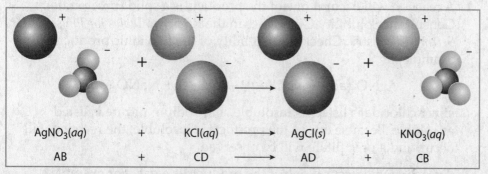

AgNO₃(aq)   +   KCl(aq) ⟶ AgCl(s)   +   KNO₃(aq)

AB   +   CD ⟶ AD   +   CB

Figure 2-11. An equation for a double replacement reaction: Although all the compounds are ionic, AgCl is an ionic compound that is not soluble in water. Crystals of AgCl form a precipitate.

Silver (Ag) is below hydrogen on the table, so it will not react with acids.

In the second column of the Activity Series is a short list of nonmetals. A nonmetal will replace a less active nonmetal in a compound according to the equation

$$A + XB \rightarrow B + XA$$

Fluorine is listed as the most active nonmetal, and it will replace chlorine, bromine, and iodine from their binary compounds.

$$F_2 + 2NaCl \rightarrow Cl_2 + 2NaF$$

Because chlorine is below fluorine on the list, it will not replace fluorine in a compound.

$$Cl_2 + NaF \rightarrow \text{no reaction}$$

When given a possible reaction between an element and an ionic compound, consult the Activity Series to determine whether or not a reaction will occur.

Double Replacement Reactions **Double replacement** reactions generally involve two soluble ionic compounds that react in solution to produce a precipitate, a gas, or a molecular compound such as water. Figure 2-11 shows that when aqueous solutions of silver nitrate and sodium chloride are mixed, a white precipitate of silver chloride is produced according to the following equation.

$$AgNO_3(aq) + NaCl(aq) \rightarrow AgCl(s) + NaNO_3(aq)$$

Double replacement equations can be represented by the general equation

$$AB + CD \rightarrow AD + CB$$

Just as not all combinations of single replacement reactants will produce a reaction, the same is true for double replacement reactions.

How can you determine if two ionic compounds will react? There are three situations that might cause a double replacement to occur.

1. A reaction will occur if one of the products is a solid (precipitate). Consult the Solubility Guidelines in the *Reference Tables for Physical Setting/Chemistry*. Check the solubility of the two ionic products. For example, in ⓡ

$$AgNO_3(aq) + NaCl(aq) \rightarrow AgCl(s) + NaNO_3(aq)$$

silver chloride is listed as insoluble, and sodium nitrate is listed as soluble. Because one of the products is insoluble, the reaction will occur, and a precipitate will be observed.

2. A reaction will occur if one of the products is a gas. For example,

$$Na_2S(aq) + 2HCl(aq) \rightarrow H_2S(g) + 2NaCl(aq)$$

3. A reaction will occur if a molecular substance such as water is formed. For example,

$$NaOH(aq) + HCl(aq) \rightarrow H_2O(\ell) + NaCl(aq)$$

Review Questions

Set 2.4

Write and balance equations for the following synthesis reactions.

44. hydrogen and bromine forming hydrogen bromide

45. fluorine and argon forming argon trifluoride

46. sulfur and oxygen forming sulfur dioxide

47. calcium and chlorine forming calcium chloride

48. nickel and oxygen forming nickel(II) oxide

Write and balance equations for the following decomposition reactions.

49. decomposition of water into hydrogen and oxygen

50. decomposition of aluminum oxide into aluminum and oxygen

51. decomposition of sodium chloride into sodium and chlorine

52. decomposition of ammonia into hydrogen and nitrogen

53. decomposition of mercury(II) oxide into mercury and oxygen

For each of the following, indicate whether or not a single replacement reaction will occur.

54. aluminum and hydrochloric acid

55. silver and magnesium chloride

56. chromium and lead(II) nitrate

57. silver and gold(III) chloride

58. chlorine and sodium iodide

59. Identify each of the following as equations for a synthesis (*S*), decomposition (*D*), single replacement (*SR*), or double replacement (*DR*) reactions.

(a) $Zn + HCl \rightarrow ZnCl_2 + H_2$

(b) $NaClO_3 \rightarrow NaCl + O_2$

(c) $P_4 + Cl_2 \rightarrow PCl_3$

(d) $HCl + Mg(OH)_2 \rightarrow MgCl_2 + H_2O$

(e) $BaO + SO_3 \rightarrow BaSO_4$

(f) $Pb + AgNO_3 \rightarrow Ag + Pb(NO_3)_2$

(g) $AgNO_3 + Na_2CrO_4 \rightarrow Ag_2CrO_4 + NaNO_3$

(h) $Al + Fe_3O_4 \rightarrow Al_2O_3 + Fe$

(i) $HNO_3 + Mg(OH)_2 \rightarrow Mg(NO_3)_2 + H_2O$

(j) $Ba(NO_3)_2 + Na_2SO_4 \rightarrow BaSO_4 + NaNO_3$

For the following, write a balanced chemical equation to show how the ions would combine in a double replacement equation.

60. sodium bromide and silver nitrate form sodium nitrate and silver bromide

61. potassium carbonate and calcium nitrate form potassium nitrate and calcium carbonate

62. ammonium sulfate and barium chloride form ammonium chloride and barium sulfate

63. barium nitrate and potassium chromate form barium chromate and potassium nitrate

64. sodium hydroxide and calcium chloride form sodium chloride and calcium hydroxide

Unknown Reactants and Products

The law of conservation of mass requires that chemical reactions neither create nor destroy matter. When given a balanced equation in which either a reactant or a product is missing, you should be able to determine the formula of the missing substance. To do so, count the atoms in the formulas on both sides of the arrow. Subtract the atoms on the side with the missing formula from the side with the known substances. Any missing element must be present in the unknown.

As an example, look at the following equation.

$$2Na + 2H_2O \rightarrow X + 2NaOH$$

The reactant side is complete and contains two sodium atoms, four hydrogen atoms, and two oxygen atoms. One product is missing from the right side of the equation. There are two hydrogen atoms, two oxygen atoms, and two sodium atoms present in the other product. For the equation to balance, the missing substance must contain only two hydrogen atoms. What is the formula of a substance that contains two hydrogen atoms? H_2, hydrogen gas.

Determining Missing Mass in Equations

Just as the formula of a missing reactant or product can be determined, the mass of a missing substance can also be found. The law of conservation of mass again is the guiding principle. Matter can be neither created nor destroyed in a chemical reaction. The total mass of the reactants must equal the total mass of the products.

SAMPLE PROBLEM

If 103.0 g of potassium chlorate are decomposed to form 62.7 g of potassium chloride and oxygen gas according to the equation $2KClO_3 \rightarrow 2KCl + 3O_2$, how many grams of oxygen are formed?

SOLUTION: Identify the known and unknown values.

Known
mass of $KClO_3$ = 103.0 g
mass of KCl = 62.7 g

Unknown
mass of O_2 = ? g

Find the total mass of the reactants.
$KClO_3$ is the only reactant; it has a mass of 103.0 g.

The total mass of the reactants and products must be equal.

$$mass\ of\ KClO_3 = mass\ of\ KCl + mass\ of\ O_2$$
$$103.0\ g = 62.7\ g + mass\ of\ O_2$$
$$mass\ of\ O_2 = 103.0\ g - 62.7\ g$$
$$mass\ of\ O_2 = 40.3\ g$$

65. Identify the missing reactant or product in each of the following equations. Include any coefficient needed to balance the equation.

(a) $2NaHCO_3 \rightarrow Na_2CO_3 + H_2O +$ _____

(b) $BaCl_2 + K_2CO_3 \rightarrow$ _____ $+ BaCO_3$

(c) $2C_6H_6 +$ _____ $\rightarrow 12CO_2 + 6H_2O$

(d) $CaCO_3 \rightarrow CaO +$ _____

66. Identify the missing reactant or product in each of the following equations. Include any coefficient needed to balance the equation.

(a) $2Al +$ _____ $\rightarrow 2AlCl_3 + 3H_2$

(b) _____ $+ H_2O \rightarrow H_2CO_3$

(c) $2NaOH +$ _____ $\rightarrow NaOCl + NaCl + H_2O$

(d) $Cr_2O_3 + 2Al \rightarrow$ _____ $+ 2Cr$

67. Identify the missing reactant or product in each of the following equations. Include any coefficient needed to balance the equation.

(a) $2HNO_3 +$ _____ $\rightarrow Mg(NO_3)_2 + 2H_2O$

(b) $2NH_4NO_3 \rightarrow$ _____ $+ 4H_2O + O_2$

(c) $H_2SO_4 + 2NaOH \rightarrow Na_2SO_4 +$ _____

(d) $3PbO +$ _____ $\rightarrow 3Pb + N_2 + 3H_2O$

68. Identify the missing reactant or product in each of the following equations. Include any coefficient needed to balance the equation.

(a) $3Cu + 8 HNO_3 \rightarrow 3Cu(NO_3)_2 + 4H_2O +$ _____

(b) $C_6H_{11}OH \rightarrow C_6H_{10} +$ _____

(c) $4NH_3 + 5O_2 \rightarrow$ _____ $+ 6H_2O$

(d) $Ca(OH)_2 +$ _____ $\rightarrow CaCl_2 + 2H_2O$

69. Identify the missing reactant or product in each of the following equations. Include any coefficient needed to balance the equation.

(a) $2AgNO_3 +$ _____ $\rightarrow Ag_2S + 2NaNO_3$

(b) $H_2C_2O_4 + 2NaOH \rightarrow$ _____ $+ 2H_2O$

(c) $CCl_4 + 2HF \rightarrow CCl_2F_2 +$ _____

(d) _____ $+ CO_2 \rightarrow K_2CO_3$

70. What mass of carbon dioxide will be produced if 144 g of carbon react with 384 g of oxygen gas according to the equation $C + O_2 \rightarrow CO_2$?

71. How many grams of HCl are produced when 16.0 g of CH_4 react with 71.0 g of Cl_2 to produce 50.5 g of CH_3Cl and HCl according to the equation $CH_4 + Cl_2 \rightarrow CH_3Cl + HCl$?

72. Consider the following equation.
$$3C_2H_4O_2 + PCl_3 \rightarrow 3C_2H_3OCl + H_3PO_3$$
How many grams of products will be produced if 90 g of $C_2H_4O_2$ completely react with 68 g of PCl_3?

73. How many grams of silver nitrate are needed to react with 156.2 g of sodium sulfide to produce 595.8 g of silver sulfide and 340.0 g of sodium nitrate?
$$2AgNO_3 + Na_2S \rightarrow Ag_2S + 2NaNO_3$$

74. Given the equation $PbO_2 \rightarrow PbO + O_2$, how many grams of oxygen will be produced if 47.8 g of lead(IV) oxide decompose to form 44.6 g of lead(II) oxide and oxygen gas?

75. Consider the following equation.
$$2Al + 3CuSO_4 \rightarrow Al_2(SO_4)_3 + 3Cu$$
Copper metal is produced when aluminum metal is reacted with copper(II) sulfate. How many grams of copper metal will be produced if 10.8 g of aluminum react with 95.8 g of copper sulfate to produce copper metal and 68.5 g of aluminum sulfate?

76. How many grams of Fe are needed to react with 8.0 g of O_2 to produce 28.9 g of Fe_3O_4 according to the equation $3Fe + 2O_2 \rightarrow Fe_3O_4$?

77. How many metric tons of nitric acid are produced from the reaction of 10.8 metric tons of N_2O_5 reacting with 1.8 metric tons of water according to the equation $N_2O_5 + H_2O \rightarrow 2HNO_3$?

78. How many pounds of sulfur will be produced from the decomposition of 318.2 pounds of copper(I) sulfide to produce 254.0 pounds of copper metal and sulfur according to the equation $Cu_2S \rightarrow 2Cu + S$?

79. Given the equation $2HgO \rightarrow 2Hg + O_2$, how many grams of mercury(II) oxide are needed to produce 12.7 g of mercury and 3.2 g of oxygen?

Directions

Review the Test-Taking Strategies section of this book. Then answer the following questions. Read each question carefully and answer with a correct choice or response.

Part A

1 What is the chemical formula of iron(III) sulfide?
   (1) $Fe_2(SO_3)_3$ (3) $FeSO_3$
   (2) Fe_2S_3 (4) FeS

2 Two molecules of hydrogen are represented by
   (1) H_2 (2) $2H_2$ (3) $2H^+$ (4) $2H$

3 Which of the following is a polyatomic ion?
   (1) CH_3COOH (3) Na^+
   (2) $Cr_2O_7^{2-}$ (4) H_2

4 Pure oxygen reacts with metals to form
   (1) oxalates   (3) oxides
   (2) oxalites   (4) oxygenates

5 Which of the following is the formula of a compound?
   (1) Fr (3) LiH
   (2) Mn (4) O_3

6 A chemical formula represents
   (1) qualitative information only
   (2) quantitative information only
   (3) both quantitative and qualitative information
   (4) neither qualitative nor quantitative information

7 An empirical formula represents
   (1) qualitative information only
   (2) only the metallic elements in the compound
   (3) the lowest integer ratio of the elements in a compound
   (4) a multiple of the simplest ratio of the elements in a compound

8 In an endothermic reaction
   (1) energy is a product and the surrounding temperature decreases
   (2) energy is a product and the surrounding temperature increases
   (3) energy is a reactant and the surrounding temperature increases
   (4) energy is a reactant and the surrounding temperature decreases

9 A reaction in which two substances combine to form a single product is called a
   (1) decomposition
   (2) synthesis
   (3) single replacement
   (4) double replacement

10 As an exothermic reaction occurs, the surrounding temperature
   (1) decreases
   (2) increases
   (3) remains the same
   (4) depends on the reaction

Part B–1

11 What is the total number of atoms of oxygen in the formula $Mg(ClO_4)_2 \cdot 6H_2O$?
   (1) 6   (2) 8   (3) 10   (4) 14

12 Which formula is correctly paired with its name?
   (1) $MgCl_2$, magnesium chlorine
   (2) K_2O, diphosphorus oxide
   (3) $CuCl_2$, copper(II) chloride
   (4) FeO, iron(III) oxide

13 What is the IUPAC name for the compound ZnO?
   (1) zinc oxalate   (3) zinc hydroxide
   (2) zinc peroxide   (4) zinc oxide

14 Given the balanced equation representing a reaction
   $$2H_2 + O_2 \rightarrow 2H_2O$$
   What is the mass of H_2O produced when 10.0 grams of H_2 reacts completely with 80.0 grams of O_2?
   (1) 800. g   (2) 180. g   (3) 70.0 g   (4) 90.0 g

15 What is the correct formula of nickel(II) oxide?
   (1) NiO (3) NiO_2
   (2) Ni_2O (4) Ni_2O_2

16 What is the name of the compound whose formula is N_2O_5?
   (1) nitrogen oxide
   (2) dinitrogen pentoxide
   (3) pentanitrogen dioxide
   (4) dinitrogen oxide

17 Which is the correct formula of dichlorine monoxide?
   (1) ClO (2) Cl_2O (3) ClO_2 (4) OCl

18 Which of the following is a synthesis reaction?
(1) $Cu + 2AgNO_3 \rightarrow Cu(NO_3)_2 + 2Ag$
(2) $2Cu + O_2 \rightarrow 2CuO$
(3) $CuCO_3 \rightarrow CuO + CO_2$
(4) $CuO + H_2 \rightarrow Cu + H_2O$

19 Which of the following reactions will *not* take place spontaneously?
(1) $Ca + AgNO_3$ (3) $Cr + Pb(NO_3)_2$
(2) $Pb + Al(NO_3)_3$ (4) $Co + HCl$

20 Consider the following unbalanced equation.

$Mg_2Si + HCl \rightarrow MgCl_2 + SiH_4$

When the equation is balanced using the smallest whole-number coefficients, the coefficient of HCl is
(1) 1   (2) 2   (3) 3   (4) 4

21 Consider the following unbalanced equation.

$Fe + H_2O \rightarrow Fe_3O_4 + H_2$

When correctly balanced using smallest whole numbers, the sum of the coefficients is
(1) 4   (2) 7   (3) 11   (4) 12

Parts B–2 and C

Base your answers to questions 22 and 23 on the information below.

In an experiment, 2.54 grams of copper completely reacts with sulfur, producing 3.18 grams of copper(I) sulfide.

22 Determine the total mass of the sulfur consumed.

23 Write the chemical formula of the compound produced.

Base your answers to questions 24 through 26 on the information below.

A tablet of one antacid contains citric acid, $H_3C_6H_5O_7$, and sodium hydrogen carbonate, $NaHCO_3$. When the tablet dissolves in water, bubbles of CO_2 are produced. This reaction is represented by the incomplete equation below.

$H_3C_6H_5O_7(aq) + 3NaHCO_3(aq) \rightarrow$
    $Na_3C_6H_5O_7(aq) + 3CO_2(g) + 3\underline{\hspace{1cm}}$ (l)

24 Complete the equation by writing the missing chemical formula.

25 State evidence that a chemical reaction occurred when the tablet was placed in the water.

26 Determine the total number of oxygen atoms in the reactants of the balanced equation.

Use the following information to answer questions 27 and 28.

In an investigation, a dripless wax candle is massed and then lighted. As the candle burns, a small amount of liquid wax forms near the flame. After 10 minutes, the candle's flame is extinguished and the candle is allowed to cool. The cooled candle is massed.

27 Identify one physical change that takes place in this investigation.

28 State one observation that indicates that a chemical change has taken place.

---

29 Balance this equation using the lowest whole-number coefficients.

$\underline{\hspace{1cm}} C_6H_{12}O_6 \rightarrow \underline{\hspace{1cm}} C_2H_5OH + \underline{\hspace{1cm}} CO_2$

30 Identify the type of reaction represented in the equation in question 29.

Use the following information to answer questions 31 and 32.

Magnesium metal reacts with hydrochloric acid to produce hydrogen. Balance the equation for the reaction using the lowest whole-number integers.

31 $\underline{\hspace{1cm}} Mg\ (s) + \underline{\hspace{1cm}} HCl\ (aq) \rightarrow MgCl_2\ (aq) + H_2(g)$

32 What type of chemical reaction occurs during this reaction?

Use the following information to answer questions 33 and 34.

Rust contains Fe_2O_3. Given the balanced equation representing the formation of rust:

$\underline{\hspace{1cm}} Fe\ (s) + \underline{\hspace{1cm}} O_2\ (g) \rightarrow \underline{\hspace{1cm}} Fe_2O_3\ (s).$

33 Balance the equation using the smallest whole-number coefficients.

34 Identify the type of reaction represented by this equation.

The Mathematics of Formulas and Equations

How Scientists Use Math to Solve Problems

? *Why do you think chemists celebrate Mole Day on October 23?* **?**

Every October 23, chemists celebrate Mole Day! Avogadro's Number or 6.02×10^{23}, is the number of particles in a mole. Look at the "molely" math problem below.

October 23

$$
\begin{array}{r}
72 \text{ g carbon} \\
12 \text{ g hydrogen} \\
+\ 96 \text{ g oxygen} \\
\hline
6.02 \times 10^{23} \text{ molecules of glucose}
\end{array}
$$

How many molecules of glucose is this?

If each molecule were one kilogram, they would equal over 20 times the mass of Earth! Calculate how many years it would take to count 1 mole of glucose atoms at the rate of 1 molecule per second. Hint: there are about 31.5 million seconds (3.15×10^7) in a year.

The Mathematics of Formulas and Equations

Vocabulary

formula mass

gram formula mass

mole

percentage composition

Topic Overview

Math is the language of chemistry. It enables us to easily determine the amount of a chemical needed for a reaction or the amount that will be produced. In this topic you will learn how to apply simple math relations to the solving of chemical problems.

SAMPLE PROBLEM

What is the formula mass of K_2CO_3?

SOLUTION: Identify the known and unknown values.

Known
formula = K_2CO_3
atomic masses from the periodic table

Unknown
formula mass = ? amu

1. Determine the number of atoms of each element from the formula.

Element:	Number of atoms:
K	2
C	1
O	3

2. Consult the table of the elements for the atomic mass of each element, and multiply it by the number of atoms to determine the total mass for each element.

For K: 2 atoms $\times$ 39.1 amu/atom = 78.2 amu
For C: 1 atom $\times$ 12.0 amu/atom = 12.0 amu
For O: 3 atoms $\times$ 16.0 amu/atom = 48.0 amu

3. Add the total mass for each element to determine the formula mass.

$$78.2 \text{ amu}$$
$$12.0 \text{ amu}$$
$$+ \ 48.0 \text{ amu}$$

Formula mass   138.2 amu

The Mathematics of Formulas

Recall that the mass of an atom is a relative value based on the mass of a carbon-12 atom. All atoms are compared to this standard. Thus, a magnesium atom with an atomic mass of 24 amu is twice as massive as the standard carbon atom with an atomic mass of 12. This relationship will remain the same in any system of weights or masses. As long as there is a mass ratio of 12 parts of carbon to 24 parts of magnesium, equal numbers of carbon and magnesium atoms are present. Twelve grams of carbon contain the same number of atoms as 24 grams of magnesium. These mass relationships of atoms are the basis for mass relationships in compounds.

Formula Mass

Remember that compounds are represented by formulas that show the type and number of atoms present in the compound. Because compounds are represented by formulas, the mass of the smallest unit of the compound is the **formula mass,** which is the sum of the atomic masses of all the atoms present. While the term *molecular mass* is often used to represent the mass of a unit of a compound, *formula mass* is preferred because ionic and network solids do not form discrete molecules. For example, sodium bromide (NaBr) is an ionic compound. No molecules of NaBr exist, so *molecular mass* does not apply to NaBr. However, formula mass can be calculated for a formula unit of the compound. The formula mass of NaBr is the mass of one atom of Na plus the mass of one atom of Br in amu.

Gram Formula Mass The **gram formula mass** of a substance is simply the formula mass expressed in grams instead of atomic mass units. Thus, the gram formula mass of K_2CO_3 is 138.2 g. Some substances, such as sucrose (table sugar), form molecules. It is common to express the gram formula masses of molecular substances as <u>gram molecular masses</u>.

Review Questions

1. What is the gram formula mass of $Ca(OH)_2$?
(1) 29 g (3) 56 g
(2) 34 g (4) 74 g

2. Which substance has the greatest molecular mass?
(1) H_2O_2 (3) CF_4
(2) NO (4) I_2

3. What is the gram formula mass of $C_3H_5(OH)_3$?
(1) 48 g (3) 74 g
(2) 58 g (4) 92 g

4. What is the gram formula mass of Na_2CO_3?
(1) 51 g (3) 106 g
(2) 74 g (4) 138 g

5. What is the gram formula mass of $(NH_4)_3PO_4$?
(1) 113 g (3) 149 g
(2) 121 g (4) 404 g

6. What is the gram formula mass of calcium nitrate $Ca(NO_3)_2$?
(1) 70.0 g (3) 150 g
(2) 102 g (4) 164 g

7. What is the gram formula mass of Li_2SO_4?
(1) 54 g (3) 110 g
(2) 55 g (4) 206 g

8. What is the gram formula mass of $Mg(ClO_3)_2$?
(1) 107 g (3) 174 g
(2) 142 g (4) 191 g

9. What is the gram molecular mass of the compound with the formula CH_3COOH?
(1) 22.4 g (2) 44.0 g (3) 48.0 g (4) 60.0 g

10. What is the gram-formula mass of $Fe(NO_3)_3$?
(1) 242 g (2) 214 g (3) 194 g (4) 146 g

11. What is the gram-formula mass of $Al_2(SO_4)_3$?
(1) 225 g (2) 342 g (3) 386 g (4) 450 g

12. What is the gram-formula mass of $C_6H_{12}O_6$?
(1) 96 g (2) 180 g (3) 360 g (4) 600 g

13. Which quantity, expressed in grams, is equal to one mole of Au?
(1) the atomic mass
(2) the atomic number
(3) the mass of neutrons
(4) the number of neutrons

Percentage Composition

Formulas represent the composition of a substance. Using the subscripts and atomic masses of the elements, the percent by mass of a substance can be calculated. The **percentage composition** of a substance represents the composition as a percentage of each element compared with the total mass of the compound.

Hydrates Ionic substances often include definite amounts of water as part of the crystal structure. The water molecules are shown as part of the formula, such as $CuSO_4 \cdot 5H_2O$. Crystals that contain attached water molecules are called <u>hydrates</u>, while substances without water are termed <u>anhydrous</u>. If it is necessary to calculate the percentage of water in such a crystal, treat the water molecule as a single unit.

SAMPLE PROBLEM

What is the percentage of oxygen in potassium chlorate ($KClO_3$)?

SOLUTION: Identify the known and unknown values.

Known
formula = $KClO_3$
atomic masses from
  the periodic table

Unknown
%O = ? %

1. Determine the formula mass of potassium chlorate.

For K: 1 atom × 39.1 amu/atom = 39.1 amu
For Cl: 1 atom × 35.5 amu/atom = 35.5 amu
For O: 3 atoms × 16.0 amu/atom = 48.0 amu
                Formula mass = 122.6 amu

2. Calculate the percent of oxygen in the compound by dividing the mass of oxygen by the formula mass and multiplying by 100%.

$$\%O = \frac{48.0\ \text{amu}}{122.6\ \text{amu}} \times 100\%$$

$$\%O = 39.2\%$$

SAMPLE PROBLEM

What is the percentage, by mass, of water in sodium carbonate crystals, $Na_2CO_3 \cdot 10H_2O$?

SOLUTION: Identify the known and unknown values.

Known
formula = $Na_2CO_3 \cdot 10H_2O$
atomic masses from
  the periodic table

Unknown
$\%H_2O$ = ? %

1. Determine the formula mass of the crystal. (Hint: Treat the water as a unit.)

For Na: 2 atoms × 23.0 amu/atom = 46.0 amu
For C: 1 atom × 12.0 amu/atom = 12.0 amu
For O: 3 atoms × 16.0 amu/atom = 48.0 amu
For H_2O: 10 units × 18.0 amu/unit = 180.0 amu
                Formula mass = 286.0 amu

2. Calculate the percent of water in the compound by dividing the mass of water by the formula mass and multiplying by 100%.

$$\%H_2O = \frac{180.0\ \text{amu}}{286.6\ \text{amu}} \times 100\%$$

$$\%H_2O = 62.9\%$$

Review Questions

Set 3.2

14. The percent by mass of nitrogen in NH_4NO_3 is closest to

(1) 15%   (3) 35%
(2) 20%   (4) 60%

15. What is the percent by mass of carbon in CO_2?

(1) 12%   (3) 44%
(2) 27%   (4) 73%

16. What is the percent by mass of water present in $CaSO_4 \cdot 2H_2O$?

(1) 10.%   (3) 21%
(2) 12%   (4) 79%

17. Which compound has the greatest percent composition by mass of sulfur?

(1) BaS   (3) CaS
(2) MgS   (4) SrS

18. What is the percent composition by mass of oxygen in $Ca(NO_3)_2$ (gram-formula mass = 164 g/mol)?

(1) 75%   (3) 48%

(2) 59%   (4) 29%

19. What is the percent by mass of oxygen in Fe_2O_3? The formula mass of Fe_2O_3 = 160 amu.

(1) 16%   (2) 30.%   (3) 56%   (4) 70.%

20. What is the percent by mass of sulfur in sulfur dioxide?

(1) 32 %   (2) 33%   (3) 50.%   (4) 67%

21. The percent by mass of Ca in $CaCl_2$ is equal to

(1) $\dfrac{40 \text{ amu}}{111 \text{ amu}} \times 100\%$ (3) $\dfrac{3 \text{ amu}}{1 \text{ amu}} \times 100\%$

(2) $\dfrac{111 \text{ amu}}{40 \text{ amu}} \times 100\%$ (4) $\dfrac{1 \text{ amu}}{3 \text{ amu}} \times 100\%$

22. Which species contains the greatest percent by mass of hydrogen?

(1) OH^- (2) H_2O (3) H_3O^+ (4) H_2O_2

23. Which quantity can be calculated for a solid compound, using only the formula of the compound and the Periodic Table?

(1) density of the compound

(2) percent composition of the elements in the compound

(3) heat of fusion of the compound

(4) melting point of the elements in the compound

Answer each of the following questions in complete sentences.

24. A crystalline material containing 30.0 g of barium chloride crystals was placed into an oven at 400°C and heated for two hours. It was then cooled and weighed. The new mass was less than before it was heated, containing 20.0 g of barium chloride. How is this possible?

25. Copper(II) sulfate is a hydrated crystal with the formula $CuSO_4 \cdot 5H_2O$ and a deep blue color. When it is heated the crystals crumble and turn white.

(a) Propose an explanation for this change of color.

(b) What would you do to restore the blue color?

26. A chemist needs to order $Na_2B_4O_7$. One supplier offers it in an anhydrous (without water) form, while another offers it as a hydrated crystal, $Na_2B_4O_7 \cdot 10H_2O$. If the prices from the two suppliers are the same for a 500.0-g bottle, which one would supply more of the desired $Na_2B_4O_7$? Explain your answer.

The Mole

We are quite familiar with collective nouns in our everyday life. *Dozen* is a convenient word to describe 12 of something. A gross of paper contains 144 sheets, while a ream contains 500. These units enable you to count by collective units of items instead of by individual items.

Chemists use a specific collective noun to define a particularly usable number of particles. A **mole** is defined as the number of atoms of carbon present in 12.000 grams of C-12. The number of particles in a mole of a substance is 6.022×10^{23}, which is called <u>Avogadro's number</u>. While it would be impossible to individually count a mole of particles, the mass of one mole of a substance can be found by determining its gram formula mass. This quantity contains 6.02×10^{23} particles of that substance. Therefore, the gram formula mass of any substance is the mass of one mole of that substance. The accepted abbreviation for mole is mol.

Converting Grams to Moles To convert grams to moles:

$$\text{moles} = \text{number of grams} \times \frac{1 \text{ mol}}{\text{gram formula mass}}$$

Converting Moles to Grams To convert moles to grams:

$$\text{grams} = \text{number of moles} \times \frac{\text{gram formula mass}}{1 \text{ mol}}$$

SAMPLE PROBLEM

How many grams are present in 40.5 mol of sulfuric acid (H_2SO_4)?

SOLUTION: Identify the known and unknown values.

Known
moles H_2SO_4 = 40.5 mol

Unknown
mass H_2SO_4 = ? g

1. Calculate the formula mass of sulfuric acid.

   For H: 2 atoms × 1.0 amu/atom = 2.0 amu
   For S: 1 atom × 32.1 amu/atom = 32.1 amu
   For O: 4 atoms × 16.0 amu/atom = 64.0 amu
   Formula mass H_2SO_4 = 98.1 amu

2. Calculate the gram formula mass of sulfuric acid.

   gram formula mass = formula mass in grams
   gram formula mass of H_2SO_4 = 98.1 g

3. Use the gram formula mass to convert the given number of moles to grams.

   $$\text{number of grams} = \text{moles} \times \frac{\text{gram formula mass}}{1 \text{ mol}}$$

   $$\text{grams } H_2SO_4 = 40.5 \text{ mol} \times \frac{98.1 \text{ g}}{1 \text{ mol}}$$

   grams H_2SO_4 = 3970 g

SAMPLE PROBLEM

How many moles are equivalent to 4.75 g of sodium hydroxide (NaOH)?

SOLUTION: Identify the known and unknown values.

Known
mass NaOH = 4.75 g

Unknown
moles NaOH = ? mol

1. Calculate the formula mass of sodium hydroxide.

   For Na: 1 atom × 23.0 amu/atom = 23.0 amu
   For O: 1 atom × 16.0 amu/atom = 16.0 amu
   For H: 1 atom × 1.0 amu/atom = 1.0 amu
   Formula mass NaOH = 40.0 amu

2. Calculate the gram formula mass of sodium hydroxide.

   gram formula mass = formula mass in grams
   gram formula mass of NaOH = 40.0 g

3. Use the gram formula mass to convert the given mass to moles.

   $$\text{moles} = \text{number of grams} \times \frac{1 \text{ mol}}{\text{gram formula mass}}$$

   $$\text{moles NaOH} = 4.74 \text{ g} \times \frac{1 \text{ mol}}{40.0 \text{ g}}$$

   moles NaOH = 0.119 mol

Review Questions

Set 3.3

27. Which quantity is equivalent to 39 g of LiF?
    (1) 0.50 mol
    (2) 1.0 mol
    (3) 1.5 mol
    (4) 2.0 mol

28. What is the total mass of 0.75 mol of SO_2?
    (1) 16 g (2) 24 g (3) 32 g (4) 48 g

29. The mass in grams of 2 mol of H_2SO_4 is
    (1) $\dfrac{98 \text{ g}}{2}$
    (2) 2(98 g)
    (3) $\dfrac{196 \text{ g}}{2}$
    (4) 2(196 g)

30. What is the mass of 1.5 moles of CO_2?
    (1) 29 g (2) 33 g (3) 66 g (4) 88 g

31. The mass of a mole of nitrogen gas is
    (1) 7 g (2) 14 g (3) 28 g (4) 56 g

32. What is the number of moles of potassium chloride (gram formula mass = 74 g) present in 148 g of KCl?
    (1) 2.0 mol
    (2) 2.5 mol
    (3) 3.0 mol
    (4) 3.5 mol

33. How many moles are in 168 g of KOH? (gram formula mass = 56 g)

(1) 0.3 mol   (3) 1.0 mol
(2) 0.5 mol   (4) 3.0 mol

34. How many moles of oxygen atoms are in one mole of $Mg_3(PO_4)_2$?

(1) 1   (2) 4   (3) 6   (4) 8

35. What is the mass of 4.5 mol of KOH?

(1) 0.080 g   (3) 56 g
(2) 36 g   (4) 252 g

36. What is the mass of 0.50 mol of $CuSO_4 \cdot 5H_2O$?

(1) 47.8 g   (3) 125 g
(2) 95.6 g   (4) 250 g

Finding Molecular Formulas from Empirical Formulas

When the molecular mass of a compound and its empirical formula are known, it is possible to determine the correct molecular formula. For example, the molecular mass of propene is 42 amu. The empirical formula of propene is CH_2, and the molecular mass of CH_2 is 14 amu. Divide the mass of the compound by the mass of the empirical formula. The result will be an integer. In this case it is 3. This tells you that the molecular formula is three times the empirical formula. Simply multiply each subscript by three to find the molecular formula, C_3H_6.

SAMPLE PROBLEM

A compound has a molecular mass of 180 amu and an empirical formula of CH_2O. What is its molecular formula?

SOLUTION: Identify the known and unknown values.

Known
molecular mass = 180 amu
empirical formula = CH_2O

Unknown
molecular formula = ?

1. Determine the molecular mass of CH_2O:

For C: 1 atom × 12.0 amu/atom = 12.0 amu
For H: 2 atoms × 1.0 amu/atom = 2.0 amu
For O: 1 atom × 16.0 amu/atom = 16.0 amu
Molecular mass of CH_2O = 30.0 amu

2. Divide the molecular mass of the compound by the mass of the empirical formula.

$$\frac{180 \text{ amu}}{30 \text{ amu}} = 6$$

3. Multiply the subscripts in the empirical formula by 6.

$$C_{1\times6}H_{2\times6}O_{1\times6} = C_6H_{12}O_6$$

The molecular formula of the compound is $C_6H_{12}O_6$.

Review Questions

Set 3.4

37. The empirical formula of a compound is CH_4. The molecular formula of the compound could be

(1) CH_4 (2) C_2H_6 (3) C_3H_8 (4) C_4H_{10}

38. A compound with an empirical formula of CH_2 has a molecular mass of 70 amu. What is its molecular formula?

(1) CH_2 (2) C_2H_4 (3) C_4H_8 (4) C_5H_{10}

39. A compound has an empirical formula of CH and a molecular mass of 78 amu. What is the molecular formula of the compound?

(1) C_2H_2 (2) C_3H_3 (3) C_4H_4 (4) C_6H_6

40. A compound has an empirical formula of CH_2 and a molecular mass of 28 amu. What is its molecular formula?

41. A compound has an empirical formula of CH_2 and a molecular mass of 56 amu. What is its molecular formula?

42. Vitamin C has an empirical formula of $C_3H_4O_3$ and a molecular mass of 176 amu. What is its molecular formula?

43. A compound has a molecular mass of 30 amu and an empirical formula of CH_3. What is its molecular formula?

44. Why can't a substance have an empirical formula of NO and a gram-formula mass of 45 g?

Mole Relations in Balanced Equations

Chemical equations include both qualitative and quantitative information about the reaction. The formulas of the compounds give qualitative information about the nature of the reactants and products, along with some quantitative information. The coefficients represent quantitative information that relates specifically to that reaction.

In problems involving chemical reactions, the relative amounts of reactants and products are represented by the coefficients. Coefficients represent both the basic unit and mole ratios in balanced equations.

Consider the equation for the combustion of ethane, C_2H_6, as shown in Figure 3-1. The coefficients tell you that 2 mol of ethane combines with 7 mol of oxygen to produce 4 mol of carbon dioxide and 6 mol of water. These ratios will remain constant for any amounts of the substances involved, as shown in the figure.

Balanced chemical equation:

$$2C_2H_6 \; + \; 7O_2 \; \rightarrow \; 4CO_2 \; + \; 6H_2O$$

Moles C_2H_6	Moles O_2	Moles CO_2	Moles H_2O
2	7	4	6
4	14	8	12
1	3.5	2	3

Figure 3-1. Mole ratios from a balanced equation: Regardless of the number of moles of any of the reactants or products, the ratio must remain 2:7:4:6 for this reaction.

Volume Relationships of Gases in Balanced Equations

Not only do coefficients represent mole ratios in balance equations, they also represent volume relations of gases. Using the same equation in the previous sample problem, we can solve for unknown quantities of gases.

SAMPLE PROBLEM

How many liters of carbon dioxide gas will be produced from the complete combustion of 30.0 liters of ethane according to the following equation?

$$2C_2H_6(g) + 7O_2(g) \rightarrow 4CO_2(g) + 6H_2O(g)$$

SOLUTION: Identify the known and unknown values.

Known
Volume of $C_2H_6(g)$ = 30.0 L
Ratio of $C_2H_6(g)$: CO_2 = 2:4

Unknown
Vol of $CO_2(g)$ = ? liters

Set up proportion and solve:

$$\frac{30.0 \text{ L}}{2} = \frac{x}{4}$$

$$x = 60 \text{ liters}$$

SAMPLE PROBLEM

How many moles of water will be produced from the complete combustion of 3.0 mol of ethane according to the following equation?

$$2C_2H_6(g) + 7O_2(g) \rightarrow 4CO_2(g) + 6H_2O(g)$$

SOLUTION: Identify the known and unknown values.

Known
moles C_2H_6 = 3.0 mol balanced equation

Unknown
moles water = ? mol

1. Use the balanced equation to determine the mole ratio between ethane and water.

   moles ethane: moles water = 2:6

2. Set up a proportion between the known moles of ethane (3.0 mol) and the coefficient of ethane, and moles of water (x) and the coefficient of water

   $$\frac{3.0 \text{ mol } C_2H_6}{2 \text{ mol } C_2H_6} = \frac{x}{6 \text{ mol } H_2O}$$

3. Solve for the number of moles of H_2O (x).

   $$x = \frac{(3.0 \text{ mol } C_2H_6)(6 \text{ mol } H_2O)}{2 \text{ mol } C_2H_6}$$

   $$x = 9.0 \text{ mol } H_2O$$

Review Questions

Set 3.5

45. Given the reaction $4Al(s) + 3O_2(g) \rightarrow 2Al_2O_3(s)$, what is the minimum number of moles of oxygen gas required to produce 1.00 mol of aluminum oxide?

    (1) 1.0 mol   (3) 3.0 mol
    (2) 1.5 mol   (4) 6.0 mol

46. Given the reaction $4NH_3 + 5O_2 \rightarrow 4NO + 6H_2O$, what is the maximum number of moles of H_2O that can be produced when 2.0 mol of NH_3 are completely reacted?

    (1) 1.0 mol   (3) 3.0 mol
    (2) 2.0 mol   (4) 6.0 mol

47. Given the reaction $2KClO_3(s) \rightarrow 2KCl(s) + 3O_2(g)$, what is the total number of moles of $KClO_3$ needed to produce 6 mol of O_2?

    (1) 1 mol   (2) 2 mol   (3) 3 mol   (4) 4 mol

48. Given the reaction $CH_4 + 2O_2 \rightarrow CO_2 + 2H_2O$, what amount of oxygen is needed to completely react with 1 mol of CH_4?

    (1) 2 mol   (3) 2 g
    (2) 2 atoms   (4) 2 molecules

49. Given the reaction $4NH_3 + 5O_2 \rightarrow 4NO + 6H_2O$, what is the total number of moles of O_2 required to produce 40 mol of NO?

    (1) 5 mol   (2) 9 mol   (3) 32 mol   (4) 50 mol

50. Given the reaction $2CH_3OH(l) + 3O_2(g) \rightarrow 2CO_2(g) + 4H_2O(g)$, how many moles of $O_2(g)$ are needed to produce exactly 20. mol of $CO_2(g)$?

    (1) 10. mol   (3) 30. mol
    (2) 20. mol   (4) 40. mol

51. Given the reaction $4Na + O_2 \rightarrow 2Na_2O$, how many moles of oxygen are completely consumed in the production of 1.00 mol of Na_2O?

    (1) 0.50 mol   (3) 2 mol
    (2) 1 mol   (4) 4.0 mol

52. Given the reaction $Ca + 2H_2O \rightarrow Ca(OH)_2 + H_2$, what is the total number of moles of Ca needed to react completely with 4.0 mol of H_2O?

    (1) 0.50 mol   (3) 2.0 mol
    (2) 1.0 mol   (4) 4.0 mol

53. Consider the following equation.
    $$CH_4(g) + 2O_2(g) \rightarrow CO_2(g) + 2H_2O(g)$$
    How many moles of oxygen are needed for the complete combustion of 3.0 mol of $CH_4(g)$?

    (1) 2.0 mol
    (2) 3.0 mol
    (3) 4.0 mol
    (4) 6.0 mol

54. According to the reaction $2Al + 3H_2SO_4 \rightarrow 3H_2 + Al_2(SO_4)_3$, the total number of moles of H_2SO_4 needed to react completely with 5.0 mol of Al is

(1) 2.5 mol   (3) 7.5 mol
(2) 5.0 mol   (4) 9.0 mol

55. Given the equation $N_2(g) + 3H_2(g) \rightarrow 2NH_3(g)$, what is the total number of moles of NH_3 produced when 10. mol of H_2 reacts completely with N_2?

(1) 2.0 mol   (3) 6.7 mol
(2) 3.0 mol   (4) 15 mol

56. According to the equation $2K(s) + Cl_2(g) \rightarrow 2KCl(s)$, potassium reacts with chlorine to form potassium chloride. If 100 atoms of potassium react with chlorine gas, how many chlorine molecules will be needed to completely react?

57. What do coefficients represent in a balanced equation?

58. A student is given the equation $N_2 + H_2 \rightarrow NH_3$ to balance. She answers with $N_2 + 2H_2 \rightarrow 2NH_2$. Explain why her answer is not correct. Balance the equation correctly.

59. Consider the equation $H_2 + Cl_2 \rightarrow 2HCl$. A student suggests that according to the ratio shown by the coefficients, 20 g of hydrogen will react with 20 g of chlorine to form 40 g of HCl. Is the student correct? Explain.

60. The process of photosynthesis can be represented by the following equation. $6CO_2(g) + 6H_2O(\ell) + \text{energy} \rightarrow C_6H_{12}O_6(s) + 6O_2(g)$ If 4 mol of $C_6H_{12}O_6$ is produced by the process, how many moles of $CO_2(g)$ and $H_2O(\ell)$ were used?

61. How many molecules of water are needed to produce 6 molecules of $C_6H_{12}O_6$ according to the equation in the previous question?

62. How many moles of oxygen gas are produced when 6 mol of CO_2 are consumed in the process of photosynthesis? (See problem 59 for the equation.)

63. Hydrogen gas and chlorine gas react to form hydrogen chloride.

$$H_2(g) + Cl_2(g) \rightarrow 2HCl(g)$$

If 2 mol of hydrogen gas are mixed with 4 mol of chlorine gas, how many moles of hydrogen chloride will be produced?

64. In the previous question, one of the reactants will not be completely used up. Which one will not be completely used, and how many moles will not react?

65. The formula $Mg(OH)_2$ contains a total of

(1) 2 atoms   (3) 4 atoms
(2) 3 atoms   (4) 5 atoms

66. Given the balanced equation:

$$4Al(s) + 3O_2(g) \rightarrow 2Al_2O_3(s)$$

How many moles of Al(s) react completely with 4.50 moles of $O_2(g)$ to produce 3.00 moles of $Al_2O_3(s)$?

(1) 1.50 mol   (3) 2.00 mol
(2) 6.00 mol   (4) 4.00 mol

67. Given the balanced equation:

$C_2H_4(g) + 3O_2(g) \rightarrow 2CO_2(g) + 2H_2O(g)$

How many liters of CO_2 are produced when 15 liters of O_2 are consumed?

(1) 10   (2) 15   (3) 30   (4) 45

68. Given the reaction: $H_2(g) + Cl_2(g) \rightarrow 2HCl(g)$

What is the total volume of $H_2(g)$ consumed when 22.4 liters of $Cl_2(g)$ completely reacts?

(1) 11.2 L   (2) 22.4 L   (3) 44.8 L   (4) 89.6 L

69. Given the reaction:
$2C_8H_{18}(g) + 25 O_2(g) \rightarrow 16CO_2(g) + 18 H_2O(g)$

What is the total number of liters of oxygen required for the complete combustion of 4.00 liters of C_8H_{18}?

(1) 25.0   (3) 100.
(2) 50.0   (4) 200.

70. Given the balanced equation representing a reaction occurring at 101.3 kPa and 298 K:
$$2H_2(g) + O_2(g) \rightarrow 2H_2O(\ell) + \text{energy}$$

What is the net amount of energy released when *one* mole of $H_2O(\ell)$ is produced (refer to Table I)?

(1) 285.8 kJ   (3) 241.8 kJ
(2) 571.6 kJ   (4) 483.6 kJ

71. Given the balanced equation representing a reaction:
$$4NH_3(g) + 5O_2(g) \rightarrow 4NO(g) + 6H_2O(g)$$

What is the number of moles of $H_2O(g)$ formed when 2.0 moles of $NH_3(g)$ react completely?

(1) 6.00 mol
(2) 3.00 mol
(3) 2.00 mol
(4) 4.00 mol

Directions

Review the Test-Taking Strategies section of this book. Then answer the following questions. Read each question carefully and answer with a correct choice or response.

Part A

1 The term *mole* is a unit used to represent
(1) density of particles   (3) numbers of particles
(2) kinds of particles   (4) reactivity of particles

2 One mole of carbon and one mole of neon both have the same
(1) mass   (3) number of particles
(2) volume   (4) number of protons

3 The mass of a mole of a substance is equal to
(1) the atomic number in grams
(2) the mass of the most common isotope in grams
(3) the gram formula mass
(4) the mass of 22.4 L of any substance

4 A hydrated crystal is one in which
(1) water molecules are part of the crystal
(2) water molecules have been removed
(3) hydrogen molecules are part of the crystal
(4) hydrogen molecules have been removed

5 To find the percent of an element in a compound
(1) divide the atomic mass of the element by its atomic number × 100%
(2) divide the total mass of an element by the total mass of the compound × 100%
(3) multiply the atomic mass of the element by the total mass of the compound × 100%
(4) multiply the atomic mass of the elements by their subscripts × 100%

6 In a balanced equation, coefficients always represent
(1) the number of atoms present
(2) the ratio of volumes of substances
(3) the mole ratios of reactants and products
(4) the volume ratios of reactants and products

Part B–1

7 What is the gram atomic mass of zinc?
(1) 1.33 g   (2) 30. g   (3) 65 g   (4) 130. g

8 The mass of a mole of $O_2(g)$ is
(1) 8.0 g   (2) 16.0 g   (3) 24.0 g   (4) 32.0 g

9 If the mass of a mole of H_2X is 34 g, then X must represent
(1) O   (2) Cl   (3) Kr   (4) S

10 The mass of a mole of $Ca(OH)_2$ is
(1) 38 g   (2) 57 g   (3) 58 g   (4) 74 g

11 The mass of 4 moles of CO_2 is
(1) 22 g   (2) 44 g   (3) 88 g   (4) 176 g

12 What is the total number of moles in 80.0 grams of C_2H_5Cl (gram-formula mass = 64.5 grams/mole)?
(1) 0.806   (2) 1.24   (3) 2.48   (4) 5.16

13 Consider the following equation.

$$2C_2H_6 + O_2 \rightarrow 4CO_2 + 6H_2O$$

When 4 mol of C_2H_6 are burned the number of moles of CO_2 produced will be
(1) 2 mol   (2) 6 mol   (3) 7 mol   (4) 8 mol

14 Given the equation $Mg + 2HCl \rightarrow MgCl_2 + H_2$, how many moles of hydrogen chloride are needed to react with 0.50 mol of magnesium?
(1) 0.5 mol   (3) 2.0 mol
(2) 1.0 mol   (4) 4.0 mol

15 Given the balanced equation representing a reaction:
$$2CO(g) + O_2(g) \rightarrow 2CO_2(g)$$

What is the mole ratio of $CO(g)$ to $CO_2(g)$ in this reaction?
(1) 1:1   (2) 1:2   (3) 2:1   (4) 3:2

Parts B–2 and C

Base your answers to questions 16 and 17 on the following information.

Glycine, NH_2CH_2COOH, is an organic compound found in proteins. Acetamide, CH_3CONH_2, is an organic compound that is an excellent solvent. Both glycine and acetamide consist of the same four elements, but the compounds have a different molecular structure.

16 Calculate the gram-formula mass of glycine. Your response must include *both* a numerical setup and the calculated result.

17 Determine the percent composition by mass of the element carbon in the acetamide compound.

Base your answers to questions 18 through 20 on the following information.

The burning of propane gas can be represented as a balanced chemical reaction as follows:

$$C_3H_8(g) + 5O_2(g) \rightarrow 3CO_2(g) + 4H_2O(g)$$

18 Determine the gram-formula mass of the propane gas.

19 State the mole ratio represented in the equation of oxygen to carbon dioxide.

20 Calculate the number of liters of water vapor produced when 25.0 liters of oxygen gas are consumed.

Base your answers on questions 21 through 23 on the following information.

A student places a 2.50 gram sample of magnesium metal in a bottle and adds hydrochloric acid. The acid reacts with The magnesium to produce hydrogen gas and $MgCl_2$.

21 Balance the equation for this reaction of magnesium and hydrochloric acid, using the smallest whole-number coefficients.

$$\_\_\_\_Mg + \_\_\_\_HCl \rightarrow \_\_\_\_MgCl_2 + \_\_\_\_H_2$$

22 How many moles of magnesium were used in this reaction?

23 How many moles of hydrogen gas were produced if all of the magnesium reacted?

Base your answers to questions 24 through 26 on the following information.

Some dry chemicals can be used to put out forest fires. One of these chemicals is $NaHCO_3$. When $NaHCO_3(s)$ is heated, one of the products is $CO_2(g)$, as shown in the following equation:

$$NaHCO_3(s) + heat \rightarrow Na_2CO_3(s) + H_2O(l) + CO_2(g)$$

24 The equation can be correctly balanced by placing a coefficient of 2 in front of one of the formulas. Give the proper name of the compound that requires the coefficient of 2.

25 Using the properly balanced version of this equation, determine the number of moles of CO_2 produced from the complete reaction of 7.0 moles of the reactant.

26 Determine the mass (in grams) of 7.0 moles of the reactant compound.

Base your answers to questions 27 through 29 on the information below.

Vitamin C, also known as ascorbic acid, is water soluble and cannot be produced by the human body. Each day, a person's diet should include a source of vitamin C, such as orange juice. Ascorbic acid has a molecular formula of $C_6H_8O_6$ and a gram-formula mass of 176 grams per mole.

27 Determine the number of moles of vitamin C in an orange that contains 0.071 grams of vitamin C.

28 Show a proper numerical setup for calculating the percent composition by mass of oxygen in ascorbic acid.

29 Write the empirical formula for ascorbic acid.

Base your answers to questions 30 and 31 on the information below.

One process used to manufacture sulfuric acid is called the contact process. One step in this process, the reaction between sulfur dioxide and oxygen, is represented by the forward reaction in the system at equilibrium shown below.

$$2SO_2(g) + O_2(g) \rightleftharpoons 2SO_3(g) + 394 \text{ kJ}$$

30 Determine the number of moles of sulfur trioxide produced when 3.5 moles of oxygen gas is consumed in the reaction.

31 If 192 grams of sulfur dioxide are reacted completely, determine both the number of moles of sulfur dioxide reacted (the formula mass for sulfur dioxide is 64 g/mol), and the number of moles of sulfur trioxide produced.

Physical Behavior of Matter

How Scientists Study Phases of Matter

? _____

Water, water everywhere. What makes it so unique? **?**

_____

The glaciers of the world hold quantities of solid water, which, if melted, would raise the oceans and change the face of the continents. Vast quantities of gaseous water—water vapor—swirl around our heads, produced by the evaporation of liquid water and sublimation of solid water. Water vapor condenses and falls as rain. Liquid water is, well, everywhere.

So why is water so unique? It's a combination of structure and bonding that gives H_2O its unusual properties.

Learn more about phases of matter in this topic.

Physical Behavior of Matter

Vocabulary

condensation	heat	solid phase
deposition	heat of fusion	sublimation
freezing	heat of vaporization	temperature
fusion	kinetic molecular theory	vaporization
gaseous phase	liquid phase	

Digging Deeper

Glass is a common substance that appears to be a solid. However, careful analysis shows that glass does not have a true crystalline structure and is not a true solid. Over time, the particles making up glass are able to slowly flow past one another. Substances like glass are called <u>supercooled liquids</u>.

There is a fourth phase of matter, plasma. A plasma is a gas or vapor in which some or all of the electrons have been removed from the atoms.

Topic Overview

In this chapter you will first examine the solid, liquid, and gaseous phases of matter. Next, you will study how to calculate the heat exchanged during heating, cooling, and phase changes. The kinetic molecular theory will then be presented to explain the behavior of gases. Finally, you'll learn about the various means of separating mixtures.

Phases of Matter

An element, compound or mixture may exist in the form of a solid, liquid, or a gas. These three forms are called the phases of matter.

The **solid phase** contains matter that is held in a rigid form. Because of this rigid form, a substance in the solid phase has a definite volume and shape. Strong attractive forces among the particles in a solid hold the particles in fixed locations. True solids have a crystalline structure.

Particles in the **liquid phase** are not held together as rigidly as those in the solid phase. Liquid phase particles are able to move past one another. The mobility of the particles prevents liquids from having a definite shape. The particles, however, are held together with sufficient attractive force to give a liquid a definite volume.

Particles in the **gaseous phase** have minimal attractive forces holding them together. Due to this lack of attraction among particles, gases have neither a definite shape nor a definite volume. Gases spread out indefinitely unless they are confined in a container. In a closed container, the gaseous particles always expand to fill the volume of the container. A vapor is the gaseous phase of a substance that is a liquid or a solid at normal conditions. Figure 4-1 summarizes the three phases of matter.

Heating and Cooling Curves

Figure 4-2 shows the heating of a hypothetical substance from the solid phase to the gaseous phase. At time = 0,

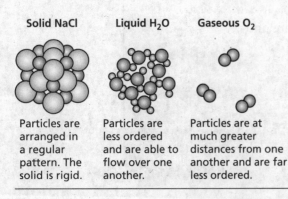

Solid NaCl	Liquid H$_2$O	Gaseous O$_2$
Particles are arranged in a regular pattern. The solid is rigid.	Particles are less ordered and are able to flow over one another.	Particles are at much greater distances from one another and are far less ordered.

Figure 4-1. Particles of matter in three phases

shown as point A on the graph, the temperature of the solid is 10°C. Heat is then added to the substance at a constant rate. From time = 0 to time = 2 minutes, the temperature rises at a constant rate until the temperature of the solid reaches its melting point (B). During this portion of the process (AB), the kinetic energy of the substance is increasing.

Eventually some of the particles in the substance possess enough kinetic energy to break the bonds holding them in the solid phase; <u>melting</u>, also known as **fusion,** begins (B). During the melting process (BC), the temperature remains constant even though heat is still being added at a constant rate. During this time, the heat is absorbed by the substance in the form of potential energy. Both solid and liquid phases of the substance are present during the melting process. As time goes on, the amount of liquid continually increases and the amount of solid continually decreases. Because the liquid phase of a substance has more potential energy than the solid phase, the potential energy of the substance increases during the melting process. The unchanging temperature during melting is evidence of the fact that the substance's kinetic energy remains constant during the process. The amount of heat needed to convert a solid at its melting point to a liquid is called the heat of fusion.

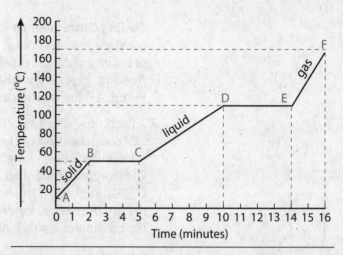

Figure 4-2. A typical heating curve: The heating of a solid (AB), liquid (CD), and gas (EF) results in an increase in the substance's temperature. Phase changes that occur during melting (BC) and boiling (DE) are not accompanied by temperature changes.

When all of the solid has melted (C) and only the liquid phase is present, the temperature once again begins to rise. This temperature rise is due to the increase in kinetic energy of the substance. The temperature continues to rise until the <u>boiling point</u> is reached (D). <u>Boiling</u>, also known as **vaporization,** begins as some of the particles in the liquid have enough kinetic energy to break free from the attractive forces holding them in the liquid phase. These particles escape the liquid and enter the gas phase. Once boiling begins, the temperature remains constant as the substance's potential energy increases. During this phase change, both the liquid and gaseous (vapor) phases are present. Because the gaseous phase of a substance has more potential energy than the liquid phase, the potential energy of the substance increases as heat is absorbed during the boiling process. If heat is added to the substance in its gas phase, the temperature of the gas begins to rise (EF).

Heating Curve Summary All of the steps (AB, BC, CD, DE, and EF) shown in Figure 4-2 are endothermic.

AB: heating of a solid, one phase present, kinetic energy increases
BC: melting of a solid, two phases present, potential energy increases, kinetic energy remains constant
CD: heating of a liquid, one phase present, kinetic energy increases
DE: boiling of a liquid, two phases present, potential energy increases, kinetic energy remains constant
EF: heating of a gas, one phase present, kinetic energy increases

Endothermic reactions absorb heat energy (heat is a reactant). Exothermic reactions release heat energy (heat is a product).

Cooling Curve Summary If a gas at high temperature is allowed to cool at a constant rate, a cooling curve results. See Figure 4-3. Note that the reverse of boiling is called **condensation,** and the reverse of melting is called **freezing.** Freezing is also called underlinesolidification. All of the steps shown in Figure 4-3 are exothermic.

AB: cooling of a gas (vapor), one phase present, kinetic energy decreases
BC: condensation of the gas (vapor) to liquid, two phases present, potential energy decreases, kinetic energy remains constant
CD: cooling of a liquid, one phase present, kinetic energy decreases
DE: solidification (freezing) of a liquid, two phases present, potential energy decreases, kinetic energy remains the same
EF: cooling of a solid, one phase present, kinetic energy decreases

Sublimation and Deposition

Heating and cooling curves show the normal transitions between phases. Some substances, however, change directly from a solid to a gas without passing through a noticeable liquid phase. An example is solid carbon dioxide (CO_2), which changes from a solid to a gas at normal atmospheric pressure. This process, in which a solid changes directly into a gas, is called **sublimation.** A substance that undergoes sublimation is said to underlinesublime. The reverse of the sublimation process, in which a gas changes directly into a solid, is called **deposition.**

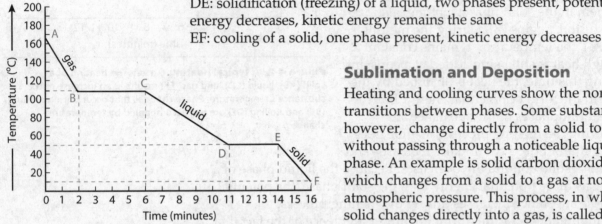

Figure 4-3. A typical cooling curve: The cooling of a gas (AB), liquid (CD), and solid (EF) results in a decrease in the substance's temperature. Phase changes occurring during condensation (BC) and freezing (DE) are not accompanied by temperature changes.

Review Questions

Set 4.1

1. Which substance has a definite shape and a definite volume at STP?

   (1) NaCl(*aq*)   (3) $CCl_4(\ell)$
   (2) $Cl_2(g)$ (4) $AlCl_3(s)$

2. At STP, which element has a definite shape and volume?

   (1) Ag   (2) Hg   (3) Ne   (4) Xe

3. Which sample is most likely to take the shape of and occupy the total volume of its container?

   (1) $CO_2(g)$
   (2) $CO_2(\ell)$
   (3) $CO_2(aq)$
   (4) $CO_2(s)$

4. As a substance changes from a liquid to a gas, the average distance between molecules

   (1) decreases
   (2) increases
   (3) remains the same

5. Which substance takes the shape of and fills the volume of any container into which it is placed?

   (1) $H_2O(\ell)$ (3) $I_2(s)$
   (2) $CO_2(g)$ (4) $Hg(\ell)$

6. Which sample of matter sublimes at room temperature and standard pressure?

   (1) $Br_2(\ell)$ (3) $CO_2(s)$
   (2) $Cl_2(g)$ (4) $SO_2(aq)$

7. Which phase change represents sublimation?

   (1) $H_2O(\ell) \rightarrow H_2O(s)$ (3) $I_2(s) \rightarrow I_2(g)$
   (2) $H_2O(\ell) \rightarrow H_2O(g)$ (4) $I_2(s) \rightarrow I_2(\ell)$

8. Which phase change represents sublimation?

   (1) $NH_3(\ell) \rightarrow NH_3(g)$ (3) $KI(s) \rightarrow KI(\ell)$
   (2) $CO_2(s) \rightarrow CO_2(g)$ (4) $H_2O(\ell) \rightarrow H_2O(s)$

9. At 1 atm, equal masses of $H_2O(s)$, $H_2O(\ell)$, and $H_2O(g)$ have

   (1) different volumes
   (2) the same density
   (3) different percent compositions
   (4) the same molecular spacing

10. A solid substance initially at a temperature below its melting point is heated at a constant rate. The heating curve for the substance is shown in the graph below.

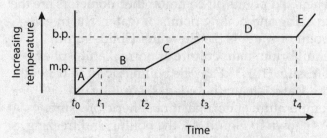

Which portions of the graph represent times when heat is absorbed and potential energy increases while kinetic energy remains constant?

(1) A and B
(2) B and D
(3) A and C
(4) C and D

11. A solid substance initially at a temperature below its melting point is heated at a constant rate. The heating curve for the substance is shown in the graph below.

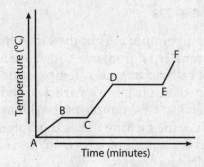

Which segment of the graph represents a time when both the solid and liquid phases are present?

(1) AB　(2) BC　(3) DE　(4) EF

12. A gaseous substance initially at a temperature above its boiling point is cooled at a constant rate. The cooling curve for the substance is shown below.

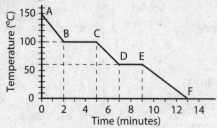

How much time passes between the first appearance of the liquid phase of the substance and the presence of the substance completely in its solid phase?

(1) 5 minutes
(2) 2 minutes
(3) 7 minutes
(4) 4 minutes

13. The heat of fusion is defined as the energy required (at constant temperature) to change a

(1) gas to a liquid
(2) gas to a solid
(3) solid to a gas
(4) solid to a liquid

14. During which process is potential energy decreasing and average kinetic energy remaining the same?

(1) A liquid is converted to a solid at its freezing point.
(2) A solid is converted to a liquid at its melting point.
(3) A gas is cooled from a temperature of 120°C to 115°C.
(4) A liquid is heated from 38°C to 58°C.

15. Which physical change is endothermic?

(1) $CO_2(\ell) \rightarrow CO_2(s)$
(2) $CO_2(g) \rightarrow CO_2(\ell)$
(3) $CO_2(g) \rightarrow CO_2(s)$
(4) $CO_2(s) \rightarrow CO_2(g)$

16. Which phase change is exothermic?

(1) $H_2O(s) \rightarrow H_2O(\ell)$
(2) $H_2O(\ell) \rightarrow H_2O(s)$
(3) $H_2O(s) \rightarrow H_2O(g)$
(4) $H_2O(\ell) \rightarrow H_2O(g)$

Temperature Scales

The **temperature** of a substance is a measure of the average kinetic energy of its particles. The particles of all substances at the same temperature have the same average kinetic energy. The temperature difference between two bodies indicates the direction of heat flow. That is, whenever two objects with different temperatures are in contact, heat flows from the object at the higher temperature to the object at the lower temperature. The heat flow continues until the two objects are at the same temperature.

The average kinetic energy depends only on the temperature of the substance, and not on the nature or amount of the material. Thus, 10 g of H_2O at 50°C has greater average kinetic energy than 500 g of Fe(s) at 20°C.

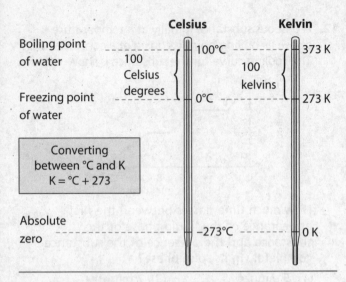

Celsius   **Kelvin**

Boiling point of water ----- 100°C ⌐ 373 K

{ 100 Celsius degrees }   { 100 kelvins }

Freezing point of water ----- 0°C ----- 273 K

Converting between °C and K
K = °C + 273

Absolute zero ----- −273°C ----- 0 K

Figure 4-4. Comparison of Celsius and Kelvin temperature scales

Temperature is measured using a thermometer. Thermometers are calibrated by establishing two fixed reference points; the distance between them is then divided into the desired number of units. The fixed points on common thermometers are the freezing and boiling points of water. The freezing point of water is the ice–water (solid–liquid) equilibrium temperature at normal atmospheric pressure (101.3 kPa). The boiling point of water is the water–steam (liquid–gas) equilibrium temperature at normal atmospheric pressure. As shown in Figure 4-4, the boiling and freezing reference points are used on both the <u>Celsius</u> and <u>Kelvin</u> temperature scales. Note that there are 100 units between the two reference points on both the Celsius and Kelvin scales.

Because there are an equal number of divisions between the fixed reference points of both the Celsius and Kelvin scales, a change of one degree Celsius is equal to a change of one Kelvin. A change of 50°C represents the same temperature change as 50 Kelvins. The Celsius and Kelvin scales are related by the following equation:

$$K = °C + 273$$

Although often confused, heat and temperature are not the same. **Heat** is a measure of the amount of energy transferred from one substance to another. Heat is measured in units of calories or joules. Temperature is a measure of the average kinetic energy of a substance's particles, and is measured in degrees Celsius or in Kelvins. An example of the difference between heat and temperature involves the melting of ice. It requires more energy to melt 10 g of ice than it does to melt 1 g of ice, yet in both cases the temperature of the ice does not change.

SAMPLE PROBLEM

What Kelvin temperature is equivalent to 35°C?

SOLUTION: Identify the known and unknown values.

Known
temperature = 35°C

Unknown
temperature = ? K

Substitute the known temperature into the equation relating Kelvin and Celsius, and solve.

$K = °C + 273$
$K = 35 + 273$
$K = 308$

308 K is equivalent to 35°C.

17. Which property is a measure of the average kinetic energy of the particles in a sample of matter?

(1) mass   (3) pressure
(2) temperature   (4) density

18. Which unit is used to express the amount of energy absorbed or released during a chemical reaction?

(1) degree   (3) gram
(2) torr   (4) joule

19. Which list includes three forms of energy?

(1) chemical, mechanical, electromagnetic
(2) chemical, mechanical, temperature
(3) thermal, pressure, electromagnetic
(4) thermal, pressure, temperature

20. The minimum number of fixed reference points required to establish the Celsius temperature scale for a thermometer is

(1) 1   (2) 2   (3) 3   (4) 4

21. What are the fixed reference points on the Celsius thermometer?

(1) 32 and 100   (3) 32 and 212
(2) 0 and 212   (4) 0 and 100

22. The difference between the boiling point and the freezing point of pure water at standard pressure is

(1) 32 K   (2) 273 K   (3) 100 K   (4) 373 K

23. What is the freezing point of water on the Kelvin scale at standard pressure?

(1) 0 K   (2) 32 K   (3) 100 K   (4) 273 K

24. Which sample of copper has atoms with the *lowest* average kinetic energy?

(1) 40. g at 15°C   (3) 20. g at 35°C
(2) 30. g at 25°C   (4) 10. g at 45°C

25. Energy is added to a substance. Compared to the Celsius temperature of the substance, the Kelvin temperature

(1) will always be 273 greater
(2) will always be 273 lower
(3) will have the same reading at 0
(4) will have the same reading at 273

26. What Kelvin temperature is equal to −73°C?

(1) 100 K   (2) 173 K   (3) 200 K   (4) 346 K

27. Which temperature is equal to 20 K?

(1) −253°C   (2) −293°C   (3) 253°C   (4) 293°C

28. Compared to a 26-gram sample of Cu(s) at STP, the atoms of a 52-gram sample of Fe(s) have

(1) a higher average kinetic energy
(2) a lower average kinetic energy
(3) the same average kinetic energy
(4) twice as much average kinetic energy

29. Which temperature change indicates an increase in the average kinetic energy of the molecules in a sample?

(1) 305 K to 0°C   (3) 15°C to 298 K
(2) 355 K to 25°C   (4) 37°C to 273 K

Measurement of Heat Energy

The amount of heat given off or absorbed in a reaction can be calculated using the following equation:

$$q = mC\Delta T$$

q = heat (in joules) C = specific heat capacity of substance
m = mass of the substance ΔT = (Temperature$_{initial}$ − Temperature$_{final}$)

SAMPLE PROBLEM

How many joules are absorbed when 50.0 g of water are heated from 30.2°C to 58.6°C?

SOLUTION: Identify the known and unknown values.

Known	*Unknown*
m = 50.0 g	q = ? J
C_{water} = 4.18 J/g•°C	
ΔT = (58.6°C − 30.2°C) = 28.4°C	

Substitute the known values into the formula $q = mC\Delta T$ and solve for q.

q = (50.0 g)(4.18 J/g•°C)(28.4°C)
q = 5936 J = 5.94 × 10^3 J

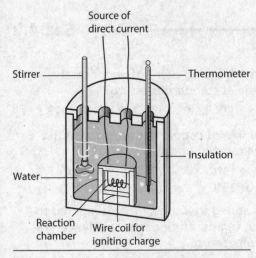

Stirrer

Source of
direct current

Thermometer

Insulation

Water

Reaction
chamber

Wire coil for
igniting charge

Figure 4-5. Cutaway drawing showing the components of a calorimeter

As shown in Figure 4-5, a device known as a calorimeter can be used to measure the amount of heat given off in a reaction. The reaction takes place in the reaction chamber, and the heat released by the reaction is absorbed by the surrounding water. By measuring the temperature increase of the water, the heat given off in the reaction can be calculated.

Whenever a substance undergoes a temperature change, the equation $q = mc\Delta T$ can be used to calculate the heat involved. However, this equation cannot be used to determine the amount of heat required to melt or boil a substance. Why? Temperature remains constant during a phase change, so there is no ΔT, and the equation cannot be used. Recall from Figure 4-2 that the line segment BC represents the melting of a substance. To determine the heat required for a phase change such as this, you must use an equation involving the substance's heat of fusion.

Heat of Fusion

The amount of heat needed to convert a unit mass of a substance from solid to liquid at its melting point is called the **heat of fusion.** The heat of fusion of solid water (ice) at 0°C and 1 atmosphere is 334 J/g. The heat absorbed by the substance during the melting process increases the potential energy of the substance without increasing the average kinetic energy of the substance's particles. Because there is no change in kinetic energy, there is no temperature change during the process.

SAMPLE PROBLEM

How many joules are required to melt 255 g of ice at 0°C?

SOLUTION: Identify the known and unknown values.

Known
$m = 255$ g
heat of fusion $= 334$ J/g

Unknown
$q = ?$ J

Multiply the heat of fusion by the total mass of ice to determine the heat required.

$q = (255 \text{ g})(334 \text{ J/g}) = 85,170$ J $= 85.2$ kJ

The process of melting is an endothermic process, that is, it requires heat. Therefore, the reverse process of freezing (also called solidification) must be exothermic. During the freezing process, water releases 334 J/g of heat and its potential energy decreases.

Heat of Vaporization

During the boiling process, a substance in the liquid phase is converted to the gaseous (vapor) phase. The temperature remains constant during the boiling process even though energy is constantly added. The heat energy increases the potential energy of the particles in the gaseous phase. The amount of heat needed to convert a unit mass of a substance from its liquid phase to its vapor phase at constant temperature is called its **heat of vaporization.** As heat is added, the particles absorb sufficient energy to overcome the attractive forces holding them in the liquid phase. The potential energy of the system increases as the temperature remains constant. The heat of vaporization of water at 100°C and 1 atmosphere is 2260 J/g.

The condensation process is the reverse of boiling process. Therefore the heat of condensation is also 2260 J/g. Condensation is an exothermic process.

SAMPLE PROBLEM

How many joules of energy are required to vaporize 423 g of water at 100°C and 1 atm?

SOLUTION: Identify the known and unknown values.

Known	*Unknown*
m = 423 g	q = ? J
heat of fusion = 2260 J/g	

Multiply the heat of vaporization by the total mass of water to determine the heat required.

q = (423 g)(2260 J/g) = 955,980 J = 956 kJ

Review Questions
Questions
Set 4.3

30. When 25.0 grams of water are cooled from 20.0°C to 10.0°C, the number of joules of heat energy released is
    (1) 42
    (2) 105
    (3) 840
    (4) 1050

31. How many joules of heat energy are released when 50.0 g of water are cooled from 70.0°C to 60.0°C?
    (1) 41.8 J
    (2) 2.09×10^3 J
    (3) 209 J
    (4) 4.18×10^3 J

32. What is the total number of joules of heat energy absorbed when the temperature of 200.0 g of water is raised from 10.0°C to 40.0°C?
    (1) 126 J
    (2) 840. J
    (3) 2.51×10^4 J
    (4) 3.36×10^4 J

33. How many kilojoules of heat energy are absorbed when 100.0 g of water are heated from 20.0°C to 30.0°C?
    (1) 4.18 kJ
    (2) 41.8 kJ
    (3) 418 kJ
    (4) 0.418 kJ

34. What is the amount of heat energy released when 50.0 grams of water is cooled from 20.0°C to 10.0°C?
    (1) 5.00×10^2 J
    (2) 1.67×10^5 J
    (3) 2.09×10^3 J
    (4) 1.13×10^6 J

35. A 100.-gram sample of $H_2O(\ell)$ at 22.0°C absorbs 8360 joules of heat. What will be the final temperature of the water?
    (1) 25.7°C
    (2) 42.0°C
    (3) 18.3°C
    (4) 20.0°C

36. When 20.0 g of a substance are completely melted at its melting point, 3444 J are absorbed. What is the heat of fusion of this substance?
    (1) 41 J/g
    (2) 172 J/g
    (3) 16,400 J/g
    (4) 68,900 J/g

37. The total amount of heat required to completely vaporize a 100.-gram sample of water at its normal boiling point is
    (1) 2.26×10 J
    (2) 2.26×10^2 J
    (3) 2.26×10^3 J
    (4) 2.26×10^5 J

For each of the following problems, be sure to show your work, use the proper units, and express your answer to the correct number of significant figures.

38. A sample of water is heated from 10.0°C to 15.0°C by the addition of 125 J of heat. What is the mass of the water?

39. What is the total number of joules absorbed by 65.0 g of water when the temperature of the water is raised from 25.0°C to 40.0°C?

40. If 100.0 J are added to 20.0 g of water at 30.0°C, what will be the final temperature of the water?

41. The temperature of 50.0 g of water was raised to 50.0°C by the addition of 1.0 kJ of heat energy. What was the initial temperature of the water?

42. What would be the temperature change if 3.0 g of water absorbed 15 J of heat?

43. What is the total number of kilojoules of heat needed to change 150. g of ice to water at 0°C?

44. What is the total number of kilojoules required to completely boil 100.0 g of water at 100.0°C and 1 atmosphere?

45. How much energy is required to vaporize 10.00 g of water at its boiling point?

46. At 1 atmosphere of pressure, 25.0 g of a compound at its normal boiling point are converted to a gas by the addition of 34,400 J. What is the heat of vaporization for this compound in J/g?

Behavior of Gases

Scientists construct models to explain the behavior of substances. While the gas laws describe how gases behave, they do not explain why gases behave the way they do. The **kinetic molecular theory** (KMT) is a model or theory that is used to explain the behavior of gases. This theory describes the relationships among pressure, volume, temperature, velocity, frequency, and force of collisions.

Kinetic Molecular Theory

The major ideas of kinetic molecular theory are summarized in the following statements:

- Gases contain particles (usually molecules or atoms) that are in constant, random, straight-line motion.
- Gas particles collide with each other and with the walls of the container. These collisions may result in a transfer of energy among the particles, but there is no net loss of energy as the result of these collisions. The collisions are said to be perfectly elastic.
- Gas particles are separated by relatively great distances. Because of this, the volume occupied by the particles themselves is negligible and need not be accounted for.
- Gas particles do not attract each other.

Relationship of Pressure and Numbers of Gas Particles The kinetic molecular theory easily explains why gases exert pressure. Not only do gas molecules collide with each other, but they also collide with the walls of their container. These collisions with the container wall exert a force over the surface area of the wall—the particles exert pressure on the wall. For example, if you add more air to a bicycle tire, the pressure is increased. The greater the number of air particles, the greater the pressure. Pressure and the number of gas molecules are directly proportional.

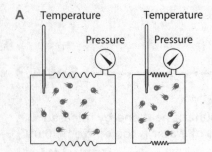

A Temperature   Temperature
Pressure   Pressure

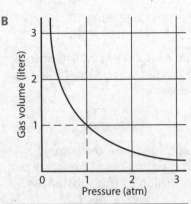

B

Gas volume (liters) vs Pressure (atm)

Figure 4-6. Pressure-volume relationship: (A) At constant temperature, as the volume of a gas decreases, the pressure it exerts increases. **(B)** This graph shows the variation of gas volume with changing pressure at constant temperature. *PV* = constant

Relationship of Pressure and Volume of a Gas Picture a cylinder with a piston at one end. If the piston can be pushed in, the volume will decrease. The molecules of the gas become more concentrated and hit the walls of the container more often. The pressure increases. If the piston is moved outward so as to increase the volume, the molecules hit the walls less often, causing a decrease in pressure. Thus volume and pressure are indirectly, or inversely, related. If one of the variables (volume or pressure) increases, the other must decrease.

Relationship of Temperature and Pressure of a Gas You may recall that the temperature of a substance is defined as a measure of the average kinetic energy of its particles. The kinetic energy (KE) is given by the formula $KE = (\frac{1}{2})mv^2$. As the temperature rises, the kinetic energy increases. This increase is due not to an increase in the mass of the particles, but rather to an increase in their velocity. As the temperature rises, the velocity of the particles increases, causing them to hit the walls of the container more often and with greater force. Thus an increase in temperature causes the pressure to increase. Pressure and temperature are directly related.

Relationship of Temperature and Volume of a Gas If the volume of a container could change while the pressure remained constant, how would volume and temperature be related? As the temperature increases, the molecules push harder on the piston of the container. When the internal pressure of the container exceeds the pressure pushing from the outside, the piston is pushed upward and the volume increases. The piston continues to move until the internal and external pressures are equal. Thus volume and temperature are directly related.

Relationship of Temperature and Velocity You know that as the temperature of a substance increases, its kinetic energy increases. What is the cause of this increase in temperature? Obviously, the masses of the particles do not increase; therefore, it must be the velocity of the particles that increases. The higher the temperature, the greater the average velocity of the particles.

Combined Gas Law Equation The relationships among pressure, temperature, and volume can be mathematically represented by an equation known as the combined gas law.

$$\frac{P_1V_1}{T_1} = \frac{P_2V_2}{T_2}$$

This law can be used to solve problems involving the gas properties of temperature (T, which must be in Kelvins to avoid introducing negative values), volume (V), and pressure (P) whenever two or more of these properties are involved. For problems in which two of the properties are involved and the third property remains constant, simply cancel out the variable representing the constant property and then solve for the remaining unknown.

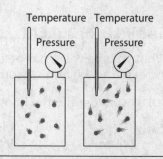

Figure 4-7. Temperature-pressure relationship: At constant volume, as the temperature of a gas increases, the pressure it exerts increases.

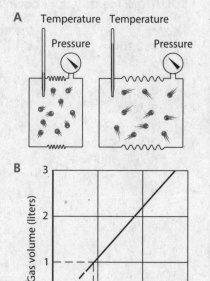

Figure 4-8. Temperature-volume relationship: (A) At constant pressure, as the temperature of a gas increases, the volume it occupies increases. **(B)** This graph shows the variation of gas volume with changing Kelvin temperature at constant pressure. V/T = a constant

SAMPLE PROBLEM

What volume will a gas occupy if the pressure on 244 cm^3 gas at 4.0 atm is increased to 6.0 atm? Assume the temperature remains constant.

SOLUTION: Identify the known and unknown values.

Known
$V_1 = 244$ cm^3
$P_1 = 4.0$ atm
$P_2 = 6.0$ atm
$T = $ constant

Unknown
$V_2 = ?$ cm^3

1. Since temperature remains constant, delete the T variable from the combined gas law equation.

$$\frac{P_1V_1}{T_1} = \frac{P_2V_2}{T_2} \quad \text{yields} \quad P_1V_1 = P_2V_2$$

2. Rearrange the equation to solve for V_2.
$$V_2 = (P_1V_1)/P_2$$

3. Substitute the known values and solve.
$$V_2 = (244 \text{ cm}^3)(4.0 \text{ atm})/(6.0 \text{ atm}) = 160 \text{ cm}^3$$

SAMPLE PROBLEM

If 75 cm^3 of a gas is at STP, what volume will the gas occupy if the temperature is raised to 75°C and the pressure is increased to 945 torr?

SOLUTION: Identify the known and unknown values:

Known
$P_1 = 760$ torr
$V_1 = 75$ cm^3
$T_1 = 0°C$
$P_2 = 945$ torr
$T_2 = 75°C$

Unknown
$V_2 = ?$ cm^3

1. Convert the known temperatures into Kelvin.
$$T_1 = 0 + 273 = 273 \text{ K}$$
$$T_2 = 75 + 273 = 348 \text{ K}$$

2. Solve the combined gas law equation for V_2.
$$V_2 = \frac{P_1V_1T_2}{P_2T_1}$$

3. Substitute the known values and solve for V_2.
$$V_2 = \frac{(760 \text{ torr})(75 \text{ cm}^3)(348 \text{ K})}{(945 \text{ torr})(273 \text{ K})}$$
$$V_2 = 77 \text{ cm}^3$$

Ideal Versus Real Gases

Kinetic molecular theory explains the behavior of gases by using a model gas called an "ideal" gas. When the gas laws are used to solve problems involving "real" gases, the answers obtained often do not exactly match the results obtained in the lab. This is because the ideal gas model does not exactly match the behavior of real gases. These discrepancies arise from the fact that two of the assumptions made by kinetic molecular theory are not exactly correct.

- **Gas particles do not attract one another.** In most cases, the attractive forces between gas particles are so small that they can be disregarded. However, when conditions become extreme, these small forces become important. For example, water molecules in the atmosphere attract each other when temperatures become cold enough. The water molecules combine to form snow or rain.

- **Gas particles do not occupy volume.** Although gas particles themselves occupy a small volume of space under normal conditions, as pressure increases the volume occupied by the particles can no longer be ignored. At high pressures, the increased concentration of particles leads to more frequent collisions and far greater chances of combining.

A gas is said to be "ideal" if it behaves exactly as predicted. Although no gas is truly "ideal," hydrogen and helium are nearly ideal in behavior. In general, gases vary from ideal behavior because of two factors: increasing mass and increasing polarity. These factors become important as pressure is increased and temperature is decreased. Gases are most ideal at low pressures and high temperatures.

Avogadro's Hypothesis

Avogadro proposed a rather startling theory about equal volumes of gases. He stated that when the volume, temperature, and pressure of two gases were the same, they contained the same number of molecules. Thus, 12 liters of nitrogen at STP would contain the same number of molecules as 12 liters of oxygen at STP, or for that matter, the same number of molecules as any gas at those conditions. Today, we believe that 22.4 liters of any gas at STP contains one mole of the gas. For example, 22.4 liters of neon contains one mole of neon—10g. One mole of any substance contains 6.02×10^{23} molecules, a number called Avogadro's number.

Memory Jogger

Standard temperature and pressure (STP) is defined as one atmosphere of pressure and a temperature of 0°C (273 K).

Pressure is defined as force per unit area. In chemistry, pressure is often expressed in units of torr, millimeters of mercury (mm Hg), atmospheres (atm), and kilopascals (kPa). Normal atmospheric pressure is 760 torr, 760 mm Hg, 1 atm, and 101.3 kPa.

Review Questions   Set 4.4

47. What volume will a 300.0 mL sample of a gas at STP occupy when the pressure is doubled at constant temperature?

(1) 150.0 mL   (3) 2000. mL
(2) 600.0 mL   (4) 4000. mL

48. The volume of a sample of a gas at 273°C is 200.0 L. If the volume is decreased to 100.0 L at constant pressure, what will be the new temperature of the gas?

(1) 0 K   (2) 100 K   (3) 273 K   (4) 546 K

49. At constant pressure, how does the volume of 1 mole of an ideal gas vary?

(1) directly with the Kelvin temperature
(2) indirectly with the Kelvin temperature
(3) directly with the mass of the gas
(4) indirectly with the mass of the gas

50. Which graph best shows the change in the volume of 1 mole of nitrogen gas as pressure increases and temperature remains constant?

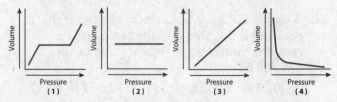

51. Which graph best shows the relationship between Kelvin temperature and average kinetic energy?

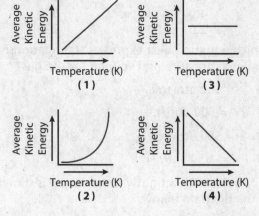

52. Under which conditions will the volume of a given sample of a gas always decrease?

(1) decreased pressure and decreased temperature
(2) decreased pressure and increased temperature
(3) increased pressure and decreased temperature
(4) increased pressure and increased temperature

53. At constant temperature, the relationship between the volume (*V*) of a gas and its pressure (*P*) is

(1) $V = (\text{constant})P$
(2) $P = (\text{constant})V$
(3) $PV = \text{constant}$
(4) $V/P = \text{constant}$

54. Which changes in pressure and temperature occur as a given mass of gas at 0.5 atm and 546 K is changed to STP?

(1) The pressure is doubled and the temperature is halved.
(2) The pressure is doubled and the temperature is doubled.
(3) The pressure is halved and the temperature is halved.
(4) The pressure is halved and the temperature is doubled.

55. As the temperature of a gas is increased from 0°C to 10°C at constant pressure, the volume of the gas

(1) increases by $\frac{1}{273}$

(2) increases by $\frac{10}{273}$

(3) decreases by $\frac{1}{273}$

(4) decreases by $\frac{10}{273}$

56. The table below shows the changes in the volume of a gas as the pressure changes at constant temperature.

Pressure (atm)	Volume (mL)
0.5	1000
1.0	500
2.0	250

Which equation best expresses the relationship between pressure and volume for the gas?

(1) $\frac{P}{V} = 500$ atm•mL

(2) $PV = 500$ atm•mL

(3) $\frac{V}{P} = 500$ atm•mL

(4) $PV = 1/500$ atm•mL

57. A cylinder with a tightly fitted piston is shown in the diagram below.

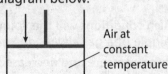

Air at constant temperature

As the piston moves downward, the number of molecules of air in the cylinder

(1) decreases
(2) increases
(3) remains the same

58. A gas has a volume of 1000 mL at a temperature of 20. K and a pressure of 760 mm Hg. What will be the new volume when the temperature is changed to 40.0 K and the pressure is changed to 380 mm Hg?

(1) 250 mL   (3) 4000 mL
(2) 1000 mL   (4) 5600 mL

59. The graph below represents the relationship between pressure and volume of a gas at constant temperature. The product of pressure and volume is constant.

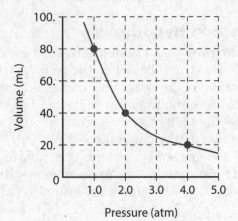

According to the graph, what is the product of pressure and volume (in atm•mL)?

(1) 20.   (2) 40.   (3) 60.   (4) 80.

60. A sample of gas has a volume of 12 liters at 0°C and 380 torr. What will be its volume when the pressure is changed to 760 torr at a constant temperature?

(1) 24 L   (2) 18 L   (3) 12 L   (4) 6.0 L

61. A 2.5 liter sample of gas is at STP. When the temperature is raised to 273°C and the pressure remains constant, the new volume of the gas will be

(1) 1.25 L   (2) 2.5 L   (3) 5.0 L   (4) 10.0 L

62. A gas occupies a volume of 500. mL at a pressure of 380. torr and a temperature of 298 K. At what temperature will the gas occupy a volume of 250. mL and have a pressure of 760. torr?

(1) 149 K
(2) 298 K
(3) 447 K
(4) 596 K

63. A gas at STP has a volume of 1.0 liter. If the pressure is doubled and the temperature remains constant, the new volume of the gas will be

(1) 0.25 L   (2) 2.0 L   (3) 0.5 L   (4) 4.0 L

64. A rigid cylinder with a movable piston contains a sample of gas. At 300. K, this sample has a pressure of 240. kPa and a volume of 70.0 mL. What is the volume of this sample when the temperature is changed to 150. K and the pressure is changed to 160. kPa?

(1) 70.0 mL   (3) 35.0 mL
(2) 105 mL   (4) 52.5 mL

65. A rigid cylinder with a movable piston contains 50.0 liters of gas at 30.0⁰C with a pressure of 1.00 atmosphere. What is the volume of the gas in the cylinder at STP?

(1) 5.49 L   (2) 55.5 L   (3) 45.0 L   (4) 455 L

66. When a sample of a gas is heated in a sealed, rigid container from 200. K to 400 K, the pressure exerted by the gas is?

(1) increased by a factor of 2
(2) decreased by a factor of 2
(3) increased by a factor of 20
(4) decreased by a factor of 20

Separation of Mixtures

The properties of a mixture's components often provide a means by which they can be separated. Density, molecular polarity, freezing point, and boiling point are a few of the properties that can be used to separate the components of mixtures. In this section you will learn some techniques that can be used to separate the components of mixtures.

Filtration

Many mixtures are made up of solids in a liquid. The solids are not dissolved in the liquid, but may be suspended. When allowed to stand undisturbed, the solids will settle to the bottom of the liquid. In some cases, you can separate the two components of the mixture by carefully pouring off the liquid without disturbing the solid. This method, though inefficient, can sometimes be used.

A filter is a material that allows small particles to pass through while trapping larger particles on or in the filter material. In essence, the filter is a material containing holes. Particles that are smaller than the holes pass through, while larger particles cannot pass through the holes and are trapped. A mixture of a solid in a liquid can often be separated by filtration. As the mixture passes through the filter, the solid is retained on the filter paper, while the liquid passes through. The substance that passes through the filter is called the filtrate, while the substance remaining on the filter is called the residue.

Filters are also commonly used to separate mixtures of solids and gases. Air conditioners have filters that allow the air to pass through while trapping solids such as lint and dust. Cars and trucks have similar filters.

Some mixtures are composed of two liquids. Two liquids that are not soluble in each other are termed <u>immiscible</u>. Oil and water is an example of such a mixture. Because the oil has a density less than water, the oil rises to the top when the mixture is allowed to stand. In some cases, it is possible to simply pour off the upper layer into a separate container. Figure 4-9 shows a separatory funnel that can be used to separate two liquids that do not dissolve in each other. After the two liquids have been allowed to separate, the valve is opened and the more dense liquid flows from the bottom of the funnel.

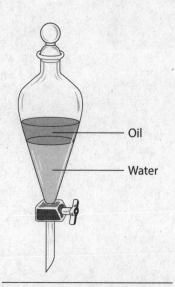

Oil

Water

Figure 4-9. Separatory funnel: Two immiscible liquids can be separated with a separatory funnel. When the valve is opened, the denser liquid flows from the funnel.

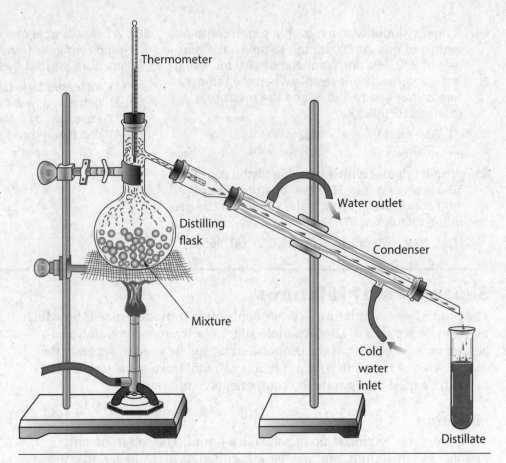

Thermometer

Water outlet

Condenser

Distilling flask

Cold water inlet

Mixture

Distillate

Figure 4-10. A simple distillation apparatus

Distillation

When solids are dissolved in liquids, making a homogeneous solution, they may be separated by distillation. Figure 4-10 shows a typical distillation apparatus. In the case of a salt and water mixture, the solution is heated and the water begins to boil. The steam passes from the distilling flask into the condensing tube. A water jacket lowers the temperature of the steam. The steam condenses and is collected. The salt remains in the distillation flask.

Liquids that mix with each other are called <u>miscible</u>. If miscible liquids have different boiling points, they may also be separated by the process of distillation. Alcohol and water are miscible liquids that form a solution. Alcohol has a lower boiling point than the water, and it vaporizes first. The alcohol vapors escape the distillation flask and are converted back to a liquid in the condenser. Water, with its higher boiling point, remains in the distillation flask.

Gasoline is obtained from crude oil by the process of distillation. Crude oil is a mixture of many different carbon compounds having different boiling points. The parts of the crude oil are separated into various parts, called fractions, by distillation. Gasoline is one of the lighter fractions. It has a relatively low boiling point when compared with other fractions such as diesel oil or home heating oil.

Chromatography

The process known as chromatography can also be used to separate the components of a mixture. The different components of a mixture often have different attractions for substances not in the mixture. For example, when a piece of paper is dipped into some inks, the water in the ink begins to rise by capillary action. The other components of the ink are drawn up along with the water, but they move up the paper at different rates. Because the components of the ink move at different rates, they begin to separate from each other as they move up the paper.

There are many types of chromatography. Gas chromatography allows gases to pass through a medium separating the components of the gaseous mixture. In all chromatography techniques, the principle remains the same—the components of the mixture have different attractions with the transporting medium. Figure 4-11 shows two common chromatography techniques.

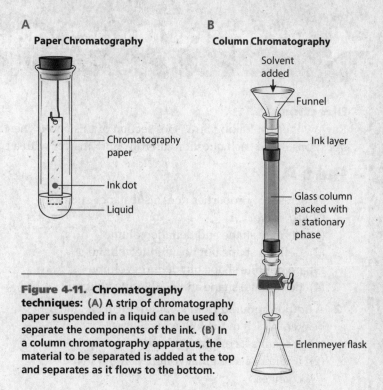

Figure 4-11. Chromatography techniques: (A) A strip of chromatography paper suspended in a liquid can be used to separate the components of the ink. **(B)** In a column chromatography apparatus, the material to be separated is added at the top and separates as it flows to the bottom.

Review Questions

Set 4.5

67. By using a paper filter, which of the following can be separated?

    (1) two immiscible liquids
    (2) two heterogeneous solids
    (3) a solid in a liquid
    (4) two miscible liquids

68. Equal amounts of ethanol and water are mixed at room temperature and at 101.3 kPa. Which process is used to separate ethanol from the mixture?

    (1) reduction   (3) filtration
    (2) distillation   (4) ionization

69. Crude oil is separated into its components by

    (1) fractional distillation
    (2) filtration
    (3) paper chromatography
    (4) column chromatography

70. The principle that allows paper chromatography to separate mixtures depends on the different components having

    (1) different boiling points
    (2) different attractions to the paper
    (3) different densities
    (4) similar solubility in water

71. A mixture consists of sand and an aqueous salt solution. Which procedure can be used to separate the sand, salt, and water from each other?

    (1) Filter out the sand, then evaporate the water.
    (2) Filter out the salt, then evaporate the water.
    (3) Evaporate the water, then filter out the salt.
    (4) Evaporate the water, then filter out the sand.

Directions
Review the Test-Taking Strategies section of this book. Then answer the following questions. Read each question carefully and answer with a correct choice or response.

Part A

1 Which set of properties does a substance such as $CO_2(g)$ have?
 (1) definite shape and definite volume
 (2) definite shape but no definite volume
 (3) no definite shape but definite volume
 (4) no definite shape and no definite volume

2 A liquid is poured from a volumetric flask into a beaker. Which of the following is true?
 (1) It retains its original volume and shape.
 (2) It retains its original volume, but its shape changes.
 (3) It retains its original shape, but its volume changes.
 (4) Both the volume and shape change.

3 The heat required to change 1 gram of a solid at its normal melting point to a liquid at the same temperature is called the heat of
 (1) vaporization   (3) reaction
 (2) fusion   (4) formation

4 Which statement best describes the molecules of H_2O in the solid phase?
 (1) They move slowly in straight lines.
 (2) They move rapidly in straight lines.
 (3) They are arranged in a regular geometric pattern.
 (4) They are arranged in a random pattern.

5 As the temperature of a substance rises, the average kinetic energy of the particles making up the substance
 (1) increases
 (2) decreases
 (3) remains the same

6 When a substance melts, it undergoes a process known as
 (1) condensation   (3) sublimation
 (2) fusion   (4) vaporization

7 Which sample of CO_2 has a definite shape and a definite volume?
 (1) $CO_2(aq)$ (3) $CO_2(s)$
 (2) $CO_2(l)$ (4) $CO_2(g)$

8 Which of the following is a unit of heat energy?
 (1) torr   (3) gram
 (2) degree   (4) joule

9 Which energy transfer occurs when ice cubes are placed in water that has a temperature of 45°C?
 (1) Chemical energy is transferred from the ice to the water.
 (2) Chemical energy is transferred from the water to the ice.
 (3) Thermal energy is transferred from the ice to the water.
 (4) Thermal energy is transferred from the water to the ice.

Part B–1

10 The graph below represents the uniform heating of a substance, starting below its melting point, when the substance is solid.

Which line segments represent an increase in average kinetic energy?

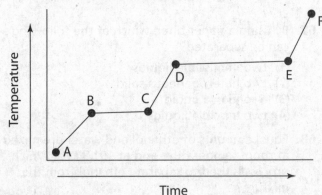

 (1) AB and BC   (3) BC and DE
 (2) AB and CD   (4) DE and EF

11 A liquid's freezing point is −38°C and its boiling point is 357°C. How many Kelvins are there between the boiling point and the freezing point of the liquid?
 (1) 319   (3) 592
 (2) 395   (4) 668

12 A mixture of sand and table salt can be separated by filtration because the substances in the mixture differ in
(1) boiling point   (3) solubility in water
(2) density at STP   (4) freezing point

13 Which Celsius temperature is equivalent to 323 K?
(1) 50°C   (3) 273°C
(2) 212°C   (4) 596°C

14 When steam condenses to water, the surrounding temperature
(1) decreases
(2) increases
(3) remains the same

15 Which grouping of the three phases of bromine is listed in order from left to right for increasing distance between bromine molecules?
(1) gas, liquid, solid
(2) liquid, solid, gas
(3) solid, gas, liquid
(4) solid, liquid, gas

16 A sealed, rigid 1.0-liter cylinder contains He gas at STP. An identical sealed cylinder contains Ne gas at STP. These two cylinders contain the same number of
(1) atoms   (3) ions
(2) electrons   (4) protons

17 Which graph best represents a change of phase from a gas to a solid?

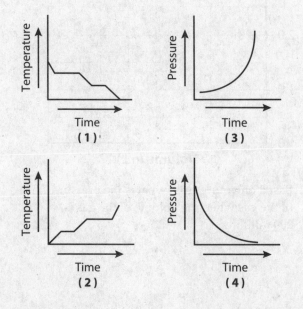

Parts B–2 and C

Base your answers to questions 18 through 20 on the following information.

A student heats a 15.0 gram metallic sphere of unknown composition to a temperature of 98°C. The sphere is transferred to a calorimeter containing 100. mL of water at a temperature of 25.0°C. The student observes that the resulting temperature of both the water and the object is 27.1°C after the object is submerged.

18 Describe, in terms of the object and the water, the flow of heat energy that took place during the experiment.

19 Calculate the amount of heat energy gained by the water in the calorimeter.

20 Using the quantity of heat calculated in the previous question, determine the specific heat of the object.

Base your answers to questions 21 through 23 on the information below.

A student prepared two mixtures, each in a labeled beaker. Enough water at 20.°C was used to make 100 milliliters of each mixture.

Information about Two Mixtures at 20.°C

	Mixture 1	Mixture 2
Composition	NaCl in H_2O	Fe filings in H_2O
Student Observations	• colorless liquid • no visible solid on bottom of beaker	• colorless liquid • black solid on bottom of beaker
Other Data	• mass of NaCl(s) dissolved = 2.9 g	• mass of Fe(s) = 15.9 g • density of Fe(s) = 7.87 g/cm³

21 Classify *each* mixture using the term "homogeneous" or the term "heterogeneous".

22 Remembering that density is equal to the mass of an object divided by its volume, determine the volume of the Fe filings used to produce mixture 2.

23 Describe a procedure to physically remove the water from mixture 1.

Base your answers to questions 24 through 26 on the information below.

Heat is added to a 200.-gram sample of $H_2O(s)$ to melt the sample at 0°C. Then the resulting $H_2O(l)$ is heated to a final temperature of 65°C.

24. Determine the total amount of heat required to completely melt the sample.

25. Show a numerical setup for calculating the total amount of heat needed to raise the temperature of the water from 0°C to its final temperature.

26. Compare the amount of heat needed to melt the sample at its melting point to the amount of heat needed to vaporize the sample at its boiling point.

___

27. A light bulb contains argon gas at a temperature of 295 K and at a pressure of 75 kilopascals. The light bulb is switched on and after 30 minutes, the temperature is 418 K. If the volume of the bulb remains constant, what is the pressure at 418 K?

Use the following information and graph to answer questions 28 through 30.

The graph below shows a compound being cooled at a constant rate starting in the liquid phase at 75°C and ending at 15°C.

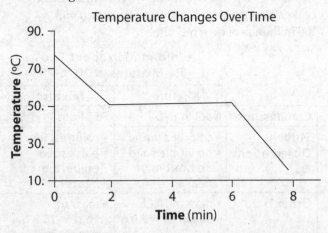

Temperature Changes Over Time

28. What is the freezing point of the compound in degrees Celsius?

29. State what is happening to the average kinetic energy of the particles of the sample between minutes 2 and 6.

30. If a total of 780 joules of energy is lost by 25.0 grams of this substance between 2 and 6 minutes, determine the heat of fusion (H_f) of this substance.

Use the following information to answer questions 31 and 32.

A gas sample is held at a constant temperature in a closed system. The volume of the gas is changed, which causes the pressure of the gas to change. Volume and pressure data are shown in the table. below.

Volume and Pressure of a Gas Sample

Volume (mL)	Pressure (atm)
1200	0.5
600	1.0
300	2.0
150	4.0
100	6.0

31. Mark an appropriate scale on the axis labeled "Volume (mL)", plot the data and connect the points.

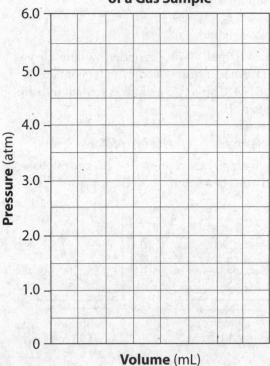

Pressure Versus Volume of a Gas Sample

32. Based on your graph, what is the pressure of the gas when the volume of the gas is 200 milliliters?

The Periodic Table

How Scientists Use the Periodic Table

Is a Russian periodic table the same as an American periodic table?

The first periodic table was developed in Russia almost 150 years ago. Look at part of the original periodic table in the picture below. Even though you might not be able to read Russian, think about what you know about the periodic table. See if you can answer these questions:

- What portion of the table is shown? How do you know?
- What information is given about each element?
- What seems to be different from a modern periodic table?

ПЕРИОДИЧЕСКАЯ СИСТЕМА ЭЛЕМЕНТОВ Д.И.МЕНДЕЛЕЕВА

The Periodic Table

Vocabulary

atomic radius	ionic radius	noble gas
electronegativity	ionization energy	nonmetal
family	metal	periodic law
group	metalloid	period

Topic Overview

Look in almost any chemistry classroom or lab here in the United States, or for that matter, almost anywhere in the world, and you will find a periodic table. The table is a brilliant arrangement of the elements used by chemists everywhere. Just finding a given element in the periodic table tells you much about an element.

Currently, more than 100 elements are known. Most of them occur naturally, while others are made artificially. These elements vary greatly in their physical and chemical properties as well as in the characteristics of their compounds. It has long been recognized that if the elements could be classified, it would simplify their study. In this topic we will present the arrangement of the periodic table. Next, we will examine different types of elements. Finally, trends of important properties will be considered.

Classifying Elements

While there were early attempts to classify and arrange the elements in some orderly fashion, it was Dmitri Mendeleev, a Russian chemist, who is given credit for first arranging elements in a usable manner. Mendeleev observed that when the elements were arranged in order of increasing atomic mass, similar chemical and physical properties appeared at regular, or periodic, intervals. Mendeleev's work in the middle of the nineteenth century laid the basis for the periodic table as we know it today.

However, in Mendeleev's periodic table, the properties of several pairs of elements, such as iodine and tellurium, seemed out of order. If they were switched on the table, the properties would match better, but they would not be in order of increasing atomic mass.

The modern periodic table is not arranged by increasing atomic mass, but rather by increasing atomic number. Henry Moseley, an English scientist, used X rays to identify the atomic number of the elements. If the elements were listed by increasing atomic number, the properties repeated periodically. Modern **periodic law** states: *The properties of the elements are periodic functions of their atomic numbers.*

Table Information about the Elements

The periodic table is an arrangement of the elements, from left to right across each descending row, in order of increasing atomic number. The periodic table used in the *Reference Tables for Physical Setting/Chemistry* displays some properties of each of the elements. To fully understand some of the information the periodic table provides, refer to Figure 5-1 as the boxes on the periodic table are discussed.

Chemical Symbols

The symbol of each element is usually found in the center of the box. With over 100 elements to refer to, a symbol is a short and easy way to indicate what element you're talking about, and scientists all over the world can identify an element by its symbol.

Each symbol has one, two, or three letters. The first letter is capitalized, and any other letters present are lower case.

The symbol is related to the name of the element, although sometimes the relationship is not obvious. For example, carbon has an obvious symbol of C. Sodium, however, has the symbol Na, which comes from its Latin name of *natrium*.

Symbols are assigned by an organization known as IUPAC after agreement on the name of a newly discovered element. Agreement has now been reached for a total of 114 elements including numbers 1-112, ending with the element copernicium, Cn. Additionally elements Fl (114) and Lv (116) have been added. Systematic names are assigned to identify these elements as shown in Fig. 5-2. For example # 118 has the systematic symbol of Ununoctium.

Other Information about the Elements

In the boxes on the periodic table in this book, the atomic number is located below and to the left of the symbol. Below the atomic number is the electron configuration showing how the electrons are arranged according to their energy levels. The atomic mass is above the symbol and to the left. Selected oxidation states are in the upper right-hand corner of the box.

Often, a periodic table will include the name of the element and its state at room temperature. Not all tables include electron configuration and common oxidation states. The information provided by a periodic table will often depend on what information is needed. A periodic table used to

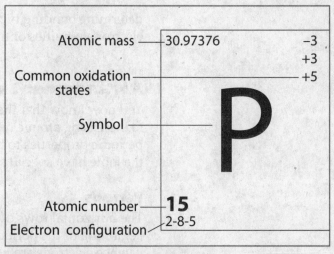

Figure 5-1. Sample information from the periodic table: Although the information about the elements can differ from one periodic table to another, some information, such as atomic mass, atomic number, and symbol, are common to almost all tables.

Roots Used for Naming Elements			
Digit	**Root**	**Digit**	**Root**
0	nil	5	pent
1	un	6	hex
2	bi	7	sept
3	tri	8	oct
4	quad	9	enn

Un un oct ium

118

Figure 5-2. Prefixes used in systematic names: To name elements with atomic numbers greater than 108, use the prefix for each digit, then add *-ium* to the end of the third prefix. For example, Element 118 would have the systematic symbol of Ununoctium.

The decimal atomic masses given for each element on the periodic table are the weighted average of the masses of the isotopes of that element.

determine bonding types, for example, might just include the symbols and electronegativities of the elements.

Arrangement of the Periodic Table

You now know that the elements on the periodic table are listed according to increasing atomic number. But how does this arrangement allow periodic properties to be seen? As you will learn, the columns and rows of the table have special significance.

Periods

The horizontal rows of the table are called **periods.** The number at the beginning of the period indicates the principal energy level in which the valence electrons are located for the atoms of that period. Potassium (K) and bromine (Br) are members of Period 4, so they have valence electrons in the fourth principal energy level.

In each period, the number of valence electrons increases from left to right, and the properties of the elements change systematically across a period. For example, the elements on the left side of the table have common properties that are described in the next section; these elements are called **metals.** Metals comprise about 75% of all the elements. To the right of the middle of the table are elements called **metalloids,** which have some properties of both metals and nonmetals. On most periodic tables, the metalloids are located adjacent to a diagonal, stair-step line. To the right of

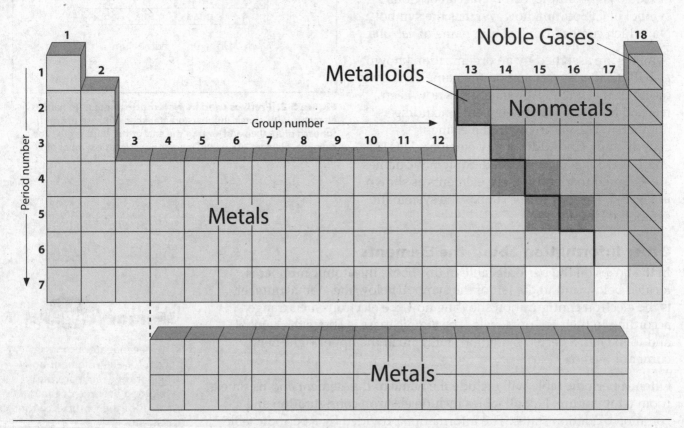

Figure 5-3. A trend from left to right across a period: Metals are found on the left of the periodic table; metalloids, on the staircase; and nonmetals and noble gases on the right side.

the metalloids, each period contains one or more elements with properties also described in the next section; these elements are known as **nonmetals**. Each period of the table ends with a noble gas. The metals and metalloids are all solid with the exception of mercury, a liquid. Nonmetals include solids, a liquid (bromine), and gases. Figure 5-3 summarizes this trend on the periodic table.

Groups, or Families

The vertical columns of the periodic table are called **groups,** or **families.** With a few exceptions, each member of a given group contains the same number of valence electrons. The number of valence electrons for each element is shown as the last number in the electron configuration. Phosphorus, in Group 15, has an electron configuration of 2-8-5. Thus, phosphorus has five valence electrons. All the members of Group 15 have five valence electrons. The elements in Group 18 have eight valence electrons. Helium, in Group 18, is an exception, having only two valence electrons. Because it is the number of valence electrons that determines much of the chemical reactivity of the element, the members of a given group have similar chemical properties.

Types of Elements

You've just seen that most elements are metals, and some are metalloids or nonmetals. An element can be classified as one of these types according to where it is located on the periodic table. The properties of each type of element are quite important in determining how it can be used.

Metals

Remember that most known elements are metals. The most active metals are located in Groups 1 and 2. In any group of the periodic table, the metallic properties of the elements increase from the top to the bottom of the group.

General Properties of Metals

- Metals are solids at room temperature, with the exception of mercury, which is a liquid.
- Most of the metals have densities greater than water, but the alkali metals (Group 1) will float.
- Metals are <u>malleable</u>, which means that they can be hammered into a shape.
- Metals are <u>ductile</u>, which means that they can be drawn or pulled into a wire.
- Metals have <u>luster</u>, which means that they are shiny.
- Metals are good conductors of heat and electricity. This property stems from the mobility of their valence electrons.
- Metals have relatively low ionization energy and electronegativity values.
- Metals tend to lose electrons to form positive ions with smaller radii. (See Figure 5-4A.)

Transition Elements The elements of Groups 3 through 12 are called the transition elements, or sometimes the transition metals. The transition elements in each period represent a series of elements in which the outermost *d* orbitals are being filled. For example, in Period 4, the transition elements proceed from scandium to zinc. Going from left to right across these elements, the 3*d* orbitals are being filled.

Transition elements are typically hard solids with high melting points, with the notable exception of mercury.

Transition elements are characterized by multiple oxidation states. When the transition elements react, they may use electrons from both *s* and *d* sublevels. The ionization energies of the *d*-orbital electrons have values close to those of their *s* electrons, and different numbers of electrons can be removed, resulting in different oxidation states. In general, the transition elements are far less reactive than the metals of Groups 1 and 2.

Another rather unique property of transition elements is that they often form ions that have color. The transition elements have several empty or half-filled *d* orbitals of nearly equal energy content. White light shining on these elements can excite electrons to slightly higher orbitals by the absorption of energy. When the electrons return to their ground state, they emit energy with the frequencies of visible colors.

Metalloids

The metalloids (B, Si, Ge, As, Sb, and Te), sometimes called semimetals, are sandwiched between the metals and the nonmetals. They can be found adjacent to the diagonal, stair-step line on the periodic table used in this book. Metalloids represent an intermediate type of element, displaying both metallic and nonmetallic properties.

Nonmetals

Although the properties of nonmetals vary more than those of metals, some standard properties can be observed.

General Properties of Nonmetals

- Many nonmetals are gases or molecular or network solids at room temperature. Bromine is an exception, being a liquid at room temperature.
- Nonmetals are not malleable or ductile; they tend to be brittle in the solid phase.
- Solid nonmetals lack luster, and their surface appears dull.
- Nonmetals have high ionization energy and high electronegativity values.
- Nonmetals are poor conductors of heat and electricity.
- Nonmetals tend to gain electrons to become negative ions with radii larger than their atoms. (See Figure 5-4B.)

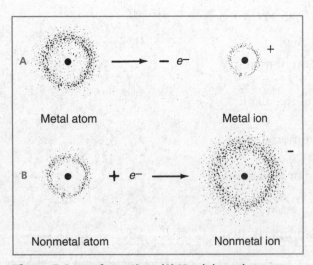

Figure 5-4. Ion formation: (A) Metals have three or fewer valence electrons. They tend to lose these electrons during chemical reactions, forming positive ions. (B) Nonmetals have four or more valence electrons. The more valence electrons a nonmetal has, up to seven, the more likely it is to gain electrons, forming a negative ion.

Noble Gases

The elements in Group 18 are called the **noble gases.** Noble gases don't have all the properties of nonmetals because they are generally unreactive. Only a few stable compounds containing noble gases have been formed.

Each of these elements has a completely filled outer energy level (valence level) of electrons. The valence level of helium is filled with only two electrons, whereas the rest of the noble gases have a complete <u>octet</u> (eight electrons), which is an extremely stable electron configuration.

Allotropes Some nonmetals can exist in two or more forms in the same phase. These forms are called <u>allotropes</u>. Oxygen ($O_2(g)$) and ozone ($O_3(g)$) are examples of allotropes. Table 5-1 compares some physical properties of oxygen and ozone.

Table 5-1. Properties of Oxygen and Ozone

Property	Oxygen (O_2)	Ozone (O_3)
Molecular mass (amu)	32	48
Melting point (K)	54.3	80.5
Boiling point (K)	90.2	161.7
Density (g/cm^3)	1.14	1.61

The table shows that allotropes have different physical properties. They also differ chemically. Ozone is a much stronger oxidizing agent than molecular oxygen and can cause serious damage to organic molecules. In the upper layers of the atmosphere, ozone absorbs harmful ultraviolet rays preventing them from reaching ground level.

Other nonmetals also show allotropy. Carbon is found as graphite, diamond, and buckminsterfullerene, which has a formula of C_{60}. Phosphorus can be found as yellow (white), red, and black allotropes.

Review Questions
Set 5.1

1. The observed regularities in the properties of the elements are periodic functions of their

   (1) atomic numbers
   (2) mass numbers
   (3) oxidation states
   (4) nonvalence electrons

2. Elements in Mendeleev's periodic table were arranged according to their

   (1) atomic number
   (2) atomic mass
   (3) relative activity
   (4) relative size

3. Most of the groups in the periodic table of the elements contain

   (1) nonmetals only
   (2) metals only
   (3) nonmetals and metals
   (4) metals and metalloids

4. An element is a gas at room temperature. It could be

   (1) a metal or a metalloid
   (2) a metal or a nonmetal
   (3) a metalloid or a nonmetal
   (4) a nonmetal only

5. Atoms of metals tend to

(1) lose electrons and form negative ions
(2) lose electrons and form positive ions
(3) gain electrons and form negative ions
(4) gain electrons and form positive ions

6. A solid element that is malleable, a good conductor of electricity, and reacts with oxygen is classified as a

(1) metalloid   (3) noble gas
(2) metal   (4) nonmetal

7. When a metal atom combines with a nonmetal atom, the nonmetal atom will

(1) lose electrons and decrease in size
(2) lose electrons and increase in size
(3) gain electrons and decrease in size
(4) gain electrons and increase in size

8. A Mg atom differs from a Mg^{2+} ion in that the atom has a

(1) smaller radius   (3) smaller nucleus
(2) larger radius   (4) larger nucleus

9. Which of the following elements has an ionic radius smaller than its atomic radius?

(1) neon   (3) sodium
(2) nitrogen   (4) sulfur

10. When a potassium atom reacts with a bromine atom, the potassium atom will

(1) lose only 1 electron   (3) gain only 1 electron
(2) lose 2 electrons   (4) gain 2 electrons

11. At room temperature, potassium is classified as

(1) a metallic solid   (3) a network solid
(2) a molecular solid   (4) an ionic solid

12. At room temperature, which substance is the best conductor of electricity?

(1) nitrogen   (3) sulfur
(2) neon   (4) silver

13. The element arsenic has the properties of

(1) metals only
(2) nonmetals only
(3) both metals and nonmetals
(4) neither metals nor nonmetals

14. Which list of elements contains two metalloids?

(1) Ga, Ge, Sn   (3) C, Si, Ge
(2) Si, P, S   (4) B, C, N

15. Which set of elements contains a metalloid?

(1) K, Mn, As, Ar   (3) Ba, Ag, Sn, Xe
(2) Li, Mg, Ca, Kr   (4) Fr, F, O, Rn

16. Which group of elements contains a metalloid?

(1) Group 2   (3) Group 8
(2) Group 18   (4) Group 16

17. Which element in Period 4 is classified as an active nonmetal?

(1) Ga   (3) Br
(2) Ge   (4) Kr

18. At STP, oxygen exists in two forms, $O_2(g)$ and $O_3(g)$. These two forms of oxygen have

(1) the same molecular structure and different properties
(2) different molecular structure and the same properties
(3) different molecular structures and different properties
(4) different molecular structures and the same properties

19. The element sulfur is classified as a

(1) nonmetal   (3) metalloid
(2) metal   (4) noble gas

20. Which element in Period 2 of the periodic table is the most reactive nonmetal?

(1) carbon   (3) oxygen
(2) nitrogen   (4) fluorine

21. Which element is brittle in the solid phase and is a poor conductor of heat and electricity?

(1) calcium   (3) sulfur
(2) strontium   (4) copper

22. Which element in Period 4 is classified as an active metal?

(1) Ca   (3) Br
(2) V   (4) Ge

23. The presence of which ion usually produces a colored solution?

(1) K^+ (3) Fe^{2+}
(2) F^- (4) S^{2-}

24. Which set of properties is most characteristic of transition elements?

(1) colorless ions in solution, multiple positive oxidation states
(2) colorless ions in solution, multiple negative oxidation states
(3) colored ions in solution, multiple positive oxidation states
(4) colored ions in solution, multiple negative oxidation states

25. Which salt contains an ion that forms a colored solution?

(1) $Mg(NO_3)_2$
(2) $Ca(NO_3)_2$
(3) $Ni(NO_3)_3$
(4) $Al(NO_3)_3$

26. Which group in the periodic table contains an element that can form a blue sulfate compound?

(1) 1
(2) 2
(3) 11
(4) 17

27. Aqueous solutions of compounds containing element X are blue. Element X could be

(1) carbon
(2) copper
(3) sodium
(4) potassium

28. Pure silicon is chemically classified as a metalloid because silicon

(1) is malleable and ductile
(2) is an excellent conductor of heat and electricity
(3) exhibits hydrogen bonding
(4) exhibits metallic and nonmetallic properties

29. Which compound forms a colored aqueous solution?

(1) $CaCl_2$
(2) $CrCl_3$
(3) NaOH
(4) KBr

Properties of Elements

Some periodic properties of elements, such as metallic character, already have been discussed. However, many other properties of elements can be predicted based on the period or group the element belongs to.

Ionization Energy

The amount of energy needed to remove the most loosely bound electron from a neutral gaseous atom is called the **ionization energy** of the element.

$$X + energy \rightarrow X^+ + e-$$

Atoms with more than one electron have more than one ionization energy, but this first ionization energy is most significant.

Trends in a Period Figure 5-5 illustrates the periodic function of ionization energy. Values from left to right across a period generally increase. Notice that the same pattern is seen in the two periods shown. As the atoms are considered from left to right of the table, an increase in the number of protons is revealed. As the nuclear charge increases, the electrons are more strongly attracted, and hence more energy is needed to remove them from the atom.

Trends in a Group Figure 5-6 shows the ionization energy from the top to the bottom of Group 2. The ionization energy decreases because valence electrons in each successive element are at a higher energy level and, thus, farther from the nucleus. It is easier to remove them when they are farther from the positive charge of the nucleus and shielded from it by other levels of electrons.

Atomic Radii

The radius of an atom is a good measure of the size of the atom. The **atomic radius** is defined as half the distance between two adjacent atoms in a crystal or half the distance between nuclei of identical atoms that are bonded together. Several methods can be used to determine the atomic radius of an element. No matter how the radius is measured, certain trends remain constant.

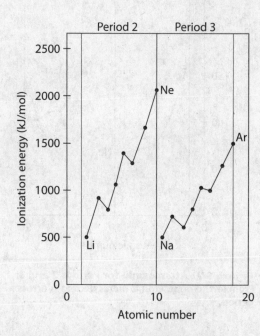

Figure 5-5. Ionization energy of Periods 2 and 3: In general, ionization energy increases from left to right across a period. The peaks in the lines result from the increased stability of filled and half-filled sublevels of electrons.

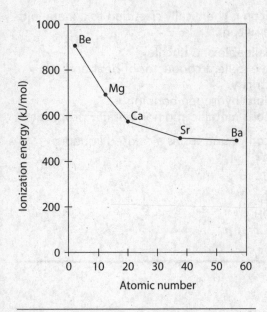

Figure 5-6. Ionization energy of Group 2: Ionization energy is less in larger atoms that have the same valence electron configuration as smaller atoms.

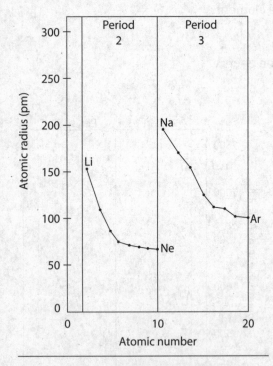

Figure 5-7. Atomic radii for Periods 2 and 3: From left to right, atomic radius decreases across a period.

Trends in a Period From left to right in a period, there is a repeating pattern of decreasing atomic radii. See Figure 5.7. In each period, metals have larger radii than nonmetals. The valence electrons of all the members of a period are at the same general energy level, but the number of protons in the nucleus attracting them increases, causing the radii to decrease.

Trends in a Group In any given group, each successive member has more inner-level electrons than the preceding member. These electrons shield the valence electrons from the nucleus, reducing the attractive force of the nucleus. Additionally, the valence electrons are more energetic than those of elements higher in the group. Thus, the atomic radius increases from top to bottom of a group. The atomic radii are shown in Table S of Appendix 1, *Reference Tables for Physical Setting/* Ⓡ *Chemistry*. Atomic radii are often measured in picometers (10^{-12} m).

Other Properties and Trends

You can easily see from the properties discussed so far that properties of elements follow predictable trends. Other properties of the elements also follow patterns.

Ionic Radii Atoms gain or lose electrons to become charged particles called ions. Metals tend to lose their valence electrons in chemical reactions to become positive ions. Nonmetals tend to gain electrons in chemical reactions and become negative ions. As these atoms gain or lose electrons, they complete an octet of valence electrons.

One way to compare an ion to the original atom is to compare the atomic radius to the ionic radius. **Ionic radius** is the distance from the nucleus to the outer energy level of the ion. As you might expect, when an atom loses its valence electrons and becomes positively charged it loses an energy level and its radius decreases. Therefore, the radius of a metallic ion is smaller than the radius of the atom. When a nonmetal gains electrons, the stable arrangement results in an increase in the radius. Thus, the radii of nonmetallic ions are greater than those of their atoms, as shown in Figure 5-4.

Electronegativity The **electronegativity** value of an atom is a measure of its attraction for electrons when bonded to another atom. Cesium, with an electronegativity value of 0.7, has the lowest attraction for bonded electrons. Fluorine, with a value of 4.0, has the highest. Electronegativity values are listed in Table S of Appendix 1, *Reference Tables for Physical Setting/* Ⓡ *Chemisty*.

Electronegativity values can be used to predict the type of bond that will be formed between two atoms. The noble gases are not generally assigned electronegativity values because they form very few stable chemical compounds.

There is a regular increase in the electronegativity value of each element when a period is considered from left to right. Metals tend to have low values, while the nonmetals of each period are higher.

In each group, the highest electronegativity value is found at the top. Attraction for bonded electrons is less toward the bottom of the group.

Reactivity of Elements Some elements can be found uncombined in nature, that is, in the atomic state. Oxygen may be simply O_2. The noble gases are always found as free elements, as they rarely react. Other elements are so reactive that they are never found in the uncombined, or free, state. Such is the case for the elements of Groups 1, 2, and 17. Some of these elements can only be obtained by the electrolysis of their fused salts.

Properties of Groups

The elements in any group of the periodic table have related chemical properties. Inspection of a group shows that all the members have the same number of valence electrons, and it is this similarity that accounts for the similarity in chemical properties. There is a regularity that can be seen quite clearly in the manner in which the members of a group react with elements of a different group.

Although each member of a group has the same number of valence electrons, there can be a change in the type of element from top to bottom. In Group 14, the top member, carbon, is clearly a nonmetal. Silicon and germanium are metalloids, while tin and lead are metals. As each group is considered from top to bottom, the metallic characteristics increase.

Examine the chemical properties of each group of the representative elements. Notice how these properties are based on the arrangements of the electrons in each group.

Hydrogen

The vertical columns of the periodic table have been previously identified as "groups." Hydrogen is unique among all of the elements as the only element not belonging to a group. Although it seems to be placed in Group 1, notice that it is separated from the rest of the group. Hydrogen does not have physical or chemical properties similar to the Group 1 metals.

In a chemical reaction, hydrogen often loses its single valence electron to become H^+. Hydrogen also can combine with metals to form metallic hydrides, such as NaH. In these compounds the metals have a positive oxidation state, while the hydrogen is assigned $1- H^-$. Hydrogen will also share electrons with another atom to gain stability. An example of hydrogen and oxygen sharing electrons can be seen in water (H_2O).

Groups 1 and 2

The elements of Group 1 (Figure 5-8), the alkali metals, and of Group 2 (Figure 5-9), the alkaline earth metals, show typical metallic characteristics. The members of both these groups easily lose their electrons and are never found in nature in their atomic state. That is, they are always found in

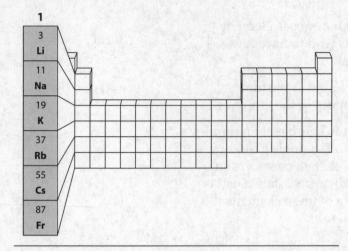

Figure 5-8. **Group 1, the alkali metals.**

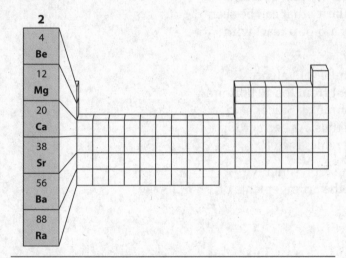

Figure 5-9. **Group 2, the alkaline earth metals.**

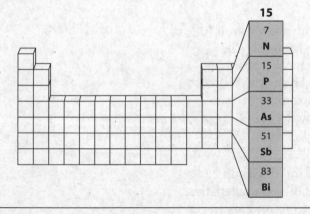

Figure 5-10. **Elements in Group 15.**

compounds. They can be reduced to their free states by electrolysis of their compounds. All of these elements have low ionization energies and electronegativity values. They typically achieve stable octets by losing electrons to form ionic bonds.

In general, from top to bottom in both groups, reactivity increases. It should be noted that each Group 1 element is more reactive than the Group 2 element of the same period. Francium is the most reactive metal.

Group 15

The members of Group 15 (Figure 5-10) show the change from nonmetallic to metallic properties from top to bottom of the group. Nitrogen and phosphorus are typical nonmetals and can accept three electrons to form 3− anions. Bismuth loses electrons to become a positive cation, which is typical of metals. Arsenic and antimony are generally classified as metalloids.

Nitrogen is a stable gas at room temperature, largely because it contains a triple bond between the two nitrogen atoms in N_2. Phosphorus forms P_4, which is far more reactive than N_2. Nitrogen is an essential component of protein synthesis and plant processes. Because atmospheric N_2 is so unreactive, it must be changed to a usable form. One way this is done is by nitrogen-fixing bacteria that release usable nitrogen compounds into the soil.

Group 16

The elements in Group 16 (Figure 5-11) also show the expected progression from nonmetal to metal with increasing atomic number. Oxygen and sulfur are typical nonmetals, while the last member, polonium, is a metal. Selenium and tellurium are metalloids.

Oxygen may well be the most important element in the group. It is a diatomic molecule at room temperature, sharing two pairs of electrons between the two atoms. Oxygen is a reactive element, easily forming compounds with other elements. Were it not for the process of photosynthesis, all of the oxygen on Earth would be in the combined state.

In a compound, oxygen normally has an oxidation value of 2−. Its negative oxidation value results from its high electronegativity as it attracts shared electrons in a bond. Only when oxygen bonds to the only element more electronegative than itself (fluorine) does oxygen have a positive oxidation value.

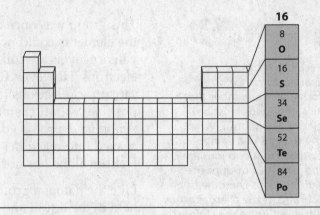

Figure 5-11. Elements in Group 16.

Group 17

The members of Group 17 (Figure 5-12) are also known as the <u>halogens</u> when they are in the free state. When atoms of elements in this group gain an electron, they become an ion with a 1– charge, and the salts formed are called <u>halides.</u> All the members of the group are nonmetals, but the normal trend of nonmetallic to metallic characteristics is seen even in this group. Iodine, the heaviest nonradioactive member, is a solid with some luster characteristic of metals.

The halogens are the only group of the table containing all three states of matter at room conditions. Fluorine and chlorine are gases; bromine is a liquid; and iodine, a solid. Astatine is a radioactive element with no practical uses. The half-life of At-210 is only 8.3 hours. Therefore, there are no sizeable amounts of astatine in nature.

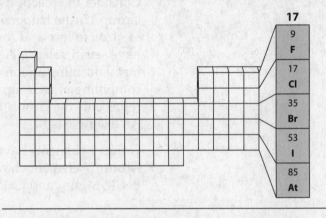

Figure 5-12. The halogens (Group 17).

As is the case with other nonpolar molecules, the halogens are held in the solid and liquid phases by weak van der Waals forces. Because these forces are the result of temporary dipoles caused by the movement of electrons, it follows that the more electrons a molecule possesses, the higher its melting and boiling points.

Because of their high reactivity, the halogens occur in nature only in their combined form. Fluorine, the most reactive halogen, can only be prepared from its fluoride compounds by electrolysis. The other halogens can be prepared by chemical means.

Group 18

The elements of Group 18 (Figure 5-13) are called the noble gases. They do not combine to form diatomic molecules, but rather exist as monatomic molecules. Each of these atoms has a complete outer energy level of electrons and therefore is chemically unreactive. The outer energy level of helium has two electrons, while each of the remaining noble gases has eight.

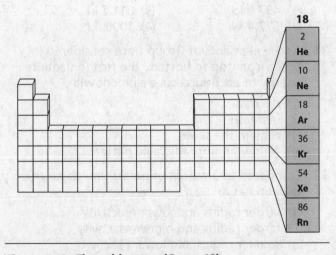

Figure 5-13. The noble gases (Group 18).

This group was once called the <u>inert gas group</u> because it was thought that the elements could not react to produce stable compounds. Because their valence levels are full, the noble gases normally would not add additional electrons. However, fluorine has such a high attraction for electrons that it can attract electrons from some of the noble gases, causing them to have a positive oxidation state. Thus, some reactivity is observed. Only argon and xenon have produced stable compounds, although even neon has been coaxed into reactions under severe conditions of temperature and pressure. Helium alone has not shown any reactivity at all.

Like the halogen group, the noble gases are nonpolar and are therefore held in the liquid and solid phases by van der Waals forces. As expected, helium, with the fewest electrons, has the lowest boiling point, and the boiling point increases from top to bottom in the group.

Reactions Between Groups

Consider the reactions of Group 1 (the alkali metals) with the members of Group 17 (the halogens). The members of Group 1 each have one valence electron to lose and form ions with a 1+ charge. Group 17 elements each have seven valence electrons and can accept one electron from the alkali metal, forming an ion with a 1− charge. The general formula for the combining of a Group 1 element with a Group 17 element is MX, where M represents the Group 1 element, and X represents the Group 17 element. An example is KI.

Group 2 elements have two valence electrons and form compounds with Group 17 elements having the general formula MX_2. Examples include $BeCl_2$, $MgBr_2$, and CaF_2.

Review Questions

Set 5.2

30. Which value represents the first ionization energy of a nonmetal?

(1) 497.9 kJ   (3) 811.7 kJ
(2) 577.4 kJ   (4) 1000. kJ

31. As the elements of Group 1 are considered in order from top to bottom, the first ionization energy of each successive element will

(1) decrease
(2) increase
(3) remain the same
(4) follow an unpredictable pattern

32. Compared to an atom of potassium, an atom of calcium has a

(1) larger radius and lower reactivity
(2) larger radius and higher reactivity
(3) smaller radius and lower reactivity

33. Which statement describes the elements in Period 3?

(1) Each successive element has a greater atomic radius.
(2) Each successive element has a lower electronegativity.
(3) All elements have similar chemical properties.
(4) All elements have valence electrons in the same principal energy level.

34. As atoms of elements in Group 16 are considered in order from top to bottom, the electronegativity of each successive element

(1) decreases
(2) increases
(3) remains the same

35. A nonmetal could have an electronegativity of
  (1) 1.0
  (2) 2.0
  (3) 1.6
  (4) 2.6

36. Which properties are most common in nonmetals?
  (1) low ionization energy and low electronegativity
  (2) low ionization energy and high electronegativity
  (3) high ionization energy and low electronegativity
  (4) high ionization energy and high electronegativity

37. A diatomic element with a high first ionization energy would most likely be a
  (1) nonmetal with a high electronegativity
  (2) nonmetal with a low electronegativity
  (3) metal with a high electronegativity
  (4) metal with a low electronegativity

38. Which element at room temperature is a poor conductor of electricity and has a relatively high electronegativity?
  (1) Cu
  (2) S
  (3) Mg
  (4) Fe

39. Within Period 2 of the periodic table, as the atomic number increases, the atomic radius generally
  (1) decreases
  (2) increases
  (3) remains the same
  (4) follows no pattern

40. Atoms of which element have the smallest radius?
  (1) Si
  (2) P
  (3) S
  (4) Cl

41. Which statement best compares the atomic radius of a potassium atom and the atomic radius of a calcium atom?
  (1) The radius of the potassium atom is smaller because of its smaller nuclear charge.
  (2) The radius of the potassium atom is smaller because of its larger nuclear charge.
  (3) The radius of the potassium atom is larger because of its smaller nuclear charge.
  (4) The radius of the potassium atom is larger because of its larger nuclear charge.

42. According to the reference table, which of the following elements has the smallest radius?
  (1) nickel
  (2) cobalt
  (3) calcium
  (4) potassium

43. In which area of the periodic table are the elements with the strongest nonmetallic properties located?
  (1) lower left
  (2) upper left
  (3) lower right
  (4) upper right

44. At which location in the periodic table would the most active metallic element be found?
  (1) in Group 1 at the top
  (2) in Group 1 at the bottom
  (3) in Group 17 at the top
  (4) in Group 17 at the bottom

45. In which section of the periodic table are the most active nonmetals located?
  (1) upper right corner
  (2) lower right corner
  (3) upper left corner
  (4) lower left corner

46. What is the total number of elements in Group 17 that are gases at room temperature and standard pressure?
  (1) 1
  (2) 2
  (3) 3
  (4) 4

47. Which of the following groups in the periodic table contain elements so reactive that they are never found in the free state?
  (1) 1 and 2
  (2) 1 and 11
  (3) 2 and 15
  (4) 11 and 15

48. Which halogen can only be prepared from its fused compounds?
  (1) I_2
  (2) Cl_2
  (3) Br_2
  (4) F_2

49. As the elements in Group 15 are considered in order of increasing atomic number, which sequence in properties occurs?
  (1) nonmetal→metalloid→metal
  (2) metalloid→metal→nonmetal
  (3) metal→metalloid→nonmetal
  (4) metal→nonmetal→metalloid

50. Which elements have the most similar chemical properties?
  (1) K and Na
  (2) K and Cl
  (3) K and Ca
  (4) K and S

51. Because of its high reactivity, which element is normally obtained by the electrolysis of its fused salts?
  (1) sulfur
  (2) lithium
  (3) argon
  (4) gold

52. Which element in Group 17 is the most active nonmetal?
  (1) Br
  (2) I
  (3) Cl
  (4) F

53. Which of the following Group 15 elements has the most nonmetallic properties?

(1) Bi (3) Sb
(2) P (4) N

54. In the ground state, an atom of each of the elements in Group 2 has a different

(1) number of valence electrons
(2) number of electrons in the first shell
(3) first ionization energy
(4) oxidation state

55. Which Group 15 element exists as a diatomic molecule at room temperature and pressure?

(1) phosphorus (3) bismuth
(2) nitrogen (4) arsenic

56. Which element is a liquid at room temperature?

(1) cesium (3) francium
(2) bromine (4) iodine

57. In which set do the elements exhibit the most similar chemical properties?

(1) N, O, and F (3) Li, Na, and K
(2) Hg, Br, and Rn (4) Al, Si, and P

58. Which of these metals loses electrons most readily?

(1) calcium (3) potassium
(2) magnesium (4) sodium

59. Element X reacts with copper to form the compounds CuX and CuX_2. In which group on the Periodic Table is element X found?

(1) Group 13 (3) Group 1
(2) Group 17 (4) Group 2

60. Which group below contains elements with the greatest variation in chemical properties?

(1) Li, Be, B (3) B, Al, Ga
(2) Li, Na, K (4) Be, Mg, Ca

61. Which element in Group 15 would most likely have luster and good electrical conductivity?

(1) N (3) Bi
(2) P (4) As

62. Which property *decreases* when the elements in Group 17 are considered in order of increasing atomic number?

(1) melting point
(2) atomic mass
(3) electronegativity
(4) atomic radius

63. Which element in Group 15 has the strongest metallic character?

(1) Bi (3) P
(2) As (4) N

64. Which halogens are gases at room temperature and pressure?

(1) chlorine and fluorine
(2) chlorine and bromine
(3) iodine and fluorine
(4) iodine and bromine

65. In which group of elements do the atoms gain electrons most readily?

(1) 1 (3) 16
(2) 2 (4) 18

66. Which element is more reactive than strontium?

(1) potassium (3) iron
(2) calcium (4) copper

67. The oxide of metal X has the formula XO. Which group in the periodic table contains metal X?

(1) Group 1
(2) Group 2
(3) Group 13
(4) Group 17

68. As elements in a group of the periodic table are considered in order from top to bottom, the metallic character of each successive element generally

(1) decreases
(2) increases
(3) remains the same

69. As the elements in Period 3 are considered from left to right, they tend to

(1) lose electrons more readily and increase in metallic character
(2) lose electrons more readily and increase in nonmetallic character
(3) gain electrons more readily and increase in metallic character
(4) gain electrons more readily and increase in nonmetallic character

70. An atom of which element in the ground state has a complete outermost energy level?

(1) He (3) Hg
(2) Be (4) H

71. Which of the following Group 15 elements has the most metallic properties?

(1) Bi (3) Sb
(2) P (4) N

72. As the atoms of the elements in Group 1 of the periodic table are considered from top to bottom, the number of valence electrons in the atoms of each successive element

   (1) decreases
   (2) increases
   (3) remains the same

73. Which element attains the structure of a noble gas when it becomes a 1^+ ion?

   (1) K
   (2) Ca
   (3) F
   (4) Ne

74. According to the reference table, which sequence correctly places the elements in order of increasing ionization energy?

   (1) H→Li→Na→K
   (2) I→Br→Cl→F
   (3) O→S→Se→Te
   (4) H→Be→Al→Ga

75. Which statement describes the general trends in electronegativity and first ionization energy as the elements in Period 3 are considered in order from Na to Cl?

   (1) Electronegativity increases, and ionization energy decreases.
   (2) Electronegativity decreases, and ionization energy increases.
   (3) Electronegativity and first ionization energy both decrease.
   (4) Electronegativity and first ionization energy both increase.

76. Which ion has the *smallest* radius?

   (1) Te^{2-}
   (2) Se^{2-}
   (3) S^{2-}
   (4) O^{2-}

77. As the elements from Group 15 are considered from top to bottom, the first ionization energy of the elements

   (1) increases, and the electronegativity decreases.
   (2) decreases, and the electronegativity decreases.
   (3) increases, and the electronegativity increases.
   (4) decreases, and the electronegativity increases.

78. Which atom in the ground state has a stable electron configuration?

   (1) neon
   (2) carbon
   (3) magnesium
   (4) oxygen

79. Which group on the Periodic Table has at least one element in each of the three phases of matter at STP?

   (1) 1
   (2) 2
   (3) 17
   (4) 18

Answer the following questions, using complete sentences when appropriate.

80. Let the letter M stand for a member of Group 13. What is the formula of the combination of this element with bromine? With oxygen? Explain.

81. Why is hydrogen not considered to be a member of Group 1 (the alkali metals)?

82. Consider atoms of the elements boron, carbon and aluminum. Which is the largest? The smallest? Which has the highest ionization energy? The lowest?

83. Why do elements in a given group of the periodic table show similar chemical properties?

84. Why do the elements of a given period always follow the progression of metal to metalloid to nonmetal to noble gas?

85. What change in charge takes place as a metal loses one or more electrons?

86. Using the law of octets, explain why it is unlikely for sodium to form a Na^{2+} ion.

87. What would be the general formula of a Group 2 element (represented by M) combined with chlorine of Group 17?

88. What would be the general formula of a Group 17 element (represented by X) combined with magnesium of Group 2?

89. What would be the general formula of a Group 1 element combined with an oxygen of Group 16?

90. Mendeleev arranged the elements on the table in order of increasing atomic mass, but it was later learned that the correct order is by increasing atomic number. Study the periodic table and locate examples where the atomic number of two successive elements increases, but the atomic mass decreases.

Directions

Review the Test-Taking Strategies section of this book. Then answer the following questions. Read each question carefully and answer with a correct choice or response.

Part A

1 The elements in the modern periodic table are arranged according to their
(1) atomic number
(2) oxidation number
(3) atomic mass
(4) nuclear mass

2 Which characteristic describes most nonmetals in the solid phase?
(1) good conductors of electricity
(2) good conductors of heat
(3) malleable
(4) brittle

3 When combining with nonmetallic atoms, metallic atoms generally will
(1) lose electrons and form negative ions
(2) lose electrons and form positive ions
(3) gain electrons and form negative ions
(4) gain electrons and form positive ions

4 At STP, both diamond and graphite are solids composed of carbon atoms. These solids have
(1) the same structure and the same properties.
(2) the same structure and different properties.
(3) different structures and the same properties.
(4) different structures and different properties.

5 Which characteristic describes most metals in the solid phase?
(1) good conductors of electricity
(2) poor conductors of heat
(3) dull
(4) brittle

6 Which element is a nonmetallic liquid at room temperature?
(1) hydrogen   (3) mercury
(2) oxygen   (4) bromine

7 Which physical characteristic of a solution may indicate the presence of a transition element?
(1) its density
(2) its color
(3) its effect on litmus
(4) its effect on phenolphthalein

8 Compared to atoms of metals, atoms of nonmetals generally
(1) have higher electronegativity values
(2) have lower first ionization energies
(3) conduct electricity more readily
(4) lose electrons more readily

9 Compared to the atoms of nonmetals in Period 3, the atoms of metals in Period 3 have
(1) fewer electron shells.
(2) more electron shells.
(3) fewer valence electrons.
(4) more valence electrons.

10 Which part of the periodic table contains elements with the strongest metallic properties?
(1) upper right
(2) upper left
(3) lower right
(4) lower left

11 Which Group 17 element is a solid at room temperature and pressure?
(1) Br_2 (3) Cl_2
(2) F_2 (4) I_2

12 Which gas is monatomic at room temperature and pressure?
(1) nitrogen
(2) neon
(3) fluorine
(4) chlorine

13 Atoms of elements in a group of the periodic table have similar chemical properties. This similarity is most closely related to the atoms'
(1) number of principal energy levels
(2) number of valence electrons
(3) atomic numbers
(4) atomic masses

14 In which group are all the elements found naturally only in compounds?
(1) 18   (3) 11
(2) 2   (4) 14

Part B-1

15 An element is a solid at room temperature. It can be a
(1) metal only
(2) metalloid only
(3) metal or a nonmetal only
(4) metal, a metalloid, or a nonmetal

16 How does the size of a barium ion compare to the size of a barium atom?
(1) The ion is smaller because it has fewer electrons.
(2) The ion is smaller because it has more electrons.
(3) The ion is larger because it has fewer electrons.
(4) The ion is larger because it has more electrons.

17 Which element is malleable and ductile?
(1) S   (3) Ge
(2) Si   (4) Au

18 Which of the following Period 4 elements has the most metallic characteristics?
(1) Ca   (3) As
(2) Ge   (4) Br

19 Which three groups of the periodic table contain the most elements classified as metalloids?
(1) 1, 2, and 13
(2) 2, 13, and 14
(3) 14, 15, and 16
(4) 16, 17, and 18

20 An aqueous solution of XCl_2 contains colored ions. Element X could be
(1) Ba   (3) Ni
(2) Ca   (4) Bi

21 Which element has the highest first ionization energy?
(1) sodium
(2) aluminum
(3) calcium
(4) phosphorus

22 An element has a first ionization energy of 1314 kJ/mol and an electronegativity of 3.5. It is classified as a
(1) metal   (3) metalloid
(2) nonmetal   (4) halogen

23 Which sequence of elements is arranged in order of decreasing atomic radii?
(1) Al, Si, P
(2) Li, Na, K
(3) Cl, Br, I
(4) N, C, B

24 Which ion has the largest radius?
(1) Na^+ (3) K^+
(2) Mg^{2+} (4) Ca^{2+}

25 In the ground state, atoms of the elements in Group 15 of the periodic table all have the same number of
(1) filled principal energy levels
(2) occupied principal energy levels
(3) neutrons in the nucleus
(4) electrons in the valence energy level

26 Which of the following Group 18 elements would be most likely to form a compound with fluorine?
(1) He   (3) Ar
(2) Ne   (4) Kr

27 The properties of carbon are expected to be most similar to those of
(1) boron
(2) aluminum
(3) silicon
(4) phosphorus

28 If M represents an alkali metal of Group 1, what is the formula for the compound formed by M and oxygen?
(1) MO_2 (3) M_2O_3
(2) M_2O (4) M_3O_2

29 An atom of an element has 28 innermost electrons and 7 valence electrons. In which period of the periodic table is this element located?
(1) 5   (3) 3
(2) 2   (4) 4

Parts B-2 and C

30 Mendeleev arranged the periodic table in order of increasing atomic masses. Locate iodine and tellurium on the table and note that they are not arranged by increasing mass, and yet Mendeleev placed iodine in Group 17 and tellurium in Group 16. What is the likely reason that he did not arrange them by increasing mass?

Base your answers to questions 31 through 33 on the following information.

In the 19th century, Dmitri Mendeleev predicted the existence of a then unknown element X with a mass of 68. He also predicted that an oxide of X would have the formula X_2O_3.

31 Determine the number of valence electrons in a neutral atom of element X.

32 On the modern periodic table, what are the group number and period number of the element X?

33 Name an element in the same group as element X that would have an atomic radius smaller than that of element X.

Base your answers to questions 34 through 37 on the information below.

A metal, M, was obtained from a compound in a rock sample. Experiments have determined that the element is a member of Group 2 of the periodic table.

34 What is the phase of element M at STP?

35 Explain, in terms of electrons, why element M is a good conductor of electricity.

36 Explain why the radius of a positive ion of the element M is smaller than an atom of element M.

37 Using the symbol M for the element, write the chemical formula for the compound that forms when element M reacts with iodine.

Base your answers to questions 38 through 41 on the following information.

The atomic radius and the ionic radius for some Group 1 and some Group 17 elements are given in the tables below.

Atomic and Ionic Radii of Some Elements

Group 1		Group 17	
Particle	**Radius (pm)**	**Particle**	**Radius (pm)**
Li atom	130.	F atom	60.
Li$^+$ ion	78	F$^-$ ion	133
Na atom	160.	Cl atom	100.
Na$^+$ ion	98	Cl$^-$ ion	181
K atom	200.	Br atom	117
K$^+$ ion	133	Br$^-$ ion	?
Rb atom	215	I atom	136
Rb$^+$ ion	148	I$^-$ ion	220.

38 Estimate the radius of a Br$^-$ ion.

39 Explain, in terms of electron shells, why the radius of a K$^+$ ion is greater than the radius of an Na$^+$ ion.

40 Write both the name and charge of the particle that is gained by an F atom when the atom becomes an F$^-$ ion.

41 State the relationship between atomic number and first ionization energy as the elements in Group 1 are considered in order of increasing atomic number.

Base your answers to questions 42 through 44 on the following information.

The ionic radii of some Group 2 elements are given in the table below.

Ionic Radii of Some Group 2 Elements

Symbol	Atomic Number	Ionic Radius (pm)
Be	4	44
Mg	12	66
Ca	20	99
Ba	56	134

42 Estimate the ionic radius of the element strontium.

43 State the trend in ionic radius as the elements of Group 2 are considered in order of increasing atomic number.

44 Explain, in terms of electrons, why the ionic radius of a Group 2 element is smaller than its atomic radius.

Bonding

What Scientists Know About Bonding

?

How does the body get energy from food?

?

We have all learned that we get energy to live from oxidizing foods, often sugar, $C_6H_{12}O_6$. But where does the energy actually come from? The answer is not what most people expect. We don't get the energy from breaking the bonds of sugar, because breaking bonds is an endothermic process. Rather, the energy is released after the body has broken the sugar bonds and made the bonds of the products, carbon dioxide (CO_2) and water (H_2O). The bonds of water and carbon dioxide have less energy than the bonds of sugar, and the difference between the energy of the two is what is used to live.

TOPIC
6 Bonding

Vocabulary

asymmetrical molecule	ionic bond	nonpolar covalent bond
covalent bond	Lewis dot diagram	octet
dipole-dipole forces	London dispersion forces	octet rule
double covalent bond	malleability	polar covalent bond
hydrogen bond	metallic bond	symmetrical molecule
ion	multiple covalent bond	triple covalent bond

Topic Overview

Chemical bonds provide the "glue" that holds all compounds together. There are different types of chemical bonds, and these different bond types account for the different properties of substances. In this section you will learn how the electron structure of atoms helps explain many aspects of chemical bonding. You will also use Lewis dot diagrams to aid in your understanding of electronic structure and its role in bonding.

Energy and Chemical Bonds

Chemical bonds are the forces that hold atoms together in a compound. Energy is required to overcome these attractive forces and separate the atoms in a compound. Thus, the breaking of a chemical bond is an endothermic process. If energy is required to break a bond, then the opposite process of forming a bond must release energy. The formation of a bond is an exothermic process.

When a chemical bond is formed, the resulting compound has less potential energy than the substances from which it was formed. Why? Energy is always released when a bond is formed. The greater the energy released during the formation of a bond, the greater its stability. Consider the following two reactions.

In exothermic reactions, heat is a product and is released; in endothermic reactions, heat is a reactant and is absorbed.

$$\text{Reaction 1} \quad B + C \rightarrow BC + 100 \text{ joules}$$
$$\text{Reaction 2} \quad K + L \rightarrow KL + 400 \text{ joules}$$

The bond formed in reaction 2 is more stable than the bond formed in reaction 1. It takes 400 joules to break apart compound KL, but only 100 joules to break apart compound BC.

1. As energy is released during the formation of a bond, the stability of the chemical system generally
   (1) decreases
   (2) increases
   (3) remains the same

2. Which kind of energy is stored in a chemical bond?
   (1) potential energy   (3) activation energy
   (2) kinetic energy   (4) ionization energy

3. Given the balanced equation:

   $$F_2 + \text{energy} \rightarrow F + F$$

   Which statement describes what occurs during this reaction?
   (1) Energy is absorbed as a bond is formed.
   (2) Energy is absorbed as a bond is broken.
   (3) Energy is released as a bond is formed.
   (4) Energy is released as a bond is broken.

4. When a chemical bond forms between two hydrogen atoms, the potential energy of the atoms
   (1) decreases
   (2) increases
   (3) remains the same

5. Given the balanced equation representing a reaction:

   $$O_2 \rightarrow O + O$$

   What occurs during this reaction?
   (1) Energy is released as bonds are broken.
   (2) Energy is released as bonds are formed.
   (3) Energy is absorbed as bonds are broken.
   (4) Energy is absorbed as bonds are formed.

Lewis Electron Dot Structures

In the next sections you will study the two types of bonds that commonly form. These two bond types result from the transfer of electrons from one atom to another and from the sharing of valence electrons between atoms. A simple modeling technique known as a Lewis dot diagram provides an easy method for showing how electrons are transferred or shared during bond formation. Learning to draw and interpret these diagrams is an important skill.

A **Lewis dot diagram,** also called an electron dot diagram, consists of a chemical symbol surrounded by one to eight dots representing valence electrons. See Figure 6-1.

Figure 6-2 shows the Lewis dot diagram of a sodium atom. The symbol of the element (Na) represents the sodium atom's nucleus along with all of its nonvalence electrons; this portion of the diagram is called the kernel. The kernel of every atom is positively charged. The valence electrons surround the kernel and are usually represented by small dots, x's, or o's.

Figure 6-3 shows the relationship between the groups of the periodic table and the electron dot diagrams of the atoms and ions in those groups.

	Group							
Period	1	2	13	14	15	16	17	18
1	H							He
2	Li	Be	Be·	C·	·N·	:O·	:F·	:Ne:
3	Na	Mg	Ai·	Si·	·P·	:S·	:Cl·	:Ar:
4	K	Ca	Ga·	Ge·	·As·	:Se·	:Br:	:Kr:

Figure 6-1. Electron dot diagrams of elements in Periods 1 through 4

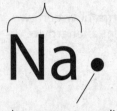

The chemical symbol Na represents the kernel of the sodium atom.

Na •

This dot represents a sodium atom's single valence electron.

Figure 6-2. The Lewis dot diagram of a sodium atom: The kernel, represented by the symbol Na, contains 11 protons and 10 electrons; the kernel has a 1+ overall charge. The 1+ charge of the kernel is balanced by the 1− charge of the single valence electron. Overall, the sodium atom is neutral.

There are slight variations in how electrons are arranged around the kernel in an electron dot diagram. Often, the first two electrons are placed at the 12 o'clock position. As the next three electrons are added, they are placed singly at the 3, 6, and 9 o'clock positions. The last three electrons are added to make pairs in the same order, at the 3, 6, and 9 o'clock positions.

When atoms gain or lose electrons they become charged particles called **ions.** Notice in Figure 6-3 that ions are represented differently than atoms. When metals react, they do so by losing their valence electrons. Thus, there aren't any dots in the electron dot diagrams of the ions for sodium (Na^+), magnesium (Mg^{2+}), or aluminum (Al^{3+}). The square brackets around the kernel and the ionic charge written as a superscript outside the brackets indicate the diagram is that of an ion. Whereas metals lose electrons to form ions, nonmetals gain electrons to form ions. The valence electrons gained when a nonmetal ion forms are shown in its electron dot diagram. It is common to show the added valence electrons with a different symbol than that used to represent the atom's originally present valence electrons.

The number of valence electrons to use in an electron dot diagram can also be determined by consulting the periodic table. The periodic table often lists the electron configuration for the elements using a modified Bohr model. For example, the electron configuration for sodium (Na) is listed as 2-8-1. This notation indicates that there is only one outermost, or valence electron for a sodium atom. The other 10 electrons belong to the kernel of the atom. The corresponding electron dot diagram for the sodium atom would show this one valence electron as a single dot, outside the kernel.

Lewis Electron-Dot Diagrams of Compounds

Lewis diagrams can also be used to show how atoms combine to form molecules. When atoms combine to form diatomic molecules, single, double, and triple covalent bonds can be shown.

The Lewis structure of a hydrogen atom is simply

H •

When two hydrogen atoms combine to form the hydrogen molecule (H_2), they share the two electrons between them in a nonpolar covalent bond:

H ⦙ H

Instead of using dots to show the pair of electrons, a single dash may be used to show the covalent bond.

H — H

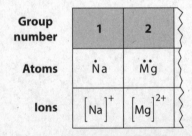

Group number	1	2
Atoms	Ṅa	M̈g
Ions	[Na]⁺	[Mg]²⁺

Group number	13	14	15	16	17	18
Atoms	Äl •	S̈i •	•P̈•	•S̈:	•C̈l:	:Är:
Ions	[Al]³⁺	*	[:P̈:]³⁻	[:S̈:]²⁻	[:C̈l:]⁻	*

*Si and Ar do not ordinarily form ions.

Figure 6-3. Electron dot diagrams of some Period 3 elements and ions

The members of column 17, the halogens, also form single bonds between them in their diatomic molecules. In addition to the single covalent bond, each atom has 6 additional valence electrons for a complete octet of 8.

$$:\ddot{C}l - \ddot{C}l:$$

Oxygen has 6 valence electrons with two atoms combining to form O_2. In this case, the two oxygen atoms share two pairs of electrons

$$:\ddot{O} = \ddot{O}:$$

Notice that each oxygen atom has a total of 8 valence electrons.

Nitrogen has five valence electrons and forms the diatomic N_2 molecule by forming a triple covalent bond

$$:N \equiv N:$$

When drawing Lewis diagrams for compounds, a pair of electrons forming a covalent bond is usually represented by a dashed line, while any unpaired electrons are represented by a pair of dots.

In drawing Lewis diagrams for compounds it is helpful to remember that the octet rule calls for each atom to have 8 valence electrons. Hydrogen is an exception, having a maximum of 2 electrons. Try to follow a pattern when drawing diagrams of compounds.

The following steps are useful in determining the dot diagrams of compounds.

1. Determine the total number of valence electrons of the atoms in the compound.

   Consider the compound CH_3Cl:
1 carbon with 4 valence electrons	=	4
3 hydrogens with 1 electron each	=	3
1 chlorine with 7 valence electrons	=	7
Total valence electrons	=	14

   The final diagram must contain 14 electrons.

2. Arrange the atoms to show bonds between them. The central atom often has the smallest electronegativity value, and generally appears once in the formula. Remember that hydrogen cannot be the central atom since it can only form one single covalent bond. If more than one atom of an element is present, they generally surround the central atom. Use a dash to show a covalent bond between the atoms. Remember that each dash represents two electrons in a covalent bond.

$$\begin{array}{c} Cl \\ | \\ H - C - H \\ | \\ H \end{array}$$

These 4 bonds account for 8 of the 14 electrons needed. The carbon atom has a complete octet of electrons. Distribute the remaining 6 electrons around the chlorine. Check to see that each atom has an octet of electrons except for hydrogen which needs only two. In this example the six remaining electrons should be distributed around the chlorine to provide it with an octet of electrons.

$$
\begin{array}{c}
:\ddot{C}l: \\
| \\
H - C - H \\
| \\
H
\end{array}
$$

If each of the atoms does not have an octet of electrons, you will probably also have some "left over" or unassigned electrons. These can be placed as double bonds or triple bonds between atoms that do not have complete octets.

Consider the compound C_2H_2:
  2 carbon atoms with
$$4 \text{ electrons} = 8 \text{ electrons}$$
  2 hydrogen atoms with
$$1 \text{ electron} = \underline{2 \text{ electrons}}$$
$$\text{Total} = 10 \text{ electrons}$$

Join the carbons and hydrogens with bonds:

$$H-C-C-H$$

The three bonds account for 6 of the 10 electrons. Distributing the four remaining electrons around the carbons will not produce octets of electrons, but forming a triple bond between the two carbons will.

$$H-C{\equiv}C-H$$

Review Questions
Set 6.2

Questions

6. Atom X has an electron configuration of 2-8-2. Which electron dot diagram correctly represents this atom?

   (1) $:\ddot{X}:$ (2) $\cdot\ddot{X}:$ (3) $X:$ (4) $\cdot X:$

7. A) Draw a Lewis dot diagram of water
   B) Draw a Lewis dot diagram of carbon dioxide

8. Which electron dot diagram represents an atom of chlorine in the ground state?

   (1) $C\,l\!:$ (2) $\cdot\dot{C}\,l\cdot$ (3) $:\ddot{C}\,l\cdot$ (4) $:\ddot{C}\,l:$

9. A) Draw an electron dot diagram of ammonia.
   B) Draw an electron dot diagram of the ammonium ion

Metallic Bonds

Metallic atoms have few valence electrons and low ionization energies. The bonds holding metallic atoms together in the solid and liquid phases, however, are apparently strong, as metals have fairly high melting and boiling points. A metallic atom may be considered to have a central portion, or kernel, made up of its nucleus and its nonvalence electrons. The atom's valence electrons surround the kernel. The kernels of the metallic atoms making up a metallic solid are arranged in the fixed positions of a crystalline lattice. The valence electrons move freely throughout the crystal and do not belong to any given atom. The freely moving valence electrons give metals properties of good electrical and thermal conductivity. A **metallic bond** results from the force of attraction of the mobile valence electrons for an atom's positively charged kernel.

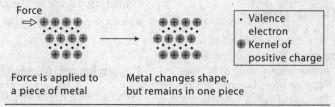

Figure 6-4. **Metallic bonding:** When hammered, the positively charged kernels are moved, but they are still attracted by the valence electrons.

As shown in Figure 6-4, metals can be hammered into shapes, which is a property known as **malleability.** Although hammering forces the kernels to move to new locations, they are still surrounded by the valence electrons. The freedom of the valence electrons often leads to the use of the term "sea of mobile electrons" to describe metallic bonding.

Review Questions
Set 6.3

10. Metallic bonding occurs between metal atoms that have

    (1) full valence orbitals, low ionization energies
    (2) full valence orbitals, high ionization energies
    (3) vacant valence orbitals, low ionization energies
    (4) vacant valence orbitals, high ionization energies

11. Which element has a crystalline lattice through which electrons flow freely?

    (1) bromine   (3) carbon
    (2) calcium   (4) sulfur

12. At STP, which substance has metallic bonding?

    (1) silver   (3) barium oxide
    (2) ammonium chloride (4) iodine

The Octet Rule

You may recall that the noble gases of Group 18 are extremely stable and undergo very few chemical reactions. Although there are a few stable compounds of argon and xenon combined with fluorine, these compounds are some of the rare exceptions to the noble gases' lack of reactivity. What is it about the structure of the noble gases that leads to their stability? The answer lies in their number of valence electrons. Except for helium (which only has two valence electrons) all of the noble gas atoms have eight valence electrons. The configuration of eight valence electrons is known as an **octet.** An octet represents the maximum number of valence electrons that an atom can have.

Ordinary chemical reactions result in changes to the valence electron configurations of the atoms involved. A complete octet of eight valence electrons results in an exceptionally stable electron configuration. This stable configuration is the reason why noble gases are so unreactive. Note that the noble gas helium requires only two electrons to fill its valence shell. The **octet rule** states that atoms generally react by gaining, losing, or sharing electrons in order to achieve a complete octet of eight valence electrons—the configuration of a noble gas.

Covalent Bonds

When two atoms approach one another, their electrons repel each other, tending to push the atoms apart. Their positive nuclei also repel each other. An attractive force between the atoms comes from the attraction of the positively charged nucleus of one atom for the negatively charged electrons of the other atom. Chemical bonds occur when the attractive forces between atoms are greater than the repulsive forces.

A **covalent bond** is formed when two nuclei share electrons in order to achieve a stable arrangement of electrons. Covalent bonds are often formed between two nonmetal atoms of the same element. The diatomic chlorine molecule (Cl_2) is an example of a covalent bond. Atoms of different elements may also combine to form covalent bonds. Sulfur and oxygen combine covalently to form sulfur dioxide (SO_2).

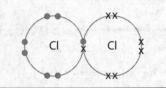

Figure 6-5. A diatomic chlorine molecule: Each chlorine atom has an octet of valence electrons.

Nonpolar Covalent Bonds When one chlorine atom forms a bond with another chlorine atom, they share a pair of electrons between them and form diatomic Cl_2. See Figure 6-5. In this way, the shared electrons of the bond are counted as part of each atom's stable octet. This bond is a **nonpolar covalent bond** because the attraction of the two chlorine nuclei for the shared electrons is equal, causing the pair of electrons to be shared equally. Nonpolar covalent bonds are formed between atoms having equal or close electronegativity values. Similar nonpolar bonds exist between each of the other Group 17 atoms in their diatomic molecules, namely F_2, Br_2, and I_2.

In a similar way, two hydrogen atoms share a pair of electrons to form diatomic H_2. See Figure 6-6. In this case there is not an octet of electrons because hydrogen only needs two electrons to fill its valence level.

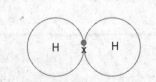

Figure 6-6. A diatomic hydrogen molecule: Each hydrogen atom has two valence electrons in its completely filled valence level.

Multiple Covalent Bonds Atoms may share more than one pair of electrons, resulting in the formation of a **multiple covalent bond.** Oxygen atoms combine with other oxygen atoms to form O_2 and achieve a stable octet configuration. In achieving this arrangement, the oxygen nuclei must share two pairs of electrons. The sharing of two pairs of valence electrons results in the type of multiple covalent bond called a **double covalent bond.** See Figure 6-7.

Diatomic nitrogen (N_2) forms when two nitrogen atoms share three pairs of valence electrons. The sharing of three pairs of valence electrons results in a **triple covalent bond.** See Figure 6-8.

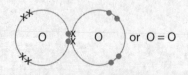

Figure 6-7. A diatomic oxygen molecule with a double covalent bond: Each oxygen atom shares two pairs of valence electrons.

Polar Covalent Bonds The different atoms involved in a bond are likely to have unequal <u>electronegativity</u> values. As you may recall, electronegativity is a measure of an atom's tendency to attract bonded electrons. When the electronegativity values of the two atoms in a covalent bond are different, the sharing of electrons in the bond is unequal. The unequal sharing of electrons in a covalent bond results in a **polar covalent bond.** The element with the higher electronegativity value attracts the shared electrons more strongly, causing that portion of the molecule to acquire a partially negative charge. Likewise, the other end of the polar covalent bond acquires a partially positive charge. Hydrogen chloride (HCl) and hydrogen iodide (HI) are examples of polar covalent compounds. Look at the electron distribution for different types of bonds, as shown in Figure 6-11.

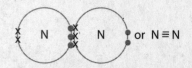

Figure 6-8. A diatomic nitrogen molecule with a triple covalent bond: Each nitrogen atom shares three pairs of valence electrons.

SAMPLE PROBLEM

Which of the following bonds is the most polar in nature? (a) O_2 (b) HCl
(c) NH_3 (d) HBr

SOLUTION: Consult the *Reference Tables for Physical Setting/Chemistry* to determine the electronegativity values of each element. For each bond, determine the difference of the two electronegativity values. The bond with the smallest difference in electronegativity is the least polar, whereas the bond with the largest difference in electronegativity is the most polar. ®

(a) Because both oxygen atoms have the same electronegativity value (3.4), the difference is 0. This is a nonpolar covalent bond.

(b) Chlorine has an electronegativity of 3.2, and hydrogen has an electronegativity of 2.2. The electronegativity difference is 1.0, and the bond is polar covalent.

(c) Nitrogen has an electronegativity of 3.0, and hydrogen has an electronegativity of 2.2. The electronegativity difference is 0.8, and the bond is polar covalent.

(d) Bromine has an electronegativity of 3.0, and hydrogen has an electronegativity of 2.2. The electronegativity difference is 0.8, and the bond is polar covalent.

The largest electronegativity difference occurs in the bonds of HCl, hence it is the most polar in nature. The bond in diatomic oxygen is the least polar; diatomic oxygen has a nonpolar covalent bond.

Review Questions

Set 6.4

13. The correct electron dot diagram for hydrogen chloride is

(1) H:Cl

(2) :H:Cl
        ··

(3) H:Cl:
        ··

(4) :H:Cl:
        ··

14. A covalent bond forms when

(1) two nuclei share electrons in order to achieve a complete octet of electrons
(2) atoms form ions and then electrostatic forces of attraction bond the ions together
(3) repulsive forces between atoms are greater than the attractive forces
(4) a metal atom combines with a nonmetal atom

15. Which of the following bonds is the most polar in nature?

(1) Cl_2
(2) HCl
(3) HBr
(4) HI

16. Polar covalent bonds are caused by

(1) unbalanced ionic charges
(2) unequal electronegativity values
(3) the transfer of electrons from one atom to another
(4) equally shared valence electrons

17. The bond in a diatomic nitrogen molecule (N_2) is best described as

(1) polar
(2) polar double covalent
(3) nonpolar triple covalent
(4) polar ionic

Molecular Substances

A <u>molecule</u> is the smallest discrete particle of an element or compound formed by covalently bonded atoms. Each atom in a molecule usually has the electron configuration of a noble gas. Molecular substances may exist as solids, liquids, or gases, depending on the strength of the forces of attraction between the molecules.

Molecules generally have properties associated with covalent bonding. Molecules are generally soft, are poor conductors of heat and electricity, and have relatively low melting and boiling points.

Water (H_2O), carbon dioxide (CO_2), and ammonia (NH_3) are examples of molecular compounds. The diatomic gases, such as oxygen (O_2) and nitrogen (N_2), are also molecular substances. Some common molecular substances are represented in Figure 6-9.

Polar Molecules Although a molecule may contain polar bonds, it does not necessarily follow that the molecule itself is polar. Molecules such as hydrogen chloride and water have polar bonds and are also polar molecules. Carbon dioxide and carbon tetrachloride, however, contain polar bonds but are not polar molecules. To understand why these molecules are polar or nonpolar, you must examine their molecular shapes.

Study the shapes of the molecules in Figure 6-10. The water, hydrogen chloride, and ammonia molecules are asymmetrical, whereas the carbon dioxide and carbon tetrachloride molecules are symmetrical. The symmetrical shape of the carbon dioxide and carbon tetrachloride molecules causes the pull of the various polar bonds to be offset by other bonds—the net result is a nonpolar molecule.

Symmetrical molecules have identical parts on each side of an axis; **asymmetrical molecules** lack identical parts on each side of an axis.

Name	Molecular Formula	Structural Formula	Ball-and-Stick Model	Space-Filling Model
Hydrogen	H_2	H—H		
Water	H_2O	O—H, H		
Ammonia	NH_3	H—N—H, H		

Figure 6-9. Models of some common molecular substances

Symmetrical Molecules		Asymmetrical Molecules		
$O = C = O$	$Cl - \overset{\displaystyle Cl}{\underset{\displaystyle Cl}{C}} - Cl$	$\overset{\displaystyle O}{H \quad H}$	$H - Cl$	$\overset{\displaystyle N}{\underset{\displaystyle H}{H \quad H}}$
Carbon dioxide	Carbon tetrachloride	Water	Hydrogen chloride	Ammonia

Figure 6-10. Five compounds with polar bonds: The symmetrical molecules are nonpolar; the asymmetrical molecules are polar.

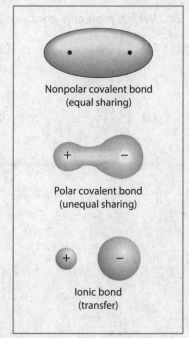

Nonpolar covalent bond (equal sharing)

Polar covalent bond (unequal sharing)

Ionic bond (transfer)

The charge distribution within a bond affects the nature of the bond. Figure 6-11 shows the changes in bond types with different electron distributions. The nonpolar covalent bond has an even electron distribution. As the electron distribution becomes unequal, a polar covalent bond is formed. When the electron is actually transferred, an ionic bond is formed. You will learn about ionic bonds in the next section.

Figure 6-11. Three bond types that are dependent on electron distribution

Review Questions

Set 6.5

18. Which electron dot diagram represents a polar molecule?

(1) H : H

(2) H : C̈l :

(3) H : C̈ : H (with H above and H below)

(4) : F̈ : F̈ :

19. Which electron dot diagram represents a polar molecule?

(1) Ö : : C : : Ö

(2) H : C̈ : H (with H above and H below)

(3) H : Ö : (with H below)

(4) : C̈l : C : C̈l : (with :C̈l: above and :C̈l: below)

20. Which electron dot diagram represents H_2?

(1) H • H

(2) H ⦙ H

(3) ⦙ H • H ⦙ (surrounded by dots)

(4) ⦙ H ⦙ H ⦙ (surrounded by dots)

21. The diagram below represents a hydrogen fluoride molecule.

H : F̈ :

This molecule is best described as

(1) polar with polar covalent bonds
(2) polar with nonpolar covalent bonds
(3) nonpolar with polar covalent bonds
(4) nonpolar with nonpolar covalent bonds

22. Which diagram best represents a polar molecule?

(1) Cl_2

(2) H_2

(3) HCl

(4) NaCl

23. Which is the correct electron dot formula for a chlorine molecule?

(1) Cl • Cl

(2) • C̈l : C̈l •

(3) : C̈l • C̈l :

(4) : C̈l ⦙ C̈l :

24. Which molecule contains a polar covalent bond?

(1) $\overset{\text{x x}}{\underset{\text{x x}}{\text{x}}}\overset{..}{\underset{..}{I}}\overset{..}{\underset{..}{I}}:$

(3) $H \overset{..}{\underset{\text{x}}{N}} H$
$\quad\;\;\overset{\text{x}}{H}$

(2) $H \overset{.}{\text{x}} H$

(4) $: N \overset{\text{x x}}{\underset{\text{x x}}{\vdots}} N \overset{\text{x}}{\text{x}}$

25. Which electron dot diagram represents the atom in Period 4 with the highest first ionization energy?

(1) $\overset{..}{\underset{..}{X}}$

(3) $\overset{..}{X} \cdot$

(2) $\overset{..}{X} \cdot$

(4) $: \overset{..}{\underset{..}{X}} :$

Ionic Bonding

Recall that when atoms gain or lose electrons they become charged particles called ions. An ionic bond is formed when ions bond together because of the electrostatic attraction of oppositely charged ions. Figure 6-12 shows the formation of an ionic bond by the transfer of an electron.

$$Na^x + \cdot \overset{..}{\underset{..}{Cl}}: \longrightarrow \left[Na \right]^+ + \left[\overset{..}{\underset{..}{\underset{\text{x}}{Cl}}}: \right]^-$$

Figure 6-12. The formation of an ionic bond by the transfer of an electron

Ion Formation in Metals As atoms form ions, they tend to do so in a manner that results in the formation of ions with noble gas electron configurations. Consider the metals of Group 1 with their single valence electron. When a Group 1 metallic atom reacts, it loses its electron and forms an ion with a 1+ charge. By losing its valence electron, the atom acquires the octet arrangement of a noble gas. The resulting ion is quite stable. The loss of the valence electron from the atom's outer energy level results in the ions having a smaller radius than the atom from which it was formed.

Ion Formation in Nonmetals Now consider a nonmetal atom from Group 17 with its seven valence electrons. This nonmetal atom reacts by gaining a single electron to form an ion with a 1− charge. By gaining an electron, the atom has acquired the noble gas electron configuration (eight valence electrons). The resulting ion is quite stable. The addition of the valence electron to the atom's outer energy level results in the ions having a larger radius than the atom from which it was formed. See Table 6-1 that summarizes the reactions of metals and nonmetals.

Ion Formation and the Octet Rule Look at Figure 6-13. Each of the atoms has a different number of electrons. When each atom reacts, it does so by losing or gaining electrons. Notice that as ions, each has an octet of valence electrons—the same number of electrons as the noble gas neon.

When metallic atoms lose electrons to form positive ions, they acquire the electron configuration of the noble gas preceding them on the

Table 6–1. Reactions of Metals and Nonmetals	
When metals react they:	**When nonmetals react they:**
1. Lose electrons	1. Gain electrons
2. Become positively charged	2. Become negatively charged
3. Have smaller radii	3. Have larger radii
4. Acquire the electron configuration of a noble gas	4. Acquire the electron configuration of a noble gas

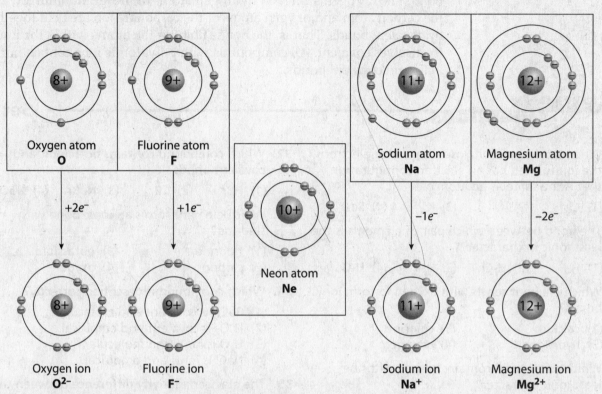

Nonmetals gain electrons

Oxygen atom
O

Fluorine atom
F

Neon atom
Ne

$+2e^-$

$+1e^-$

Oxygen ion
O^{2-}

Fluorine ion
F^-

Metals lose electrons

Sodium atom
Na

Magnesium atom
Mg

$-1e^-$

$-2e^-$

Sodium ion
Na^+

Magnesium ion
Mg^{2+}

Figure 6-13. **Atoms tend to gain or lose electrons and acquire the electron configuration of the nearest noble gas:** All of the ions and neon are isoelectronic, that is, they have the same electron configuration.

periodic table. When nonmetals gain electrons, they form negative ions and acquire the electron configuration of the noble gas that follows them on the table.

Electronegativity As you just learned, as the electronegativity difference between two atoms in a bond increases, the bond becomes more polar in nature. Figure 6-14 summarizes the relationship between electronegativity and bond type. As shown, as the electronegativity difference increases, the bond becomes more ionic in character. At some point the bond can no longer be considered as a sharing of electrons, but rather as a bond in which one or more electrons have actually been transferred from one atom to another. The transfer of electrons from one atom to another results in an ionic bond.

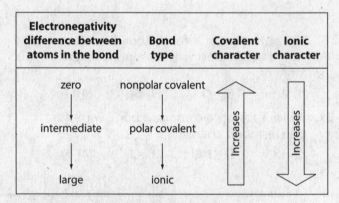

Electronegativity difference between atoms in the bond	Bond type	Covalent character	Ionic character
zero	nonpolar covalent		
intermediate	polar covalent	Increases	Increases
large	ionic		

Figure 6-14. **Electronegativity and bond type**

If the electronegativity difference between the bonding atoms is 1.7 or greater, the bond is generally considered to be ionic. Ionic bonds are generally formed between metals and nonmetallic atoms. Refer to Table S in the *Reference Tables for Physical Setting/Chemistry* for Ⓡ electronegativity values.

Polyatomic Ions Any compound containing a polyatomic ion must also contain an ionic bond. Consider the ionic compound ammonium carbonate $(NH_4)_2CO_3$. The ammonium ion is attracted to the carbonate ion by an ionic bond. Within the ammonium and carbonate ions, there is a second type of bond. The nitrogen atom and hydrogen atoms of the ammonium ion and the carbon atom and oxygen atoms of the carbonate ion are held together by covalent bonds. That is, the bonds holding the atoms within the ion are themselves covalent. All compounds with polyatomic ions contain both ionic and covalent bonds.

Review Questions

26. When a calcium atom loses its valence electrons, the ion formed has an electron configuration that is the same as an atom of

    (1) Cl   (2) Ar   (3) K   (4) Sc

27. The bond between which pair of elements is the least ionic in character?

    (1) H-F   (2) H-Cl   (3) H-I   (4) H-O

28. Which element reacts with oxygen to form ionic bonds?

    (1) calcium   (3) chlorine
    (2) hydrogen   (4) nitrogen

29. Which compound contains a bond with the least ionic character?

    (1) CO   (2) CaO   (3) K_2O (4) Li_2O

30. Look at the electron dot formula shown below.

    $$H : \overset{\cdot\cdot}{\underset{\cdot\cdot}{X}} :$$
    $$H$$

    The attraction of X for the bonding electrons would be greatest when X represents an atom of

    (1) S   (2) O   (3) Se   (4) Te

31. Which substance contains a bond with the greatest ionic character?

    (1) KCl   (2) HCl   (3) Cl_2 (4) F_2

32. Which compound contains both ionic and covalent bonds?

    (1) HBr   (2) CBr_4 (3) NaBr   (4) NaOH

33. Which element forms an ionic bond with fluorine?

    (1) fluorine   (3) potassium
    (2) carbon   (4) oxygen

34. Which compound is described correctly?

    (1) $BaCl_2$ is covalent and molecular.
    (2) H_2O_2 is covalent and empirical.
    (3) H_2O is ionic and molecular.
    (4) NaCl is ionic and empirical.

35. The electronegativity difference between the atoms in a molecule of HCl can be used to determine

    (1) the entropy of the atoms
    (2) the atomic number of the atoms
    (3) the first ionization energy of the atoms
    (4) the polarity of the bond between the two atoms

36. An atom of which element has the same electron configuration as O^{2-}?

    (1) Li   (2) Na   (3) Ar   (4) Ne

37. Which ion has the electron configuration of a noble gas?

    (1) Cu^{2+} (2) Fe^{2+} (3) Ca^{2+} (4) Hg^{2+}

Distinguishing Bond Types

Metallic, covalent, and ionic bonds have different properties that can be used to distinguish among them. Metals generally have high melting points. Mercury, which is a liquid at standard conditions, is an exception, as are the metals of Group 1. Ionic compounds also have high melting points, while covalently bonded molecules have relatively low melting points.

Of course, melting point alone will not accurately differentiate between bond types. Other properties must also be considered. Metallic bonds are the only type that result in good thermal and electrical conductivity. Neither ionic solids nor molecular solids are good conductors. Ionic substances become conductors when they are melted (fused) or dissolved in aqueous solutions.

Molecular substances are held together by covalent bonds. Thus, there are no charged particles to conduct an electric current. Molecular substances are poor conductors, whether they are in the solid state, in the liquid state, or in aqueous solution.

The three bond types also differ in hardness. Ionic and metallic solids are generally hard, while a majority of covalently bonded solids are soft. Table 6-2 summarizes some of the properties of the various bond types.

Table 6-2. Properties of Metallic, Ionic, and Covalent Bonds					
Bond Type	Melting and Boiling Points	Hardness	Conductivity		
			Solid	Liquid	Aqueous
Metallic	High	Hard	Yes	Yes	Yes
Covalent	Low	Soft	No	No	No
Ionic	High	Hard	No	Yes	Yes

Digging Deeper

Why do ionic substances conduct electricity when melted or when in aqueous solution, but not when in the solid state? In solids, electrical current is carried by electrons. In liquids, however, electrical current is carried by charged particles (ions). The ions in an ionic solid are not able to move from their fixed positions and conduct electrical current. When the ionic solid is melted or dissolved in water, the ions are free to move and conduct electrical current.

Intermolecular Forces

Dipole-Dipole Forces Just as atoms are held together by chemical bonds, molecules also have attractive forces acting on them in the solid and liquid states. It is fairly easy to understand how polar molecules are attracted to each other. Because polar molecules have positive and negative ends, polar molecules are also called dipoles. The positive area of one dipole molecule is attracted to the negative portion of an adjacent dipole molecule. These attractive forces are known as **dipole-dipole forces.**

Hydrogen Bonds **A hydrogen bond** is an intermolecular bond between a hydrogen atom in one molecule and a nitrogen, oxygen, or fluorine atom in another molecule. See Figure 6-15. Perhaps the most important example of hydrogen is found in water.

Water is a polar molecule, so you might expect it to be held to other water molecules by dipole-dipole attractions. However, if only dipole-dipole forces acted to hold water molecules together, all of the water on earth

Memory Jogger

You should recall the difference between *intra-* and *inter-*. When you play *intra*mural sports, you play against students from within your own school. In chemistry, *intra*molecular forces refer to the covalent bonds between atoms within a molecule. When you play *inter*scholastic sports, you play against teams from other schools. In chemistry, *inter*molecular forces refer to attractions between and among molecules.

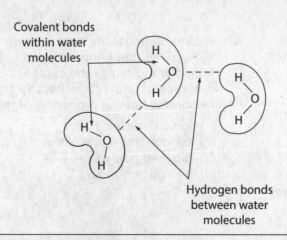

Covalent bonds within water molecules

Hydrogen bonds between water molecules

Figure 6-15. Covalent and hydrogen bonding in water

Digging Deeper

Perhaps you remember from your biology class that thymine and adenine are bonded to each other as are cytosine and quanine in the DNA molecule. The bonds that hold these parts to each other are hydrogen bonds. Hydrogen bonds are also important in holding many enzymes on to their targets.

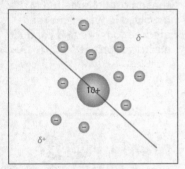

Figure 6-16. Possible instantaneous position of electrons around nucleus of a neon atom showing uneven distribution. Uneven distribution could result in polarity which accounts for London Dispersion Forces.

would have boiled away. The water has not boiled away because there are relatively strong hydrogen bonding forces acting on the water molecules. Hydrogen bonding forces are much stronger than dipole-dipole attractions. Hydrogen bonding is responsible for the relatively high boiling point of water. Ammonia (NH_3) and hydrogen fluoride (HF) are two other examples of substances with strong hydrogen bonds.

London Dispersion Forces For substances that lack polarity or the presence of hydrogen bonding, there seems to be no cause for attraction between their molecules. However, we know that such substances do demonstrate attractive forces, and can form liquids or solids as they lose energy. These forces of attraction are due to uneven distribution of electrons within the molecules (even if the molecule is symmetrical), and the resulting polarity of the molecule allows for a weak attraction between molecules called **London Dispersion Forces**. These forces are present in any molecule, but are far less apparent in asymmetrical molecules where stronger dipole-dipole attractions exist.

The probability of having an uneven distribution of electrons within a molecule increases as the size of the particle (and overall number of electrons) increases. This accounts for the higher freezing points and boiling points exhibited by the larger molecules. (See Figure 6-16.) Noble gas atoms have no obvious polarity, however, when we consider the possible instantaneous position of their electrons, we see that their distribution can be uneven – resulting in a slight polarity. This polarity can be observed at low temperatures and high pressures when these gases can be liquefied. Observe that the freezing points and boiling points of these elements increase in direct correlation with their size. The greater the number of electrons present, the greater the possibility of an uneven distribution of electrons. Larger particles have stronger London Dispersion Forces.

Review Questions

Set 6.7

38. The electrical conductivity of KI(*aq*) is greater than the electrical conductivity of $H_2O(\ell)$ because the KI(*aq*) contains mobile

(1) molecules of H_2O (3) molecules of KI
(2) ions from H_2O (4) ions from KI

39. Which substance has a high melting point and conducts electricity in the liquid phase?

(1) Ne   (2) Hg   (3) NaCl   (4) CO

40. Which of the following compounds consists of dipole molecules?

(1) H_2S (2) CH_4 (3) CO_2 (4) N_2

41. Which atom has the least attraction for the electrons in a bond between that atom and an atom of hydrogen?

(1) carbon   (3) nitrogen
(2) oxygen   (4) fluorine

42. Which element is expected to demonstrate the strongest London dispersion forces and have the highest boiling point?

(1) Ne   (2) Kr   (3) Xe   (4) Rn

43. A compound has the molecular formula $C_{30}H_{62}$. The compound is known to have nonpolar molecules and exists as a solid at room temperature. Which is the biggest factor responsible for the properties of this compound?

(1) ionic attractive forces
(2) London dispersion forces
(3) dipole-dipole attractions
(4) hydrogen bonding

Directions

Review the Test-Taking Strategies section of this book. Then answer the following questions. Read each question carefully and answer with a correct choice or response.

Part A

1 Which kind of energy is stored within a chemical bond?
   (1) free energy   (3) kinetic energy
   (2) activation energy   (4) potential energy

2 Which particles may be gained, lost, or shared by an atom when it forms a chemical bond?
   (1) protons   (3) neutrons
   (2) electrons   (4) nucleons

3 The forces between atoms that create chemical bonds are the result of the interactions between
   (1) nuclei
   (2) electrons
   (3) protons and electrons
   (4) protons and nuclei

4 At STP, potassium is classified as
   (1) a metallic solid   (3) a network solid
   (2) a molecular solid   (4) an ionic solid

5 Which element consists of positive ions immersed in a "sea" of mobile electrons?
   (1) sulfur
   (2) nitrogen
   (3) calcium
   (4) chlorine

6 The degree of polarity of a bond is indicated by
   (1) ionization energy difference
   (2) the shape of the molecule
   (3) electronegativity difference
   (4) the charge on the kernel

7 In a nonpolar covalent bond, electrons are
   (1) located in a mobile "sea" shared by many ions
   (2) transferred from one atom to another
   (3) shared equally by two atoms
   (4) shared unequally by two atoms

8 Which type of bond is formed when an atom of potassium transfers an electron to a bromine atom?
   (1) metallic
   (2) ionic
   (3) nonpolar covalent
   (4) polar covalent

9 Which type of bonding is characteristic of a substance that has a high melting point and is a good electrical conductor only when in the liquid phase?
   (1) nonpolar covalent   (3) ionic
   (2) polar covalent   (4) metallic

10 Which terms describe a substance that has a low melting point and poor electrical conductivity?
   (1) covalent and metallic
   (2) covalent and molecular
   (3) ionic and molecular
   (4) ionic and metallic

11 At standard pressure, CH_4 boils at 112 K and H_2O boils at 373 K. What accounts for the higher boiling point of H_2O at standard pressure?
   (1) the covalent bonding
   (2) metallic bonding
   (3) ionic bonding
   (4) hydrogen bonding

12 When two atoms form a chemical bond by sharing electrons, the resulting molecule will be
   (1) polar only
   (2) nonpolar only
   (3) either polar or nonpolar
   (4) neither nonpolar nor polar

13 Which type of substance is soft, has a low melting point, and is a poor conductor of electricity?
   (1) covalent solid   (3) metallic solid
   (2) ionic solid   (4) network solid

14 Oxygen, nitrogen, and fluorine bond with hydrogen to form molecules. These molecules are attracted to each other by
   (1) ionic bonds
   (2) hydrogen bonds
   (3) polar covalent bonds
   (4) nonpolar covalent bonds

15 What occurs in order to break the bond in a Cl_2 molecule?
   (1) The molecule creates energy.
   (2) The molecule destroys energy.
   (3) Energy is absorbed.
   (4) Energy is released.

Part B–1

16 Which statement is true concerning the reaction
N(g) + N(g) → N₂(g) + energy?
(1) A bond is broken and energy is absorbed.
(2) A bond is broken and energy is released.
(3) A bond is formed and energy is absorbed.
(4) A bond is formed and energy is released.

17 The bond between which pair of elements is the least ionic in character?
(1) H—F   (3) H—S
(2) H—Br   (4) H—O

18 Which compound has the greatest degree of ionic character?
(1) NaCl   (3) AlCl₃
(2) MgCl₂   (4) SiCl₄

19 Look at the electron dot diagram below.

H:F:

The electrons in the bond between hydrogen and fluorine are more strongly attracted to the atom of
(1) hydrogen, which has the higher electronegativity
(2) hydrogen, which has the lower electronegativity
(3) fluorine, which has the higher electronegativity
(4) fluorine, which has the lower electronegativity

20 Which type of bond is formed between the two chlorine atoms in a chlorine molecule?
(1) polar covalent
(2) nonpolar covalent
(3) metallic
(4) ionic

21 Which diagram best represents the structure of a water molecule?

(3) O—H—O

(4) H—H—O

22 Which electron dot formula represents a substance that contains a nonpolar covalent bond?

23 Which electron dot diagram represents a molecule that has a polar covalent bond?

24 When a sodium atom reacts with a chlorine atom to form a compound, the electron configuration of the ions forming the compound are the same as those in which noble gases?
(1) krypton and neon   (3) neon and helium
(2) krypton and argon   (4) neon and argon

25 Which atom will form an ionic bond with a Br atom?
(1) N   (3) O
(2) Li   (4) C

26 A white crystalline salt conducts electricity when it is melted and when it is dissolved in water. Which type of bond does this salt contain?
(1) ionic   (3) nonpolar covalent
(2) metallic   (4) polar covalent

27 In which molecule is hydrogen bonding the strongest?
(1) HF   (3) HBr
(2) HCl   (4) HI

28 Which statement correctly describes the bonds in the electron dot diagram shown below?

(1) One of the bonds is ionic.
(2) One of the bonds is metallic.
(3) All of the bonds are covalent.
(4) None of the bonds are covalent.

29 Which electron dot diagram best represents a compound that contains both ionic and covalent bonds?

(1) H :S: H

(3) K$^+$ [:Br:]$^-$

(2) Ca^{2+} [:O: :O:S:O: :O:]$^{2-}$

(4) :Br:Br:

30 Which statement explains why Br_2 is a liquid at STP and I_2 is a solid at STP?
(1) Molecules of Br_2 are polar, and molecules of I_2 are nonpolar.
(2) Molecules of Br_2 are nonpolar, and molecules of I_2 are polar.
(3) Molecules of Br_2 have stronger intermolecular forces than molecules of I_2.
(4) Molecules of I_2 have stronger intermolecular forces than molecules of Br_2.

Parts B-2 and C

Base your answers to questions 31 through 33 on your knowledge of chemical bonding and on the Lewis electron-dot diagrams of H_2S, CO_2, and F_2 below.

H :S: H   :O: :C: :O: :F: :F:

31 Which atom, when bonded as shown, has the same electron configuration as an atom of argon?

32 Explain, in terms of *structure* and/or *distribution of charge*, why CO_2 is a nonpolar molecule.

33 Explain, in terms of *electronegativity*, why a C=O bond in CO_2 is more polar than the F—F bond in F_2.

Base your answers to questions 34 through 36 on the following information.

In 1864, the Solvay process was developed to make soda ash. One step in the process is represented by the balanced equation below.

$$NaCl + NH_3 + CO_2 + H_2O \rightarrow NaHCO_3 + NH_4Cl$$

34 Write the chemical formula for *one* compound in the equation that contains *both* ionic bonds and covalent bonds.

35 Explain, in terms of electronegativity difference, why the bond between hydrogen and oxygen in a water molecule is more polar than the bond between hydrogen and nitrogen in an ammonia molecule.

36 Draw a Lewis electron-dot diagram for the reactant containing nitrogen in the equation.

Base your answers to questions 37 through 39 on the following information.

The hydrides of Group 16 are all dipoles. The graph below shows the boiling points of H_2S, H_2Se, and H_2Te.

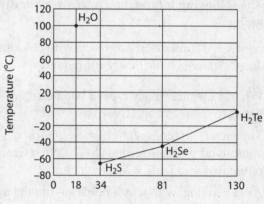

Boiling Points of the Group 16 Hydrides

37 Based on the plotted boiling points, write the formula of the compound that shows the greatest intermolecular forces of attraction.

38 As molecular mass is considered from 34 g/mol to 130 g/mol, what general trend is observed in the boiling points of the Group 16 compounds?

39 Construct a Lewis electron-dot structure to illustrate the compound with the lowest boiling point.

Base your answers to questions 40 and 41 on the information below.

Physical Properties of CF₄ and NH₃ at Standard Pressure

Compound	Melting Point (°C)	Boiling Point (°C)	Solubility in Water at 20.0°C
CF_4	−183.6	−127.8	insoluble
NH_3	−77.7	−33.3	soluble

40 State evidence that indicates NH_3 has stronger intermolecular forces than CF_4.

41 Draw a Lewis electron-dot formula for CF_4.

Use the following information to answer questions 42 through 45.

Element X is a solid metal that reacts with chlorine to produce a water-soluble binary compound.

42 What is the most likely type of bond formed between the metal and chlorine?

43 The metal combines with chlorine to form a compound with the formula MCl_2. What Group of the Periodic Table is M a member of?

44 After reacting, with which noble gas are the metal and chlorine isoelectronic?

45 Explain, in terms of particles, why an aqueous solution of the binary compound conducts an electric current.

Use the following information to answer questions 46 through 48.

Metal X is recovered from a rock sample and found to combine with iodine in a 1:1 ratio according to the equation

$$2X + I_2 \rightarrow 2XI$$

46 What is the most likely type of bond formed between element X and iodine?

47 Explain, in terms of electrons, why element X is a good conductor of electricity.

48 Once bonded, the iodine atom will have an electron configuration resembling that of what element?

Base your answers to questions 49 through 51 on the following information.

Ozone, $O_3(g)$, is produced from oxygen, $O_2(g)$ by electrical discharge during thunder-storms. The following chart provides a description of each gas that includes some basic physical properties.

Table of Properties for Oxygen and Ozone

	Oxygen gas	Ozone gas
Molecular Formula	O_2	O_3
Appearance	transparent	bluish colored
Melting Point	54.36 K	80.7 K
Boiling Point	90.20 K	161.3 K

49 Identify the type of bonding between the atoms in an oxygen molecule.

50 Explain, in terms of electron configuration, why an oxygen molecule is more stable than an oxygen atom.

51 Explain, in terms of intermolecular forces of attraction, the difference in boiling points between the two substances.

Properties of Solutions

What You Know About Solutions

What can you tell about the saturation of a solution using a crystal of the solute?

Can you do an experiment to determine if a solution is saturated?

Sure. Take a crystal of the solute and drop it into the solution, then observe what happens:

If it dissolves, the solution is unsaturated.

If it falls to the bottom, the solution is saturated.

If more crystals form, the solution is supersaturated.

Learn more about solutions and their properties while studying this topic.

Properties of Solutions

Vocabulary

boiling point	percent mass	supersaturated
ion-dipole forces	saturated	unsaturated
molarity	solute	vapor
parts per million (ppm)	solution	vapor pressure
percent by volume	solvent	

Topic Overview

Most of the materials that you use every day are not pure substances. It is more likely that they are mixtures. This topic will explore an important type of mixture, the solution. The nature and properties of solutions are important concepts used in chemistry. One reason they are so important is that most chemical reactions take place in solutions. In this topic you will study the nature and properties of solutions and ways to express the concentration of solutions.

Solutions

A **solution** is a homogeneous mixture of substances in the same physical state. Solutions contain atoms, ions, or molecules of one substance spread uniformly throughout a second substance. When salt (NaCl) is stirred into water, the individual ions of the salt separate and uniformly spread throughout the water, forming a solution.

Types of Solutions

A solid may be dissolved in another solid. Brass is a mixture of zinc and copper. When metals are mixed to form a solution, the result is called an alloy. Air is an example of a mixture of gases forming a solution.

Although solutions exist in all three states, the discussion in this topic will be limited to liquid solutions. Perhaps the most common type of solution is one in which a solid or a liquid is dissolved in a liquid.

The terms *solute* and *solvent* are commonly used to identify the parts of a solution. In general terms, the **solute** is the substance that is being dissolved, and it is the substance present in the smaller amount. When solid sodium nitrate dissolves in water, the sodium nitrate is the solute. The substance that dissolves the solute is the **solvent**, and it is present in the greater amount. Water is, perhaps, the most common solvent. Water solutions are called aqueous solutions, and the notation (aq) is used in equations to show that the substance is dissolved in water.

$$NaCl(s) \rightarrow Na^+(aq) + Cl^-(aq)$$

Memory Jogger

Mixtures do not have definite composition. For example, air is a mixture. The percentage of water vapor present in the air varies from day to day. Photosynthesis increases the concentration of oxygen in the air and reduces carbon dioxide. Respiration has the opposite effect, decreasing oxygen and increasing carbon dioxide.

Once the salt and water are stirred and the mixture becomes homogeneous, the dissolved particles will not settle. Liquid solutions are clear, and light will pass through a solution without being dispersed, as shown in Figure 7-1.

Solutions may or may not have color. For example, solutions of copper salts have a characteristic blue color, while a solution of sodium nitrate is colorless.

The following list summarizes characteristics of liquid solutions.

- Solutions are homogeneous mixtures.
- Solutions are clear and do not disperse light.
- Solutions can have color.
- Solutions will not settle on standing.
- Solutions will pass through a filter.

Solubility Factors

You've noticed that some things easily dissolve in water or other solvents. When you make a cup of coffee, certain materials in the coffee grounds dissolve but other materials don't. Sugar will readily dissolve in the cup of coffee but the spoon you use to stir the solution does not dissolve. How much of a solute will dissolve in a certain amount of solvent at a certain temperature is known as solubility. Materials with a high solubility are said to be soluble; materials with a low solubility are said to be insoluble. What factors determine the solubility of a solute in a solvent?

Nature of Solute and Solvent When sodium chloride dissolves in water it does so because its positively and negatively charged ions are attracted to the oppositely charged ends of the polar water molecule. The dissolving process is shown in Figure 7-2. The positively charged sodium ions are attracted to the negative pole of the water molecules. In like manner, the negatively charged chloride ions are attracted to the positive end of the water dipole and are dissolved. The attractive forces between the ions and water molecules are called **ion-dipole forces**, and are greater than the forces of attraction between the ions themselves. Ionic and polar substances dissolve in polar solvents.

Nonpolar substances, such as fats, do not dissolve in water because there aren't strong attractive forces between the fat molecules and the water molecules. Fat molecules will dissolve in nonpolar solvents. The forces that hold the nonpolar molecules to each other are quite weak, and the molecules simply mix together. The term "like

Memory Jogger

Dissolved particles are small enough that they will pass through a filter, so filtration cannot be used to separate the parts of a solution. Distillation is one method that can be used to separate the components of a solution. If a solution consists of a solid dissolved in a liquid, distillation removes the solvent, leaving the solute behind.

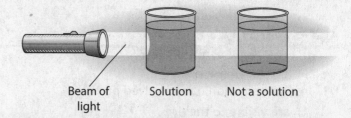

Beam of light   Solution   Not a solution

Figure 7-1. Light passing through a solution: The particles in a solution are too small to disperse light. When light passes through a liquid with larger particles, such as gelatin in water, you can see the beam because larger particles disperse light.

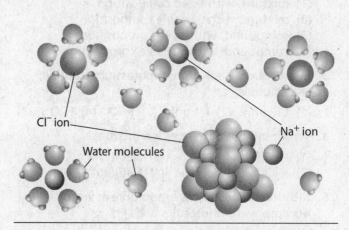

Cl^- ion   Water molecules Na^+ ion

Figure 7-2. The dissolving process: Ionic and polar solutes dissolve in polar solvents because unlike charges attract each other.

Table 7-1. Solubility Summary		
Solute Type	**Nonpolar Solvent**	**Polar Solvent**
nonpolar	soluble	insoluble
polar	insoluble	soluble
ionic	insoluble	soluble

dissolves like" is often used to describe what solutes will dissolve in what solvents. Table 7-1 summarizes this concept.

An interesting and important case of "like dissolves like" is found in the action of soaps. Greases, which are nonpolar, won't easily wash off our hands in water, which is polar. Soaps are long carbon chains that have one end that is polar, allowing the soap to dissolve in water. The other end of the soap is nonpolar, and grease will dissolve in it.

Temperature As temperature increases, most solids become more soluble in water. A few exceptions exist. Gases react in the opposite manner. As temperature rises, the solubility of all gases in liquids decreases.

Pressure Pressure has little or no effect on the solubility of solid or liquid solutes. Pressure does affect the solubility of gases in liquids. As pressure increases, the solubility of gases in liquids increases. When a can of soda is opened, the pressure decreases. The carbon dioxide is no longer as soluble at the lowered pressure, and it escapes as bubbles.

Review Questions   Set 7.1

1. In a true solution, the dissolved particles

   (1) are visible to the eye
   (2) will settle out on standing
   (3) are always solids
   (4) cannot be removed by filtration

2. Salt water is classified as a

   (1) mixture, with fixed composition
   (2) mixture, with variable composition
   (3) compound, with fixed composition
   (4) compound, with variable composition

3. In an aqueous solution of potassium chloride, the solute is

   (1) Cl^- only (2) K^+ only (3) K^+Cl^- (4) H_2O

4. Which sample of matter is a mixture?

   (1) $H_2O(s)$ (3) $NaCl(\ell)$
   (2) $H_2O(\ell)$ (4) $NaCl(aq)$

5. Most ionic substances are soluble in water because water molecules are

   (1) nonpolar   (3) ionic
   (2) inorganic   (4) polar

6. An aqueous solution of copper sulfate is poured into a filter paper cone. What passes through the filter paper?

   (1) only the solvent
   (2) only the solute
   (3) both solvent and solute
   (4) neither the solute nor solvent

7. Nonpolar solvents will most easily dissolve solids that are

   (1) ionic   (3) metallic
   (2) covalent   (4) colored

8. As the temperature rises, the solubility of all gases in water

   (1) decreases   (2) increases
   (3) remains the same

9. A decrease in pressure has the greatest effect on a solution that contains

   (1) a gas in a liquid   (3) a solid in a solid
   (2) a liquid in a liquid (4) a solid in a liquid

10. Which diagram best illustrates the ion-molecule attractions that occur when the ions of NaCl(s) are added to water?

11. What happens when NaCl(s) is dissolved in water?

(1) Cl^- ions are attracted to the oxygen atoms of the water.

(2) Cl^- ions are attracted to the hydrogen atoms of the water.

(3) Na^+ ions are attracted to the hydrogen atoms of the water.

(4) No attractions are involved; the crystal just falls apart.

12. Two grams of potassium chloride are completely dissolved in a sample of water in a beaker. This solution is classified as

(1) an element.

(2) a compound.

(3) a homogeneous mixture.

(4) a heterogeneous mixture.

Looking at Solubility

Solubility information may be presented in different ways. Solubility Curves in the *Reference Tables for Physical Setting/Chemistry* presents quantitative information showing the relationship of grams of solute that may be dissolved at various temperatures. Solubility Guidelines provides some general guidelines about the solubility of ionic substances. You will need to be able to interpret information from both tables.

Solubility Graphs The Solubility Curves table shows the number of grams of a substance that can be dissolved in 100. g of water at temperatures between 0°C and 100°C. Each line represents the maximum amount of that substance that can be dissolved at a given temperature. All of the lines that show an increase in solubility as temperatures increase represent solids being dissolved in water. Although these lines on the graph show an increase in solubility as temperature increases, a few solids, such as cesium sulfate, become less soluble as temperature increases.

Three lines show decreasing solubility with increasing temperature. These three lines represent the gases NH_3, HCl, and SO_2. The solubility of all gases decreases with increasing temperature.

Figure 7-3 shows four positions relative to a line of maximum solubility. Position A is below the maximum line of solubility. At this position, the temperature is 35°C, and 25 g of solute X dissolve. Because at this point the solution holds less solute than the maximum it can hold, the solution is said to be **unsaturated.** If there is not a temperature change, an additional 30 g can be added to bring X to position B.

Position B is on the line of maximum solubility. A solution that contains a maximum amount of solute that will dissolve at a specific temperature is **saturated.** At this position, the solution contains 55 g of X. The addition of more solid solute will not result in more being dissolved. Any additional solid that is added will simply settle to the bottom of the container.

If the temperature is reduced to 20°C, only 35 g of X can dissolve. When the temperature of the solution at B is reduced, the most likely event is that the excess 20 g of X will precipitate, and the solution will remain

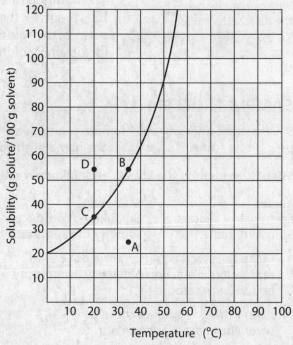

Figure 7-3. A solubility curve

saturated at point C. On rather rare occasions, as the temperature decreases, crystals do not form and the substance may be at position D.

At position D, there is more solid dissolved than normal. A solution that holds more solute than is present in a saturated solution at that temperature is **supersaturated.** These solutions are quite unstable. The addition of a single solid crystal of the substance will cause additional solid to form, and the solution will return to a saturated condition. If no temperature change occurred, the solution would become saturated at point C, with 20 g of the substance precipitating. The only way to make a supersaturated solution is to cool a saturated solution in which there are no crystals or impurities, such as dust, present.

Solubility Tables The Solubility Guidelines of *Reference Tables for Physical* ®
Setting/Chemistry contains some guidelines for the solubility of common ionic compounds. The table shows that all compounds of the ammonium and the nitrate ion are soluble. All of the halide ions, such as Cl^-, form compounds that are soluble, but three exceptions are listed. Silver chloride is not soluble, nor are Pb^{2+} nor Hg_2^{2+} chlorides, and they are precipitates if they form in a double-replacement reaction. This table is useful in predicting whether or not a precipitate will form when two ionic solutions are mixed. A reaction will take place if one or both of the products is listed as insoluble.

Recognizing Unsaturated, Saturated, and Supersaturated Solutions Because solutions are clear, it is difficult to simply look at a solution and determine whether it is unsaturated, saturated, or supersaturated.

One method of recognizing the type of solution narrows the choices. If a solution contains some undissolved solute, it must be a saturated solution.

The addition of a solute crystal can also be used to determine its condition. If it dissolves, the original solution was unsaturated. If it simply falls to the bottom, the solution is saturated. If it causes additional crystals to form, the original solution was supersaturated.

SAMPLE PROBLEM

Silver nitrate and sodium chromate solutions are mixed together. Will a precipitate form? If so, what is the name of the precipitate?

SOLUTION: Identify the known and unknown values.

Known
Formulas of reactants
Solubility table

Unknown
Solubility of products
Identity of precipitate

1. Write the word equation for a double-replacement reaction between silver nitrate and sodium carbonate.

    silver nitrate + sodium chromate →
    silver chromate + sodium nitrate

2. Check the solubilities of the products.

    Chromates are listed as insoluble, with the exception of Group 1 ions or the ammonium ion. Nitrates are soluble.

    A precipitate of silver chromate will form.

Use the tables in *Reference Tables for Physical Setting/Chemistry* as needed in answering the following questions.

13. Which compound's solubility decreases most rapidly as the temperature changes from 10°C to 70°C?

(1) NH₄Cl   (2) NH₃   (3) HCl   (4) KCl

14. Solubility for salt X is shown in the table below.

Temperature (°C)	Solubility (g salt *X*/100 g H₂O)
10	5
20	9
30	13
40	18
50	27
60	35

Which graph most closely represents the data shown in the table?

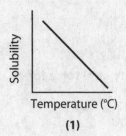

(1)

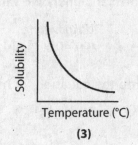

(3)

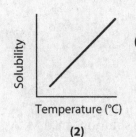

(2)

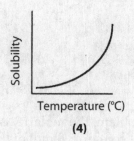

(4)

15. A solution contains 14 g of KCl in 100. g of water at 40°C. What is the minimum amount of KCl that must be added to make this a saturated solution?

(1) 14 g   (2) 19 g   (3) 25 g   (4) 44 g

16. After being thoroughly stirred at 10.°C, which substance will produce a heterogenous mixture with 100. G of water? (Hint: see Table G)

(1) 25.0 g of KNO₃   (3) 25.0 g of NaCl

(2) 25.0 g of KCl   (4) 25.0 g of NaNO₃

17. Which of the following substances is least soluble in 100. g of water at 50°C?

(1) NaCl   (2) KCl   (3) NH₄Cl   (4) HCl

18. A student obtained the following data in a chemistry laboratory.

Trial	Temperature (°C)	Solubility (g KNO₃/100 g H₂O)
1	25	40
2	32	50
3	43	70
4	48	60

Based on the reference tables, which of the four trials listed seems to be in error?

(1) 1   (2) 2   (3) 3   (4) 4

19. How many grams of the compound potassium chloride (KCl) must be dissolved in 200. g of water to make a saturated solution at 60°C?

(1) 30 g   (2) 45 g   (3) 56 g   (4) 90 g

20. According to Table F, which ions combine with chloride ions to form an insoluble compound?

(1) Fe²⁺ ions   (3) Ag⁺ ions

(2) Ca²⁺ ions   (4) Li⁺ ions

21. Which ion combines with Ba²⁺ to form a compound that is most soluble in water?

(1) S²⁻   (2) OH⁻   (3) CO₃²⁻   (4) SO₄²⁻

22. A 1-gram sample of a compound is added to 100 grams of H₂O(ℓ) and the resulting mixture is stirred thoroughly. Some of the compound is then separated from the mixture by filtration. Based on Table F, the compound could be?

(1) AgCl   (2) CaCl₂   (3) NaCl   (4) NiCl₂

23. Which amount of a compound dissolved in 100. g of water at the stated temperature represents a solution that is saturated?

(1) 20 g KClO₃ at 80°C
(2) 40 g KNO₃ at 25°C
(3) 40 g KCl at 60°C
(4) 60 g NaNO₃ at 40°C

Concentration of Solutions

Because solutions are homogeneous mixtures, their compositions can vary. Sometimes, it is adequate to refer to a solution as dilute or concentrated. However, *dilute* and *concentrated* are relative terms and are not precise regarding the amount of solute involved. In most cases it is the specific amount, or concentration, of the solute that is important. In this section you will learn several methods of expressing the specific concentration of solute in a solution.

Molarity

One of the most important methods of stating the concentration of a solution is in terms of the number of moles of solute in a given volume of solution. The **molarity** (M) of a solution is the number of moles of solute in 1 L of solution. The relationship is listed in Important Formulas and Equations of *Reference Tables for Physical Setting/Chemistry*.

$$\text{molarity} = \frac{\text{moles of solute}}{\text{liters of solution}}$$

SAMPLE PROBLEM

What is the molarity of a solution that contains 4.0 mol of NaOH in 0.50 L of solution?

SOLUTION: Identify the known and unknown values.

Known
amount NaOH = 4.0 mol
volume of solution = 0.50 L

Unknown
molarity = ? M

Substitute known values into the equation for molarity, and solve for molarity.

$$M = \frac{\text{moles of solute}}{\text{liters of solution}}$$

$$M = \frac{4.0 \text{ moles NaOH}}{0.50 \text{ liter}}$$

$$M = 8.0$$

In the previous sample problem, the molarity of the solution is 8.0 M. A liter of this solution would contain 8.0 mol of the solute, NaOH. However, in many problems, the mass of solute is given instead of the number of moles. To solve this type of problem, convert grams of solute to moles of solute and solve as above.

What is the molarity of a solution containing 82.0 g of $Ca(NO_3)_2$ in 2.0 liters of solution?

SOLUTION: Identify the known and unknown values.

Known
mass of $Ca(NO_3)_2$ = 82.0 g
volume of solution = 2.0 L

Unknown
molarity = ? M

1. Calculate the formula mass of $Ca(NO_3)_2$.

For Ca: 1 atom × 40. amu/atom = 40 amu
For N: 2 atoms × 14 amu/atom = 28 amu
For O: 6 atoms × 16 amu/atom = <u>96 amu</u>
        Formula mass $Ca(NO_3)_2$ = 164 amu

2. Change the formula mass to gram formula mass.

gram formula mass = formula mass in grams
gram formula mass $Ca(NO_3)_2$ = 164 g/mol

3. Convert grams of $Ca(NO_3)_2$ to moles.

$$\text{moles } Ca(NO_3)_2 = \frac{\text{grams } Ca(NO_3)_2}{\text{gram formula mass } Ca(NO_3)_2}$$

$$\text{moles } Ca(NO_3)_2 = \frac{82.0 \text{ g}}{164 \text{ g/mol}} = 0.500 \text{ mol}$$

4. Calculate molarity.

$$M = \frac{\text{moles of solute}}{\text{liters of solution}}$$

$$M = \frac{0.500 \text{ mol NaOH}}{2.0 \text{ L solution}}$$

$$M = 0.250$$

Percent by Mass

It is common to find labels that list the concentration of the ingredients by percent mass. Fertilizers often list the active ingredients as a percentage of the entire mass of the fertilizer. **Percent mass** is simply the mass of an ingredient divided by the total mass, expressed as a percent (parts per hundred). Percent mass problems are essentially the same as the percent composition problems found in Topic 3. To calculate the percent mass, use the following relationship.

$$\text{percent mass} = \frac{\text{mass of part}}{\text{mass of whole}} \times 100\%$$

Percent by Volume

When two liquids are mixed to form a solution, it is common to express the concentration of the solute as a percent by volume. A label on a bottle of rubbing alcohol shows a common example. Usually the label will show that the solution is 70% isopropyl alcohol by volume. The rest of the solution is water.

Percent by volume is the ratio of the volume of an ingredient divided by the total volume and expressed as a percent.

$$\text{percent by volume} = \frac{\text{volume of solute}}{\text{volume of solution}} = 100\%$$

Memory Jogger

In math class you have learned how to rearrange an equation to solve for an unknown variable. Analyze these formulas to remind yourself how to do it.

$$a = bc$$
$$b = a/c$$
$$c = a/b$$

Recognize that the molarity equation can also be rearranged to solve for any variable included in the equation.

$$\text{molarity} = \frac{\text{moles solute}}{\text{liters of solution}}$$

$$\text{moles solute} = (\text{molarity})(\text{liters of solution})$$

$$\text{liters of solution} = \frac{\text{moles solute}}{\text{molarity}}$$

SAMPLE PROBLEM

What is the percent mass of sodium hydroxide if 2.50 g of NaOH are added to 50.00 g of H_2O?

SOLUTION: Identify the known and unknown values.

Known
mass of NaOH = 2.50 g
mass of H_2O = 50.00 g

Unknown
Percent mass
  NaOH ?%

Substitute known values into the percent mass equation, and solve for percent mass.

$$\% \text{ mass} = \frac{\text{mass of part}}{\text{mass of whole}} \times 100\%$$

$$\% \text{ mass NaOH} = \frac{2.50 \text{ g NaOH}}{(2.50 + 50.00) \text{ g solution}} \times 100\%$$

$$\% \text{ mass NaOH} = 4.76\%$$

SAMPLE PROBLEM

What is the percent by volume of alcohol if 50.0 mL of ethanol is diluted with water to form a total volume of 300. mL?

SOLUTION: Identify the known and unknown values.

Known
volume of ethanol = 50.0 mL
total volume = 300. mL

Unknown
percent by volume
  ethanol = ? %

Substitute known values into the percent by volume equation, and solve for percent by volume.

$$\% \text{ by volume} = \frac{\text{volume of solute}}{\text{volume of solution}} \times 100\%$$

$$\% \text{ by volume ethanol} = \frac{50.0 \text{ mL ethanol}}{300. \text{ mL solution}} \times 100\%$$

$$\% \text{ by volume ethanol } 16.7\%$$

Parts per Million

Parts per million is similar to percent composition because it compares masses. **Parts per million (ppm)** is a ratio between the mass of a solute and the total mass of the solution. This method of reporting concentrations is useful for extremely dilute solutions when molarity and percent mass would be difficult to interpret. For example, chlorine is used as a disinfectant in swimming pools. Only about 2 g of chlorine per 1,000,000 g of swimming pool water is necessary to keep the pool sanitized. Finding molarity and percent mass would result in numbers too small to be useful. Parts per million is often used to report a measured amount of air or water pollutants.

Percent composition uses the amount present per hundred parts because it is a percent. The only difference in finding ppm is that you multiply by 1,000,000 ppm instead of 100 percent.

$$\text{ppm} = \frac{\text{grams of solute}}{\text{grams of solution}} \times 1,000,000 \text{ ppm}$$

SAMPLE PROBLEM

Approximately 0.0043 g of oxygen can be dissolved in 100. mL of water at 20°C.
Express this in terms of parts per million.

SOLUTION: Identify the known and unknown values.

Known
mass of O_2 = 0.0043 g
volume of H_2O = 100. mL

Unknown
ppm O_2 = ?

Substitute known values into the ppm equation,
and solve for ppm O_2.

$$ppm = \frac{grams\ of\ solute}{grams\ of\ solution} \times 1{,}000{,}000\ ppm$$

$$ppm\ O_2 = \frac{0.0043\ \cancel{g}}{100.0043\ \cancel{g}} \times 1{,}000{,}000\ ppm$$

$$ppm\ O_2 = 43\ ppm$$

Preparation of a Solution of Known Concentration

It is important to be able to calculate the amount of solute to be added to
a known volume of solvent to make a solution of specified concentration.
The following sample problem shows you how to determine the amount
of solute needed to prepare a solution of known molarity.

You now know how much solute and solvent you need to actually prepare
the solution in the sample problem, but the procedure used in preparation

SAMPLE PROBLEM

What mass of sodium carbonate is required to prepare 2.00 L of a 0.250 M
sodium carbonate solution?

SOLUTION: Identify the known and unknown values.

Known
concentration of
 solution = 0.250 M
volume of solution = 2.00 L

Unknown
mass of Na_2CO_3 = ? g

Determine the number of moles of solute needed
by using molarity and volume.

moles = MV = molarity × liters of solution

$$moles\ Na_2CO_3 = \frac{0.250\ mol}{1\ \cancel{L}} \times 2.00\ \cancel{L} = 0.500\ mol$$

The following steps are used to convert moles
Na_2CO_3 to grams Na_2CO_3:

1. Determine the formula mass of Na_2CO_3.

For Na: 2 atoms × 23.0 amu/atom = 46.0 amu
For C: 1 atom × 12.0 amu/atom = 12.0 amu
For O: 3 atoms × 16.0 amu/atom = 48.0 amu
         formula mass Na_2CO_3 = 106.0 amu

2. Change the formula mass to gram formula
mass.

gram formula mass = formula mass in grams
gram formula mass Na_2CO_3 = 106.0 g/mol

3. Convert moles of Na_2CO_3 into grams of
Na_2CO_3.

mass = moles × gram formula mass
mass Na_2CO_3 = 0.500 $\cancel{mol}$ × 106.0 g/$\cancel{mol}$
mass Na_2CO_3 = 53.0 g

is also essential. The steps listed below apply to the preparation of any solution of known concentration:

1. Add the desired amount of solute to a volumetric flask.
2. Add some distilled water and mix until the solute is dissolved and the solution is homogeneous.
3. Fill the volumetric flask to the mark on the neck of the flask, stopper, and again mix to ensure that the solution is homogeneous.

The reason the water is added in two steps is that it is easier to dissolve the solute if the flask is not full and there is room for the water to be adequately stirred or shaken.

Review Questions — Set 7.3

24. What is the molarity of a KF(aq) solution containing 116 g of KF in 1.00 L of solution?

    (1) 1.00 M (2) 2.00 M (3) 3.00 M (4) 4.00 M

25. What is the molarity of an H_2SO_4 solution if 0.25 L of the solution contains 0.75 mol of H_2SO_4?

    (1) 0.33 M (2) 0.75 M (3) 3.0 M (4) 6.0 M

26. What is the total number of moles of the solute H_2SO_4 needed to prepare 5.0 L of a 2.0 M solution of H_2SO_4?

    (1) 2.5 mol   (3) 10. mol
    (2) 5.0 mol   (4) 20. mol

27. What volume of a 2.0 M solution is needed to provide 0.50 mol of NaOH?

    (1) 0.25 L (2) 0.50 L (3) 1.0 L (4) 2.0 L

28. What is the molarity of a solution that contains 40. g of NaOH in 0.50 L of solution?

    (1) 1.0 M (2) 2.0 M (3) 0.50 M (4) 0.25 M

29. If 100. mL of a 1.0 M solution is evaporated to a volume of 25 mL, what will be the concentration of the resulting solution?

    (1) 0.25 M (2) 0.50 M (3) 2.0 M (4) 4.0 M

30. What is the percent by mass of a solution in which 60. g of NaOH are dissolved in sufficient water to make 100 g of solution?

    (1) 16% (2) 40% (3) 60% (4) 160%

31. What is the percent by mass of a solution if 60. g of acetic acid are added to 90. g of water?

    (1) 20% (2) 30% (3) 40% (4) 67%

32. Carbon dioxide gas has a solubility of 0.0972 g/100 g H_2O at 40°C. Expressed in parts per million, this concentration is closest to

    (1) 0.972 ppm   (3) 97.2 ppm
    (2) 9.72 ppm   (4) 972 ppm

33. An aqueous solution has a mass of 490 grams, and contains 8.5×10^{-3} grams of calcium ions. The concentration of calcium ions in this solution is

    (1) 4.3 ppm
    (2) 17 ppm
    (3) 8.5 ppm
    (4) 34 ppm

34. What is the percent by mass of solute in a saturated solution of $KClO_3$ at a temperature of 60°C?

    (1) 0.218%   (3) 21.8%
    (2) 0.28%   (4) 28%

35. A 2400.-gram sample of an aqueous solution contains 0.012 gram of NH_3. What is the concentration of NH_3 in the solution, expressed in parts per million?

    (1) 5.0 ppm   (3) 20. ppm
    (2) 15 ppm   (4) 50. ppm

36. The concentration of a solution can be expressed in

    (1) kelvins
    (2) moles per liter
    (3) joules per kilogram
    (4) milliliters

37. Concentration of a solution can be expressed in

    (1) milliliters per minute
    (2) parts per million
    (3) grams per kelvin
    (4) joules per gram

Colligative Properties

The freezing and boiling points of water change when nonvolatile solutes are added. When any salt is added to water, the freezing point of the water decreases. This helps explain why salt is applied to roads and sidewalks when they are covered with snow and ice. The added salt lowers the freezing point and helps to melt the snow or ice. The amount of the lowering of the freezing point is not dependent on the nature of the added particle but only on the total number of dissolved particles. One mole of any particles will have the same effect on the freezing point. One mole of particles lowers the freezing point of 1000 g of water by 1.86°C.

Molecular Versus Ionic

When one mole of sugar, a molecular substance, is dissolved in water, one mole of particles is produced in solution.

$$C_{12}H_{22}O_{11}(s) \rightarrow C_{12}H_{22}O_{11}(aq)$$
$$\text{1 mol} \qquad\qquad \text{1 mol}$$

When one mole of an ionic substance is dissolved in water, the results are different. The ionic substance separates into individual ions.

$$NaCl(s) \rightarrow Na^+ (aq) \quad + Cl^- (aq)$$
$$\text{1 mol NaCl} \rightarrow \text{1 mol } Na^+ + \text{1 mol } Cl^-$$

Thus, one mole of sodium chloride produces two moles of particles and will depress the freezing point of water twice as much as the mole of sugar. The greater the number of ions, the greater the effect on the freezing point. $CaCl_2$ contains three ions, and one mole of this salt will depress the freezing point three times as much as a mole of sugar.

The situation is similar with the boiling point. One mole of particles will elevate the boiling point of 1000. g of water by 0.52°C. One mole of dissolved sugar will elevate the boiling point of 1000. g of water by 0.52°C. One mole of dissolved sodium chloride contains two moles of ions, and will raise the boiling point of 1000.g of water by 1.04°C.

Review Questions
Set 7.4

38. Why is salt (NaCl) put on icy roads and sidewalks in the winter?

(1) It is ionic and lowers the freezing point of water.

(2) It is ionic and raises the freezing point of water.

(3) It is covalent and lowers the freezing point of water.

(4) It is covalent and raises the freezing point of water.

39. What occurs as a salt dissolves in water?

(1) The number of ions in the solution decreases, and the freezing point decreases.

(2) The number of ions in the solution decreases, and the freezing point increases.

(3) The number of ions in the solution increases, and the freezing point decreases.

(4) The number of ions in the solution increases, and the freezing point increases.

40. Assume equal aqueous concentrations of each of the following substances. Which has the lowest freezing point?

(1) $C_2H_{12}O_6$ (3) $C_{12}H_{22}O_{11}$

(2) CH_3OH (4) NaOH

41. What occurs when sugar is added to water?

(1) The freezing point of the water will decrease, and the boiling point will decrease.

(2) The freezing point of the water will decrease, and the boiling point will increase.

(3) The freezing point of the water will increase, and the boiling point will decrease.

(4) The freezing point of the water will increase, and the boiling point will increase.

42. Which solution has the highest boiling point?

(1) 1.0 M KNO_3

(2) 2.0 M KNO_3

(3) 1.0 M $Ca(NO_3)_2$

(4) 2.0 M $Ca(NO_3)_2$

43. Which property of a distilled water solution will not be affected by adding 50 mL of CH_3OH to 100. mL of the water solution at 25°C?

(1) conductivity

(2) mass

(3) freezing point

(4) boiling point

Memory Jogger

Hydrogen bonds are formed when a hydrogen atom in one molecule is attracted to an oxygen, nitrogen, or fluorine atom in another molecule. Because hydrogen bonding is stronger than dipole-dipole attraction, substances with hydrogen bonding have abnormally high boiling points.

Vapor Pressure

The molecules in a liquid are held together by rather weak forces. Polar molecules called dipoles are held in the liquid phase by dipole-dipole forces. In molecules containing hydrogen and one atom of oxygen, nitrogen, or fluorine, the force of attraction holding them in the liquid phase are hydrogen bonds.

In any sample of a liquid, some of the particles at the surface have sufficient energy to escape from their neighboring molecules and enter the gas phase. When a substance that is normally a solid or a liquid at room temperature enters the gas phase it is called a **vapor.** Thus, you will often hear about water vapor or gasoline vapor, as water and gasoline are normally liquids at room temperature.

As the temperature of a liquid increases, the particles have more energy, and more particles escape from the surface. These vapor particles are gaseous particles and exert pressure in the gaseous phase. The pressure that a vapor exerts is called **vapor pressure.** Table H of *Reference Tables for Physical Setting/Chemistry* is a graph showing the vapor pressure of four substances measured in pressure units of kilopascals (kPa).

Of the substances shown on the graph, propanone exerts the most pressure, about 93 kPa at a temperature of 50°C. It can be inferred that propanone has the weakest intermolecular forces holding it in the liquid phase, while ethanoic acid has the greatest, exerting only about 8 kPa of pressure.

Boiling Point

As the temperature of a liquid rises, vapor pressure increases. Finally the vapor pressure becomes equal to atmospheric pressure. At this point the gas may vaporize, not only on the surface but at any point in the container. A bubble of vapor below the surface has enough pressure that it does not collapse from the atmospheric pressure pushing against it. When a bubble can occur at any point in the liquid, the process is called boiling. The normal **boiling point** of a liquid is the temperature at which the vapor pressure of the liquid is 101.3 kPa, standard atmospheric pressure. Equivalent pressures are 1 atm, 760 mm Hg, and 760 torr. The heat required to change 1 mol of a substance from a liquid at its boiling point to 1 mol of a vapor is termed the <u>heat of vaporization.</u>

The normal boiling point of water is 100.°C. At this temperature, the vapor pressure of water is 101.3 kPa. The line representing 101.3 kPa on Table H shows the normal boiling point of ethanol to be 78°C. When the pressure is less than 101.3 kPa, the boiling point will be less than the normal value. Water will boil at about 70°C when the pressure is about 30 kPa. If the pressure is greater than normal, liquids will boil at temperatures above their normal boiling points. When atmospheric pressure is about 145 kPa, water boils at 110.°C.

Review Questions

Set 7.5

Use the tables in *Reference Tables for Physical Setting/Chemistry* as needed in answering the following questions.

44. What is the vapor pressure of water at 105°C?

(1) 100 kPa
(2) 101.3 kPa
(3) 110 kPa
(4) 120 kPa

45. As the pressure on a liquid is changed from 100. kPa to 120. kPa, the temperature at which the liquid will boil

(1) decreases
(2) increases
(3) remains the same

46. In a closed system at 40°C, a liquid has a vapor pressure of 50 kPa. The liquid's normal boiling point could be

(1) 10°C   (3) 40°C
(2) 30°C   (4) 60°C

47. If the pressure on the surface of water in the liquid state is 30 kPa, the water will boil at

(1) 0°C   (3) 70°C
(2) 30°C   (4) 100°C

48. A sample of ethanoic acid at 100°C has a vapor pressure of

(1) 53 kPa
(2) 100 kPa
(3) 101.3 kPa
(4) 125 kPa

49. Which substance has the greatest intermolecular forces of attraction between molecules?

(1) propanone
(2) ethanol
(3) water
(4) ethanoic acid

50. The vapor pressure of ethanol at its normal boiling point would be

(1) 80 kPa
(2) 101.3 kPa
(3) 273 kPa
(4) 373 kPa

Directions

Review the Test-Taking Strategies section of this book. Then answer the following questions. Read each question carefully and answer with a correct choice or response.

Part A

1 When a teaspoon of sugar is added to water in a beaker, the sugar dissolves. The resulting mixture is
   (1) a compound
   (2) a homogeneous solution
   (3) a heterogeneous solution
   (4) an emulsion

2 A small quantity of a salt is stirred into a liter of water until it dissolves. In the resulting mixture, the water is
   (1) the solvent
   (2) the solute
   (3) dispersed material
   (4) a precipitate

3 A solution
   (1) will separate on standing
   (2) may have color
   (3) can be cloudy
   (4) can be heterogeneous

4 A nonpolar solvent would most easily dissolve which of the following substances?
   (1) NH_3 (3) $NaCl$
   (2) CCl_4 (4) H_2SO_4

5 What happens when a crystal of a salt is dropped into an unsaturated solution of the same salt?
   (1) Excess solute crystals form.
   (2) The crystal dissolves.
   (3) The crystal drops to the bottom, unchanged.
   (4) The solution becomes colorless.

6 The depression of the freezing point is dependent on
   (1) the nature of the solute
   (2) the formula mass of the solute
   (3) the concentration of dissolved particles
   (4) hydrogen bonding

7 Which compound becomes *less* soluble in water as the temperature of the solution is increased?
   (1) HCl (3) $NaCl$
   (2) KCl (4) NH_4Cl

8 What happens when a crystal of solute is dropped into a supersaturated solution of the salt?
   (1) The crystal dissolves.
   (2) Excess solute crystals form.
   (3) The crystal drops to the bottom, unchanged.
   (4) The solution begins to boil.

9 Under which conditions are gases most soluble in water?
   (1) high temperature and high pressure
   (2) high temperature and low pressure
   (3) low temperature and high pressure
   (4) low temperature and low pressure

10 As the temperature of a liquid decreases, the amount of a gas that can be dissolved
   (1) decreases
   (2) increases
   (3) remains the same

11 As the temperature of liquid water decreases, its vapor pressure
   (1) decreases
   (2) increases
   (3) remains the same
   (4) disappears

12 At standard pressure, how do the boiling point and freezing point of $NaCl(aq)$ compare to that of $H_2O(\ell)$?
   (1) The boiling point of $NaCl(aq)$ is higher, and the freezing point of $NaCl(aq)$ is lower.
   (2) The boiling point of $NaCl(aq)$ is lower, and the freezing point of $NaCl(aq)$ is higher.
   (3) Both the boiling point and freezing point of $NaCl(aq)$ are lower.
   (4) Both the boiling point and freezing point of $NaCl(aq)$ are lower.

Part B-1

13 Which substance increases in solubility as the temperature decreases?
(1) KClO₃   (2) NH₃   (3) KNO₃   (4) NaCl

14 The diagrams below represent an ionic crystal being dissolved in water.

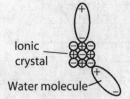

According to the diagrams, the dissolving process takes place by
(1) hydrogen bond formation
(2) metallic bonding
(3) dipole-dipole attractions
(4) molecule-ion attractions

15 If solutions of barium nitrate and sodium sulfate are mixed and then poured into a filter, the solid remaining on the filter will be
(1) barium nitrate   (3) barium sulfate
(2) sodium nitrate   (4) sodium sulfate

16 A student tested the solubility of a salt at different temperatures and then used the *Reference Tables for Physical Setting/Chemistry* to identify the salt. The student's data appears below.

Temperature (°C)	Solubility Data (g of salt per 10 g of water)
30	1.2
50	2.2
62	3.0
76	4.0

What is the identity of the salt?
(1) potassium nitrate   (3) potassium chlorate
(2) sodium chloride   (4) ammonium chloride

17 A student drops a crystal of NaCl into a beaker of NaCl(aq) and the crystal dissolves. The original solution must have been
(1) supersaturated
(2) saturated
(3) unsaturated
(4) heterogeneous

18 If 100. g of water at 80°C contains 45 g of KCl and 45 g of NaNO₃, the solution is
(1) saturated with respect to both KCl and NaNO₃
(2) saturated with respect to KCl and unsaturated with respect to NaNO₃
(3) unsaturated with respect to both KCl and NaNO₃
(4) supersaturated with respect to both KCl and NaNO₃

19 What happens when KI(s) is dissolved in water?
(1) I⁻ ions are attracted to the oxygen atoms of the water.
(2) K⁺ ions are attracted to the oxygen atoms of the water.
(3) K⁺ ions are attracted to the hydrogen atoms of the water.
(4) No attractions are involved; the crystal just falls apart.

20 Which compound is soluble in water?
(1) PbS   (3) Na₂S
(2) BaS   (4) Fe₂S₃

21 A saturated solution of potassium chloride at 10°C is heated to 30°C. As the solution is heated in a closed container, the total mass of the solution
(1) decreases   (3) remains the same
(2) increases

22 Water boils at 90°C when the pressure exerted on the liquid equals
(1) 65 kPa   (3) 101.3 kPa
(2) 90 kPa   (4) 120 kPa

23 A solution consists of 0.50 mole of CaCl₂ dissolved in 100. grams of H₂O at 25°C. Compared to the boiling point and freezing point of 100. grams of pure H₂O at standard pressure, the solution at standard pressure has
(1) a higher boiling point and a lower freezing point
(2) a higher boiling point and a higher freezing point
(3) a lower boiling point and a lower freezing point
(4) a lower boiling point and a higher freezing point

24 Which sample of ethanol will have the highest vapor pressure?
   (1) 10. mL at 62°C   (3) 30. mL at 42°C
   (2) 20.0 mL at 52°C   (4) 40 mL at 32°C

25 The vapor pressure of water is 50 kPa. The temperature of this sample of water is
   (1) 37°C   (2) 62°C   (3) 82°C   (4) 92°C

Parts B–2 and C

Base your answers to questions 26 through 28 on the information below.

A solution of $KClO_3$ is prepared using 75 grams of the solute in enough water to make 0.250 liters of solution. The gram-formula mass of $KClO_3$ is 122 grams per mole.

26 Determine the molarity (concentration in mol/L) of the solution.

27 Determine the percent by mass of solute in the solution.

28 Assuming the solution is saturated, determine the temperature of the solution.

Base your answers to questions 29 through 31 on the information below.

Four flasks are prepared, each containing 100 mL of aqueous solution as described in the data table.

Flask	Solution	Concentration	Solute Type
A	KCl(aq)	1.0 M	ionic
B	CH_3OH(aq)	1.0 M	molecular
C	$Ba(OH)_2$(aq)	1.0 M	ionic
D	CH_3OCH_3(aq)	1.0 M	molecular

29 Which solution has the lowest freezing point?

30 For aqueous solutions, the boiling point is elevated by 0.52°C for each mole of particles (ions or molecules) present in 1 liter of the solution. Determine the boiling point of solution C.

31 Solution A is an unsaturated solution with 74.54 grams (1 mol) of solute dissolved in 1 liter of solution. According to Table G, at a temperature of 30°C, how much additional solute would be required to saturate the solution at that temperature?

Base your answers to questions 32 through 35 on the information below.

The following graph displays the Solubility Curve for substance X. The points labeled **A** through **F** represent various solutions of the substance at different concentrations and temperatures.

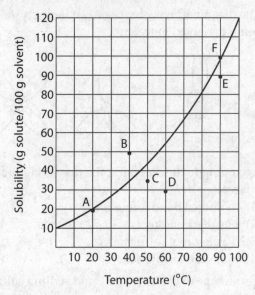

32 State a letter that indicates a position on this graph where solution X is saturated.

33 Describe, in terms of solute and solvent interaction, what could happen if additional solute crystals were added to the solution indicated at Point B.

34 What could be done to the solution at Point D to make the solution saturated?

35 If the gram-formula mass of substance X is 180 g/mol, determine the molarity of the solution at Point E.

Base your answers to questions 36 through 38 on the following information.

A scientist makes a solution that contains 44.0 grams of hydrogen chloride gas, HCl(g), in 200. grams of water, $H_2O(\ell)$, at 20.°C. This process is represented by the balanced equation below.

$$HCl(g) \xrightarrow{H_2O} H^+(aq) + Cl^-(aq)$$

36 Based on Reference Table G, identify, in terms of saturation, the type of solution made by the scientist.

37 Explain, in terms of distribution of particles, why the solution is a homogeneous mixture.

38 Knowing that the gram-formula mass of HCl is 36 g/mol, determine the molarity of this solution.

Kinetics and Equilibrium

8

What Scientists Know About Chemical Reactions

? What do car accidents and chemical reactions have in common? ?

Well, they both must involve collisions. Just like all car collisions do not cause damage, not all chemical collisions cause a reaction. Consider that most cars have bumpers that can absorb energy at low speeds and avoid damage. But at higher speeds—CRUNCH! Colliding molecules also need a minimum amount of energy, called the activation energy, to cause changes and start chemical reactions.

135

8 Kinetics and Equilibrium

Vocabulary

activated complex	entropy	potential energy diagram
activation energy	equilibrium	stress
catalyst	Le Châtelier's principle	

Topic Overview

In this topic you will be introduced to two important ideas in chemistry—the collision theory and equilibrium. The collision theory explores why reactions occur, and the factors that affect those reactions. Equilibrium introduces an important surprise. Not only do reactant particles produce products, but often, these products can react to regenerate the reactants. Many reactions can proceed in two directions. These processes are not only vital in industry, but even more in our own bodies. We have many equilibrium systems that help maintain our health on an even keel.

Kinetics

Kinetics is the branch of chemistry that is concerned with the rates of chemical reactions. Several different factors affect how quickly chemical reactions occur. One of the basic concepts of kinetics is that in order for a reaction to occur, reactant particles must collide. This is called the collision theory. Collisions between particles can produce a reaction if both the spatial orientation and energy of the colliding particles are conducive to a reaction.

Factors Affecting Rates of Reaction

The rate of a chemical reaction is dependent on factors such as the nature of the reactants, concentration, surface area, the presence of a catalyst, and temperature. All these factors affect rate of reaction by changing the number of effective collisions that take place between particles. Pressure can also be a factor that affects the rate of reactions involving gases.

Nature of the Reactants Reactions involve the breaking of existing bonds and the formation of new ones. In general, covalently bonded substances are slower to react than ionic substances due to the greater number of bonds that must be broken before a reaction can occur. Breaking more bonds requires that the particles must have more energy when they collide.

Concentration Most chemical reactions will proceed at a faster rate if the concentration of one or more reactants is increased. An obvious example is the rate of combustion of paper in air, which is 20% oxygen, compared with the much faster rate in pure oxygen. The kinetic molecular theory would predict that because there are more collisions between the paper and oxygen in pure oxygen than in air, the rate in pure oxygen would be faster. Indeed, this is the case.

Surface Area When more surface area of a substance is exposed, there are more chances for reactant particles to collide, thus increasing the reaction rate. A finely divided powder will react more rapidly than a single lump of the same mass.

Pressure While pressure has little or no effect on the rate of reactions between solids or liquids, it has a pronounced effect on gases. An increase in pressure has the effect of increasing the concentration of gaseous particles. Therefore, it increases the rate of a reaction that involves gases.

The Presence of a Catalyst **Catalysts** are substances that increase the rate of a reaction by providing a different and easier pathway for a reaction. Catalysts take part in a reaction, but they are unchanged when the reaction is complete.

Temperature By definition, temperature implies that the greater the temperature of a substance, the faster the molecules move. The kinetic molecular theory states that collisions must occur in order for a reaction to take place. When these two concepts are put together you can see that if the particles are moving faster, there will be more collisions, thus increasing the likelihood that a reaction will occur. At a higher temperature, not only will there be more collisions, but the reacting particles will have more energy, making it more likely that the collisions will be effective.

Table 8-1. Factors that Affect Rate of Reaction	
Factor	**Increases Rate**
Nature of reactants	ionic more than covalent
Concentration	increased concentration
Pressure	increased pressure for gases
Temperature	increased temperature
Surface area	increased surface area
Catalyst	presence of a catalyst

Review Questions

Set 8.1

1. As the number of effective collisions between reacting particles increases, the rate of the reaction
   (1) decreases
   (2) increases
   (3) remains the same

2. Which of the following pairs of reactants will react most quickly?
   (1) sodium chloride and silver nitrate
   (2) water and hydrogen chloride
   (3) hydrogen and propene
   (4) oxygen and methane

3. In the reaction $2Mg(s) + O_2(g) \rightarrow 2MgO(s)$, as the surface area of $Mg(s)$ increases, the rate of the reaction
   (1) decreases
   (2) increases
   (3) remains the same

4. Consider the following equation.
   $$A(g) + B(g) \rightarrow C(g)$$
   As the concentration of $A(g)$ increases, the frequency of collisions of $A(g)$ with $B(g)$
   (1) decreases
   (2) increases
   (3) remains the same

5. The reaction $A(g) + B(g) \rightarrow C(g)$ is occurring in the apparatus shown below.

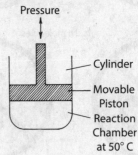

Pressure

Cylinder

Movable Piston

Reaction Chamber at 50° C

The rate of the reaction can be decreased by increasing the
   (1) pressure on the reactants
   (2) temperature of the reactants
   (3) concentration of reactant $A(g)$
   (4) volume of the reaction chamber

6. Consider the following equation.
   $$Mg(s) + 2H_2O(\ell) \rightarrow Mg(OH)_2(s) + H_2(g)$$
   For the reaction to occur at the fastest rate, 1 g of $Mg(s)$ should be added in the form of
   (1) large chunks
   (2) small chunks
   (3) a ribbon
   (4) a powder

7. Raising the temperature speeds up the rate of chemical reaction by increasing

(1) the effectiveness of the collisions only
(2) the frequency of the collisions only
(3) both the effectiveness and frequency of the collisions
(4) neither the effectiveness nor frequency of the collisions

8. Which statement explains why increasing the temperature increases the rate of a chemical reaction, while other conditions remain the same?

(1) The reacting particles have more energy and collide more frequently.
(2) The reacting particles have more energy and collide less frequently.
(3) The reacting particles have less energy and collide more frequently.
(4) The reacting particles have less energy and collide less frequently.

9. If the pressure on gaseous reactants is increased, the rate of reaction is increased because there is an increase in the

(1) temperature   (3) concentration
(2) volume   (4) heat of reaction

10. Which factors have the greatest effect on the rate of a chemical reaction between $AgNO_3(aq)$ and $Cu(s)$?

(1) solution concentration and pressure
(2) solution concentration and temperature
(3) molar mass and pressure
(4) molar mass and temperature

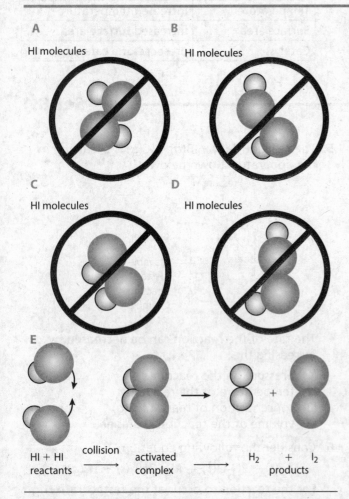

Figure 8-1. Collisions of molecules: If HI molecules collide in any arrangement other than the one shown in part E, the collision is not effective and no products form.

Potential Energy Diagram

As was mentioned when discussing the nature of the reactants, chemical bonds contain energy. Specifically, they contain potential chemical energy. A diagram, called a **potential energy diagram,** illustrates the potential energy change that occurs during a chemical reaction. The vertical axis of this diagram represents the change in potential energy. The horizontal axis is called the <u>reaction coordinate</u>, which represents the progress of the reaction.

In order for a reaction to occur, the reactants must have sufficient energy to collide effectively. As the reactant particles approach each other, kinetic energy is converted into potential energy.

Not only must the particles collide in order for a reaction to occur, they must be properly positioned. Look at Figure 8-1. If the particles collide in the proper orientation, an activated complex is formed. This **activated complex** is a temporary, intermediate product that may either break apart and reform the reactants or rearrange the atoms and form new products.

Figure 8-2 shows a potential energy diagram for the following reaction.

$$A + B \rightarrow C + D + heat$$

Line 1 extends from the origin of the y-axis to the reactants and represents the amount of potential

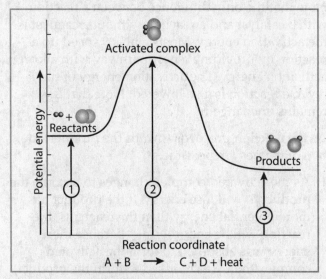

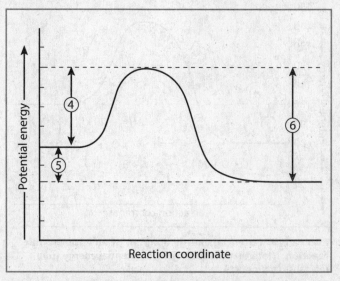

Figure 8-2. **Potential energy diagram:** This figure shows the potential energy of the reactants, the activated complex, and the products of the reaction.

Figure 8-3. **Activation energies and heat of reaction**

energy of the reactants. Line 2 extends from the origin of the *y*-axis to the activated complex and represents the potential energy of the complex. Line 3 represents the potential energy of the products. Any line that begins at the origin of the *y*-axis of such a graph is a measure of potential energy.

Figure 8-3 shows the same potential energy diagram, but the lines represent the differences between the potential energies of different substances. Line 4 represents the difference in potential energy between the reactants and the activated complex. The amount of energy needed to form the activated complex from the reactants is called the **activation energy.** Because the diagram is read from left to right, it is also called the activation energy of the forward reaction.

Line 5 represents the difference between the potential energy of the reactants and the potential energy of the products. The difference between the potential energy of the reactants and products is called the <u>heat of reaction</u> and is represented by ΔH.

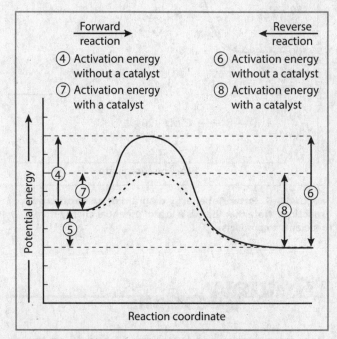

Figure 8-4. **Effect of a catalyst on activation energy:** Note that the heat of reaction is unchanged with the addition of a catalyst, but the activation energy is decreased.

Line 6 represents the difference between the potential energies of the products and the activated complex. How can this be useful? Some reactions can proceed, not only in the forward direction, but also in the reverse, or right to left on the diagram. In this case, the line represents the activation energy of the reverse reaction.

Figure 8-4 is similar to the previous diagrams, but a new line has been added. This new line represents the effect of a catalyst on the reaction.

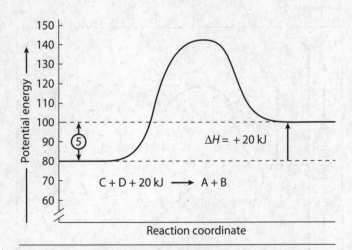

Figure 8-5. **Potential energy diagram of an endothermic reaction:** Note that there is a gain in potential energy from reactants to products.

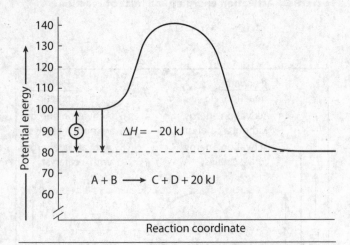

Figure 8-6. **Potential energy diagram of an exothermic reaction:** Note that there is a loss of potential energy from reactants to products.

Note that the only difference between a reaction with a catalyst and a reaction without a catalyst is the activation energy. Most catalysts speed up a reaction by providing a new pathway with a lower activation energy. The activation energy of the reverse reaction is also lowered. Note that ΔH remains unchanged.

As the reaction proceeds toward the product side, two outcomes are possible.

1. As the activated complex changes to become the product, it will lose energy. If the product has more potential energy than the reactants, the reaction will be <u>endothermic</u>. Because more energy was absorbed to form the activated complex than was released to form the product, there was a net gain of energy. Because there has been a gain in energy, the heat of reaction has a positive value ($\Delta H = +$), as shown in Figure 8-5.

2. If the product is lower on the vertical axis than the reactants, all of the energy that was absorbed to form the activated complex is recovered, plus the difference between the potential energy of the reactants and products. This represents a loss of potential energy compared to the reactants, indicating a release of energy and an <u>exothermic</u> reaction. In this case the heat of reaction has a negative value ($\Delta H = -$), as shown in Figure 8-6.

Review Questions

Set 8.2

Base your answers to Questions 11 and 12 on the diagram below, which represents the reaction:

$$A + B \rightarrow C + energy$$

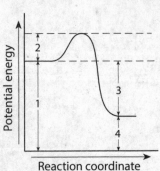

Reaction coordinate

11. Which statement correctly describes this reaction?

   (1) It is endothermic and energy is absorbed.
   (2) It is endothermic and energy is released.
   (3) It is exothermic and energy is absorbed.
   (4) It is exothermic and energy is released.

12. Which numbered interval will change with the addition of a catalyst to the system?

   (1) 1
   (2) 2
   (3) 3
   (4) 4

13. A potential energy diagram of a chemical system is shown below.

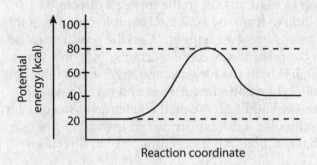

Reaction coordinate

What is the difference between the potential energy of the reactants and the potential energy of the products?

(1) 20. kcal
(2) 40. kcal
(3) 60. kcal
(4) 80. kcal

14. Consider the reaction for which $\Delta H = +$ 33 kJ/mol.

$$N_2(g) + 2O_2(g) \rightleftarrows 2NO_2(g)$$

The potential energy diagram of the reaction is shown below.

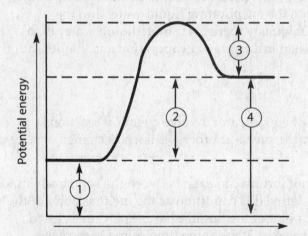

Which arrow represents the heat of reaction for the reverse reaction?

(1) 1
(2) 2
(3) 3
(4) 4

15. The potential energy diagram of a chemical reaction is shown below.

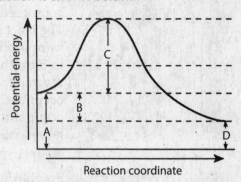

Reaction coordinate

Which letter in the diagram represents the heat of reaction?

(1) A   (2) B   (3) C   (4) D

16. A potential energy diagram is shown below.

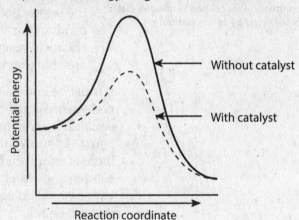

Reaction coordinate

Which reaction would have the lowest activation energy?

(1) the forward catalyzed reaction
(2) the forward uncatalyzed reaction
(3) the reverse catalyzed reaction
(4) the reverse uncatalyzed reaction

17. In the potential energy diagram below, which arrow represents the potential energy of the activated complex?

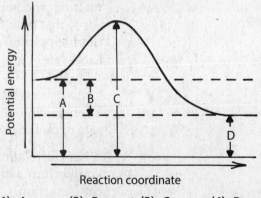

Reaction coordinate

(1) A   (2) B   (3) C   (4) D

Open container
$H_2O(\ell) \rightarrow H_2O(g)$

Closed container
$H_2O(\ell) \rightleftarrows H_2O(g)$

Figure 8-7. Equilibrium in a closed container: In the open container, the liquid evaporates at a constant rate until it is all evaporated. In the closed container, evaporation continues, but it is balanced by condensation.

Equilibrium

Each of the potential energy diagrams shown depicts a reaction that is proceeding from left to right, that is, in the forward direction. The reactants first collide to form the activated complex, and then they form products. Can the reverse ever happen? Can the products collide to form the activated complex and become reactants? Not only can a reverse reaction occur, but both the forward and reverse reactions can occur at the same time. When both the forward and reverse reactions occur at the same rate, the condition is called **equilibrium.** An equation representing equilibrium uses a double arrow ($\rightleftarrows$) instead of a single arrow ($\rightarrow$) to show that reactions are proceeding in both directions.

Equilibrium is a state of balance between the rates of two opposite processes that are taking place at the same rate. Equilibrium can only occur in a system in which neither reactants nor products can leave the system.

Equilibrium is a dynamic process, that is, it implies motion in which the interactions of reactant particles are balanced by the interactions of product particles. Equilibrium is an important concept because many chemical reactions and physical processes are reversible, that is, they are able to proceed in both directions.

It must be emphasized that the quantities of reactants and products are not necessarily equal at equilibrium. Indeed, it would be unusual if they were equal. It is the rates of the two reactions, forward and reverse, that are equal. As shown in Figure 8-7, in a closed container half-filled with water, there is equilibrium between the evaporating liquid water and the condensing water vapor. Obviously there is far more liquid water than water vapor. At equilibrium, it is the rate of evaporation and condensation that are equal.

Physical Equilibrium

Although many examples of equilibrium involve chemical reactions, equilibrium also occurs during physical processes such as change of state (phase) or dissolving.

Phase Equilibrium Phase equilibrium can exist between the solid and liquid phases of a substance. We define this condition as the melting point of the solid phase or the freezing point of the liquid phase. At 0°C in a closed container, both water and ice exist at the same time. Some of the ice is melting, and some of the water is freezing. An equation can be written to show that both the forward and reverse processes are taking place. The double-pointed arrow shows that both reactions are taking place at the same rate.

$$H_2O(s) \rightleftarrows H_2O(\ell)$$

There may not be the same amounts of solid and liquid present, but the rate of melting will be equal to the rate of freezing.

A similar relationship can exist in a closed container for liquid-gas equilibrium, where the rate of evaporation is equal to the rate of condensation.

$$H_2O(\ell) \rightleftarrows H_2O(g)$$

Solution Equilibrium Solids dissolved in liquids exist in equilibrium in a saturated solution. When solid sugar is first placed into water, the sugar dissolves, but no sugar is recrystallizing. When all of the sugar dissolves that can be dissolved at that temperature, the solution is saturated. If additional solid sugar is placed into the saturated solution, the process of dissolving will continue, but it is exactly balanced by the process of recrystallization. When the rate of dissolving and recrystallizing are equal, equilibrium exists, and the solution is saturated.

$$C_{12}H_{22}O_{11}(s) \rightleftharpoons C_{12}H_{22}O_{11}(aq)$$

Equilibrium may also be attained in a closed system between a gas dissolved in a liquid and the undissolved gas. In a closed bottle or can of soda there is equilibrium between the gaseous and dissolved state of carbon dioxide.

$$CO_2(g) \rightleftharpoons CO_2(aq)$$

In both of these cases, the equilibrium can be disturbed by a change in temperature. If the temperature is raised, a solid generally becomes more soluble in a liquid. For a short time the rate of dissolving exceeds the rate of recrystallization. As more solid is placed into solution, the rate of recrystallization increases until a new equilibrium is reached.

The opposite is true when the temperature of a solution of a gas in a liquid is raised. As the temperature increases, the rate of the gas escaping from the liquid increases, while the rate at which gas particles dissolve decreases. This decreases the solubility of the gas in the liquid. As the temperature rises, the solubility of all gases decreases in a liquid.

Chemical Equilibrium

When reactants are first mixed and no products are present, only the forward reaction can occur. Examine what happens in the chemical reaction between water vapor and methane.

$$CH_4(g) + H_2O(g) \rightarrow 3H_2(g) + CO(g)$$

As time progresses, the concentrations of $CH_4(g)$ and $H_2O(g)$ decrease, causing the forward reaction to slow, while the concentrations of $H_2(g)$ and $CO(g)$ increase, causing the rate of the reverse reaction to increase.

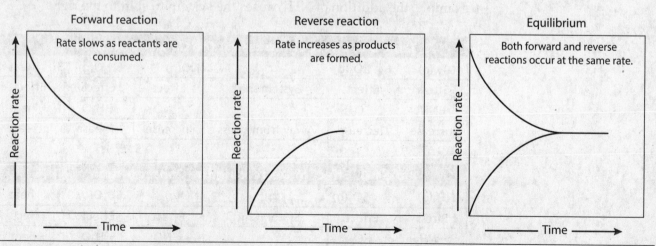

Figure 8-8. Chemical equilibrium: Equilibrium occurs when opposite reactions occur at the same rate.

This slowing of the forward reaction and speeding up of the reverse reaction continues until the rates of the two reactions become the same. At this point, chemical equilibrium exists. Figure 8-8 summarizes this process.

As with physical equilibrium, it is important to remember that no reactant or product can leave the system. If a precipitate is formed or a gas is formed in a system that is not closed, equilibrium will not be reached. The effect of any change in equilibrium is explained by Le Châtelier's principle.

Le Châtelier's Principle

Any change in temperature, concentration or pressure on an equilibrium system is called a **stress**. **Le Châtelier's principle** explains how a system at equilibrium responds to relieve any stress on the system. Examined below are several types of stress and how equilibrium shifts to relieve them.

Concentration Changes Again consider the reaction represented by the following equation.

$$CH_4(g) + H_2O(g) \rightleftarrows 3H_2(g) + CO(g)$$

If the stress is the addition of more methane (CH_4), the rate of the forward reaction will increase and more products will form. If the concentration of one substance is increased, the reaction that reduces the amount of the added substance is favored. In this example, the system is said to shift to the right as more product is formed. As more product forms, the rate of the reverse reaction also increases until once again the rates of the forward and reverse reactions are equal.

If the concentration of methane is reduced, the rate of the forward reaction decreases. When the concentration of a substance decreases, the reaction that produces that substance is favored. Initially the reverse reaction will take place faster than the forward reaction, and the system is said to be shifting to the left, or toward the reactant side.

Tables 8-2 and 8-3 show how a change in concentration affects equilibrium. A plus sign (+) means the concentration increases, and a minus sign (−) means that the concentration decreases. An increase causes the system to shift away from the stress, causing the stress to be lessened. In this example, the addition of NH_3 causes the system to shift to the right.

Table 8-2. Effect of Increasing the Concentration of NH_3					
$4NH_3(g)$ + $5O_2(g)$		$\rightleftarrows$	$4NO(g)$ +	$6H_2O(g)$ +	heat
Stress	Effect	System shift	Effect	Effect	Effect
$+NH_3$	$-O_2$	$\rightarrow$	$+NO$	$+H_2O$	+ heat
Increase	Decrease	Away from stress	Increase	Increase	Increase

Table 8-3. Effect of Decreasing the Concentration of NH_3					
$4NH_3(g)$ + $5O_2(g)$		$\rightleftarrows$	$4NO(g)$ +	$6H_2O(g)$ +	heat
Stress	Effect	System shift	Effect	Effect	Effect
$-NH_3$	$+O_2$	$\leftarrow$	$-NO$	$-H_2O$	$-$heat
Decrease	Increase	Toward the stress	Decrease	Decrease	Decrease

A decrease of NH_3 causes the system to move toward the stress, or a shift to the left, replacing some of the lost substance.

Notice that all factors on the same side of the arrow as the stress do the opposite of the stress. For example, as the NH_3 increases, O_2 decreases. All factors on the opposite side of the arrow from the stress increase or decrease in the same way as the stress.

A second consideration about equilibrium is important. While the rates of the forward and reverse reactions are equal, the concentrations of the reactants and products are most likely not equal. Figure 8-9 shows a situation in which carbon dioxide [$CO_2(g)$] and hydrogen [$H_2(g)$] are beginning to react to form carbon monoxide [$CO(g)$] and water [$H_2O(g)$]. At the beginning of the reaction (t_0) both CO_2 and H_2 are present while there is no $CO(g)$ or $H_2O(g)$. As the reaction proceeds these two reactants [$CO_2(g)$ and $H_2(g)$] are consumed and their concentrations decrease while the products [$CO(g)$ and $H_2O(g)$] begin to appear and their concentrations increase (t_1). As time progresses, a point is finally reached (t_2) when the concentrations of both reactants and products no longer change, but remain constant (t_3). This is the second characteristic of a system at equilibrium. The concentrations of reactants and products at equilibrium remain constant.

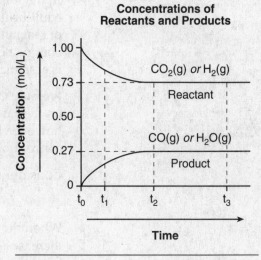

Concentrations of Reactants and Products

Figure 8-9
$$CO_2(g) + H_2(g) \rightleftarrows CO(g) + H_2O(g)$$

Important Concepts to Remember:

- The rates of reactions can be changed by changes in concentrations, temperature and the presence of a catalyst.

At Equilibrium:

- The rates of forward and reverse reactions are equal.
- The concentrations of reactants and products are constant, but the amounts of reactant and products are not necessarily equal.

Temperature Changes Consider the production of ammonia:

$$N_2(g) + 3H_2(g) \rightleftarrows 2NH_3(g) + heat$$

Le Châtelier's principle states that a system will undergo changes to reduce a stress. For this reaction, heat can be considered as a product. If the temperature is raised, the rates of both the forward and reverse reactions are increased, but not equally. The reverse reaction is endothermic and will absorb some of the applied heat. The endothermic reverse reaction is favored over the exothermic forward reaction. In other words, more reactants will form when temperature is increased in this reaction. A decrease in temperature will favor the exothermic reaction and, for this reaction, more products will form.

Table 8-4: Effect of Increasing the Heat					
4NH$_3$(*g*)	+ 5O$_2$(*g*)	$\rightleftarrows$	4NO(*g*)	+ 6H$_2$O(*g*)	+ heat
Effect	Effect	System shift	Effect	Effect	Stress
+NH$_3$	+O$_2$	←	−NO	−H$_2$O	+ heat
Increase	Increase	Away from stress	Decrease	Decrease	Increase

Table 8-5: Effect of Decreasing the Heat					
$4NH_3(g)$ + $5O_2(g)$		$\rightleftarrows$	$4NO(g)$ +	$6H_2O(g)$ +	heat
Effect	Effect	System shift	Effect	Effect	Stress
$-NH_3$	$-O_2$	$\rightarrow$	$+NO$	$+H_2O$	$-$ heat
Decrease	Decrease	Toward the stress	Increase	Increase	Decrease

In the following representation of how a temperature change affects equilibrium, note that the results are seen in a change of concentration of reactants and products, even though the stress is actually a change of energy. Because heat is a product of the reaction, a change in temperature is essentially a change in the concentration of that product.

Pressure Changes Remember that pressure changes do not have an effect on the rate of reaction when only solids and liquids are involved. They do, however, have an effect on gases. An increase in pressure increases the concentration of the gases.

Consider the following system.

$$CO_2(g) \rightleftarrows CO_2(aq)$$

When the pressure increases, the concentration of the gaseous CO_2 increases. Le Châtelier's principle predicts that the system will move away from the added stress—the system will shift to the right, causing more dissolved CO_2. Conversely, when the pressure on this system is reduced, the system shifts to the left, forming more gaseous CO_2. Recall what happens when a soda bottle is opened. The pressure is reduced, and the dissolved gas becomes bubbles of gaseous CO_2.

In the $CO_2(g) \rightleftarrows CO_2(aq)$ reaction, only one side of the equation contains a gaseous molecule. How will a system react when there are gaseous molecules on both sides? An increase in pressure will increase the concentration of gaseous molecules on both reactant and product sides of the equation, but the effects will be unequal. An increase in pressure will favor the reaction toward the side with fewer gas molecules. In the system:

$$N_2(g) + 3H_2(g) \rightleftarrows 2NH_3(g)$$

there are four gaseous molecules on the reactant side and only two on the product side. An increase in pressure will favor the reaction toward the product side, increasing the amount of NH_3 formed.

A decrease in pressure has the opposite effect. A decrease in pressure favors the reaction toward the side with the greater number of gas molecules. Thus, when the pressure is reduced the reaction shifts to the left, forming more $N_2(g)$ and $H_2(g)$ and decreasing the amount of $NH_3(g)$.

One more case remains. What happens if there are the same number of gaseous molecules on both sides? In the equation, $H_2(g) + Cl_2(g) \rightleftarrows 2HCl(g)$, the reactant and product sides each have two gaseous molecules. Where there are the same number of gaseous reactants and product molecules, pressure changes have no effect on the system.

The following points summarize how pressure changes affect the rate of reaction when gases are involved.

- An increase in pressure will favor the reaction toward the side with the fewer number of gas molecules.
- A decrease in pressure will favor the reaction toward the side with the greater number of gas molecules.
- A change in pressure will not affect a system if there are no gas molecules or the same number of gas molecules on both sides.
- A catalyst has no net effect on an equilibrium system.

Effect of a Catalyst The addition of a catalyst changes the rates of both the forward and reverse reactions equally. This is because the catalyst equally lowers the activation energy for both the forward and the reverse reactions. A catalyst may cause equilibrium to be established more quickly but does not change any of the equilibrium concentrations.

Review Questions
Set 8.3

18. Which factors must be equal when a reversible chemical process reaches equilibrium?
    (1) mass of the reactants and mass of the products
    (2) rate of the forward reaction and rate of the reverse reaction
    (3) concentration of the reactants and concentration of the products
    (4) activation energy of the forward reaction and activation energy of the reverse reaction

19. When a chemical reaction is at equilibrium, the concentration of each reactant and the concentration of each product must be
    (1) variable   (3) equal
    (2) constant   (4) zero

20. An open flask is half filled with water at 25°C. Phase equilibrium can be reached after
    (1) more water is added to the flask
    (2) the temperature is decreased to 15°C
    (3) the temperature is increased to 35°C
    (4) the flask is stoppered

21. Solution equilibrium always exists in a solution that is
    (1) unsaturated   (3) dilute
    (2) saturated   (4) concentrated

22. Given the reaction at equilibrium:

$$A(g) + B(g) \rightleftarrows C(g) + D(g)$$

The addition of a catalyst will
    (1) shift the equilibrium to the right
    (2) shift the equilibrium to the left
    (3) increase the rate of forward and reverse reactions equally
    (4) have no effect on the forward or reverse reactions

23. If a catalyst is added to a system at equilibrium and the temperature and pressure remain constant, there will be no effect on the
    (1) rate of the forward reaction
    (2) rate of the reverse reaction
    (3) activation energy of the reaction
    (4) heat of reaction

24. For a reaction at equilibrium, which change can increase the rates of the forward and reverse reactions?
    (1) a decrease in the concentration of the reactants
    (2) a decrease in the surface area of the products
    (3) an increase in the temperature of the system
    (4) an increase in activation energy of the forward reaction

25. In a reversible reaction, chemical equilibrium is attained when the
   (1) rate of the forward reaction is greater than the rate of the reverse reaction
   (2) rate of the reverse reaction is greater than the rate of the forward reaction
   (3) concentration of the reactants reaches zero
   (4) concentration of the products remains constant

26. Which temperature change indicates an increase in the average kinetic energy of the molecules in a sample?
   (1) 255 K to 0°C
   (2) 355 K to 25°C
   (3) 115°C to 298 K
   (4) 37°C to 273 K

27. Given the equation representing a system at equilibrium:

$$N_2(g) + 3H_2(g) \leftrightarrows 2NH_3(g)$$

Which statement describes this reaction at equilibrium?
   (1) The rate of the reverse reaction deceases.
   (2) The rate of the reverse reaction increases.
   (3) The concentration of $N_2(g)$ is constant.
   (4) The concentration of $N_2(g)$ decreases.

28. Consider the following equation.

$$Zn(s) + HCl(aq) \rightarrow ZnCl_2(aq) + H_2(g)$$

As the concentration of the HCl(aq) decreases at constant temperature, the rate of the forward reaction
   (1) decreases
   (2) increases
   (3) remains the same

29. Given the equation representing a reaction at equilibrium:

$$2SO_2(g) + O_2(g) \rightleftarrows 2SO_3(g) + heat$$

Which change causes the equilibrium to shift to the right?
   (1) adding more $O_2(g)$
   (2) adding a catalyst
   (3) increasing the temperature
   (4) decreasing the pressure

30. Consider the following equation.

$$H_2(g) + Cl_2(g) \rightleftarrows 2HCl(g)$$

As the pressure increases at constant temperature, the mass of $H_2(g)$
   (1) decreases
   (2) increases
   (3) remains the same

Entropy and Enthalpy

What are the factors that cause chemical and physical changes to occur? There are two fundamental tendencies in nature that help determine whether or not these changes will occur.

Enthalpy

There is a tendency in nature to change to a state of lower energy (enthalpy). Exothermic reactions move toward a lower energy state because some of the energy contained in the reactants is released. The products have less potential energy than do the reactants.

A study of potential energy diagrams for reversible chemical reactions shows that the activation energy for the exothermic direction is less than that for the endothermic direction. Therefore, at any given temperature, the particles in a system are more likely to collide with enough energy to react in the exothermic direction than in the endothermic direction. On the basis of energy change alone, we expect reactions to go in the exothermic direction. This drive toward lower energy is also called a drive toward lower enthalpy.

Entropy

There is a tendency in nature to change to a state of greater randomness or disorder, which refers to the lack of regularity in a system. **Entropy** is a measure of the disorder or randomness of a system. The greater the disorder, the higher the entropy. Figure 8-10 illustrates the concept of increasing entropy as an originally ordered state becomes "messy" or more random.

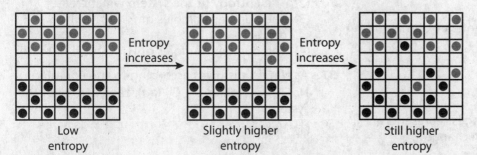

Figure 8-10. Entropy: Entropy is a measure of disorder or randomness.

It is usually necessary for particles to collide in a special way in order to form a more highly organized or regular arrangement. On the other hand, there are many ways in which they can collide to produce more disorder. Therefore, it is to be expected that systems will often go from conditions of greater order (lower entropy) to conditions of greater disorder (higher entropy). On the basis of entropy change alone, we expect reactions to go in the direction of greater entropy.

Examples of entropy change are physical changes from the solid, crystalline phase (great order, low entropy), to the liquid phase (more randomness, higher entropy), to the gaseous phase (maximum randomness, highest entropy). For chemical changes, compounds represent a state of greater order and lower entropy than the free elements of which they are composed.

To identify whether reactants or products have the greater amount of entropy consider:

1. The solid phase has less entropy than the liquid phase, which has less entropy than the gaseous phase.
2. Generally, the side of the equation with the greater number of molecules has the greater amount of entropy.

Review Questions
Set 8.4

31. Which change in a sample of water is accompanied by the greatest increase in entropy?

(1) $H_2O(\ell)$ at 100°C is changed to $H_2O(g)$ at 200°C

(2) $H_2O(g)$ at 100°C is changed to $H_2O(g)$ at 200°C

(3) $H_2O(s)$ at −100°C is changed to $H_2O(s)$ at 0°C

(4) $H_2O(s)$ at 0°C is changed to $H_2O(\ell)$ at 0°C

32. What occurs when a sample of $CO_2(s)$ changes to $CO_2(g)$?

(1) The gas has greater entropy and less order.

(2) The gas has greater entropy and more order.

(3) The gas has less entropy and less order.

(4) The gas has less entropy and more order.

33. The diagram below shows a system of gases with the valve closed.

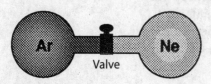

Valve

As the valve is opened, the entropy of the gaseous system

(1) decreases
(2) increases
(3) remains the same

34. Which series of physical changes represents an entropy increase during each change?

(1) gas → liquid → solid
(2) liquid → gas → solid
(3) solid → gas → solid
(4) solid → liquid → gas

35. In terms of entropy and energy, systems in nature tend to undergo changes toward

(1) higher entropy and higher energy
(2) higher entropy and lower energy
(3) lower entropy and higher energy
(4) lower entropy and lower energy

36. Consider the following equation.

$$H_2O(\ell) + heat \rightleftarrows H_2O(g)$$

Which will occur if the temperature of the system is increased?

(1) The average kinetic energy of the system will decrease.
(2) The entropy of the system will increase.
(3) The number of moles of $H_2O(g)$ will decrease.
(4) The number of moles of $H_2O(\ell)$ will increase.

37. As NaCl(s) dissolves according to the equation NaCl(s) → Na^+(aq) + Cl^-(aq), the entropy of the system

(1) decreases
(2) increases
(3) remains the same

38. Which change results in an increase in entropy?

(1) $H_2O(g) \rightarrow H_2O(\ell)$
(2) $H_2O(s) \rightarrow H_2O(\ell)$
(3) $H_2O(\ell) \rightarrow H_2O(s)$
(4) $H_2O(g) \rightarrow H_2O(s)$

39. A reaction must be spontaneous if its occurrence is

(1) endothermic with an increase in entropy
(2) endothermic with a decrease in entropy
(3) exothermic with an increase in entropy
(4) exothermic with a decrease in entropy

The Equilibrium Expression

The mathematical expression that shows the relationship of reactants and products in a system at equilibrium is called the equilibrium expression. It is a fraction with the concentrations of reactants and products expressed in moles per liter. Each concentration is then raised to the power of its coefficient in a balanced equation. This expression equals a value called the equilibrium constant (K_{eq}), which remains the same for a particular reaction at a specified temperature.

To write an equilibrium expression, follow these steps.

1. Write a balanced equation for the system.
2. Place the products as factors in the numerator of a fraction and the reactants as factors in the denominator.
3. Place a square bracket around each formula. The square bracket means *molar concentration*.
4. Write the coefficient of each substance as the power of its concentration. The resulting expression is the equilibrium expression, which should be set equal to the K_{eq} for that reaction.

SAMPLE PROBLEM

Write the equilibrium expression for the equilibrium system of nitrogen, hydrogen, and ammonia.

SOLUTION: Identify the known and unknown values.

Known
reactants = N_2, H_2
product = NH_3

Unknown
equilibrium expression = K_{eq}

1. Write a balanced equation for the reaction.

$$N_2(g) + 3H_2(g) \rightleftarrows 2NH_3(g) + heat$$

2. Place the products as factors in the numerator of a fraction and the reactants as factors in the denominator.

$$\frac{NH_3}{H_2 \times N_2}$$

3. Place a square bracket around each formula to show the concentration of each.

$$\frac{[NH_3]}{[H_2][N_2]}$$

4. Write the coefficient of each substance as the power of its concentration. This is the equilibrium expression, labeled K_{eq}.

$$K_{eq} = \frac{[NH_3]^2}{[H_2]^3[N_2]}$$

The equilibrium constant is a specific numerical value for a given system at a specified temperature. Changes in concentrations will not cause a change in the value of K_{eq}, nor will the addition of a catalyst. Only a change in temperature will affect the value of K_{eq}.

When the value of K_{eq} is large, the numerator is larger than the denominator, indicating that the products are present in larger concentration than the reactants. Chemists would simply say that the products are favored. If the value is small, the opposite is true, and the reactants are favored.

Directions

Review the Test-Taking Strategies section of this book. Then answer the following questions. Read each question carefully and answer with a correct choice or response.

Part A

1 In order for a chemical reaction to occur, there must always be
   (1) an effective collision between reacting particles
   (2) a bond that breaks in a reactant particle
   (3) reacting particles with a high charge
   (4) reacting particles with high kinetic energy

2 As the number of effective collisions between reacting particles increases, the rate of reaction
   (1) decreases
   (2) increases
   (3) remains the same

3 Activation energy is required to initiate
   (1) exothermic reactions only
   (2) endothermic reactions only
   (3) both endothermic and exothermic reactions
   (4) neither endothermic nor exothermic reactions

4 For a chemical reaction, the difference between the potential energy of the products and the potential energy of the reactants is equal to the
   (1) heat of fusion.
   (2) heat of reaction.
   (3) activation energy of the forward reaction.
   (4) activation energy of the reverse reaction.

5 Which conditions will increase the rate of a chemical reaction?
   (1) decreased temperature and decreased concentration of reactants
   (2) decreased temperature and increased concentration of reactants
   (3) increased temperature and decreased concentration of reactants
   (4) increased temperature and increased concentration of reactants

6 What will change when a catalyst is added to a chemical reaction?
   (1) activation energy
   (2) heat of reaction
   (3) potential energy of the reactants
   (4) potential energy of the products

7 The energy needed to start a chemical reaction is called
   (1) potential energy
   (2) kinetic energy
   (3) activation energy
   (4) ionization energy

Use the potential energy diagram of a chemical reaction shown below to answer questions 8 and 9.

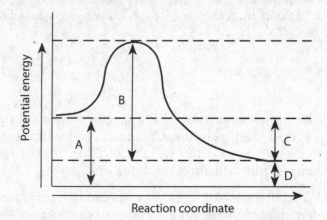

8 Which arrow represents the part of the reaction most likely to be changed by the addition of a catalyst?
   (1) A   (3) C
   (2) B   (4) D

9 Which letter represents the activation energy for the reverse reaction?
   (1) A   (3) C
   (2) B   (4) D

10 Adding a catalyst to a chemical reaction will
(1) lower the activation energy needed
(2) lower the potential energy of the reactants
(3) increase the activation energy
(4) increase the potential energy of the reactants

11 Given the equation and potential energy diagram representing a reaction:

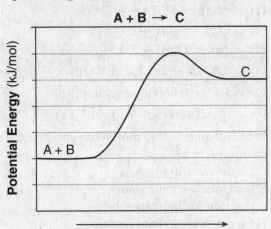

A + B → C

If each interval on the axis labeled "Potential Energy (kJ/mol)" represents 10. kJ/mol, what is the heat of reaction?
(1) +60. kJ/mol   (3) +20. kJ/mol
(2) +30. kJ/mol   (4) +40. kJ/mol

12 The graph below is a potential energy diagram of a compound that is formed from its elements. Which interval represents the heat of reaction?

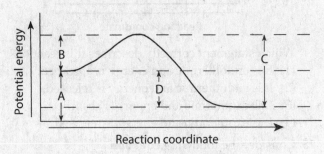

(1) A   (3) C
(2) B   (4) D

13 For any chemical reaction at equilibrium, the rate of the forward reaction is
(1) less than the rate of the reverse
(2) greater than the rate of the reverse
(3) equal to the rate of the reverse
(4) unrelated to the rate of the reverse

14 Which term is defined as a measure of the disorder of a system?
(1) heat   (3) kinetic energy
(2) entropy   (4) activation energy

15 Which potential energy diagram represents the reaction A + B → C + energy?

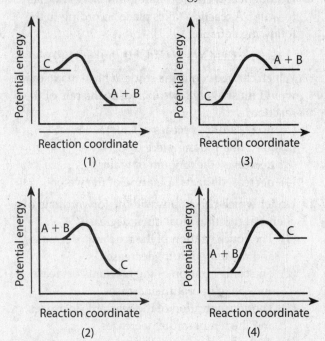

(1)   (3)

(2)   (4)

16 Given the potential energy diagram below, what does interval B represent?

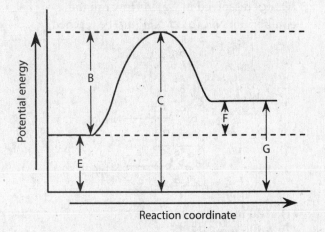

(1) potential energy of the reactants
(2) potential energy of the products
(3) activation energy
(4) activated complex

17 Solution equilibrium most likely exists in which type of solution?
(1) supersaturated
(2) unsaturated
(3) saturated
(4) dilute

Part B–1

18 A student adds two 50-milligram pieces of Ca(s) to water. A reaction takes place according to the following equation.

$$Ca(s) + 2H_2O(\ell) \rightarrow Ca(OH)_2(aq) + H_2(g)$$

Which change could the student have made that would most likely have increased the rate of the reaction?
(1) used 10 10-mg pieces of Ca(s)
(2) used one 100-mg piece of Ca(s)
(3) decreased the amount of water
(4) decreased the temperature of the water

19 Under which conditions will the forward rate of a chemical reaction most often decrease?
(1) The concentration of the reactants decreases, and the temperature decreases.
(2) The concentration of the reactants decreases, and the temperature increases.
(3) The concentration of the reactants increases, and the temperature decreases.
(4) The concentration of the reactants increases, and the temperature increases.

20 The diagram below shows a bottle containing $NH_3(g)$ dissolved in water. How can the equilibrium $NH_3(g) \rightleftarrows NH_3(aq)$ be reached?

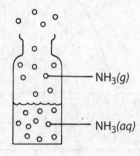

(1) Add more water.
(2) Add more NH_3.
(3) Cool the contents.
(4) Stopper the bottle.

21 A 1-cm³ cube of sodium reacts more rapidly in water at 25°C than does a 1-cm³ cube of calcium at 25°C. This difference in rate of reaction is most closely associated with the different
(1) surface area of the metal cubes
(2) nature of the metals
(3) density of the metals
(4) concentration of the metals

22 At room temperature, which reaction would be expected to have the fastest reaction rate?
(1) $Pb^{2+}(aq) + S^{2-}(aq) \rightarrow PbS(s)$
(2) $2H_2(g) + O_2(g) \rightarrow 2H_2O(\ell)$
(3) $N_2(g) + 2O_2(g) \rightarrow 2NO_2(g)$
(4) $2KClO_3(s) \rightarrow 2KCl(s) + 3O_2(g)$

23 Consider the following equation.

$$A(s) + B(aq) \rightarrow C(aq) + D(s)$$

Which change would most likely increase the rate of this reaction?
(1) a decrease in pressure
(2) an increase in pressure
(3) a decrease in temperature
(4) an increase in temperature

24 The potential energy diagram shown below represents the reaction A + B → AB.

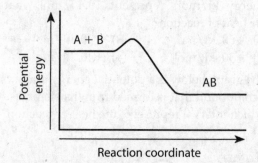

Which statement correctly describes this reaction?
(1) It is endothermic and energy is absorbed.
(2) It is endothermic and energy is released.
(3) It is exothermic and energy is absorbed.
(4) It is exothermic and energy is released.

25 Consider the following equation.

$$AgBr(s) \rightleftarrows Ag^+(aq) + Br^-(aq)$$

Which change occurs when KBr(s) is dissolved in the reaction mixture?
(1) The amount of AgBr(s) decreases.
(2) The amount of AgBr(s) remains the same.
(3) The concentration of $Ag^+(aq)$ decreases.
(4) The concentration of $Ag^+(aq)$ remains the same.

26 Consider the following equation.

$$C(s) + O_2(g) \rightleftarrows CO_2(g) + heat$$

Which stress on the system will increase the concentration of $CO_2(g)$?
(1) increasing the temperature of the reaction
(2) increasing the concentration of $O_2(g)$
(3) decreasing the pressure on the reaction
(4) decreasing the amount of $C(s)$

27 Which compound is formed from its elements by an exothermic reaction at 298 K and 101.3 kPa?
(1) $C_2H_4(g)$ (3) $H_2O(g)$
(2) $HI(g)$ (4) $NO_2(g)$

28 Which equation represents a change that results in an increase in disorder?
(1) $I_2(s) \rightarrow I_2(g)$
(2) $CO_2(g) \rightarrow CO_2(s)$
(3) $2Na(s) + Cl_2(g) \rightarrow 2NaCl(s)$
(4) $2H_2(g) + O_2(g) \rightarrow 2H_2O(\ell)$

29 Consider the following change of phase.

$$CO_2(g) \rightarrow CO_2(s)$$

As $CO_2(g)$ changes to $CO_2(s)$, the entropy of the system
(1) decreases (3) remains the same
(2) increases

30 Which reaction system tends to become less random as reactants form products?
(1) $C(s) + O_2(g) \rightarrow CO_2(g)$
(2) $S(s) + O_2(g) \rightarrow SO_2(g)$
(3) $I_2(s) + Cl_2(g) \rightarrow 2ICl(g)$
(4) $2Mg(s) + O_2(g) \rightarrow 2MgO(s)$

31 In which reaction will the point of equilibrium shift to the left when the pressure on the system is increased?
(1) $C(s) + O_2(g) \rightleftarrows CO_2(g)$
(2) $CaCO_3(s) \rightleftarrows CaO(s) + CO_2(g)$
(3) $2Mg(s) + O_2(g) \rightleftarrows 2MgO(s)$
(4) $2H_2(g) + O_2(g) \rightleftarrows 2H_2O(g)$

32 Consider the following equation.

$$A(g) + B(g) \rightleftarrows C(g) + D(g)$$

Which relationship is an indication that this reaction has reached equilibrium?
(1) The concentration of A equals the concentration of B.
(2) The concentration of C equals the concentration of D.
(3) The concentrations of A, B, C, and D are constant.
(4) The concentrations of A, B, C, and D are equal.

33 Consider the following equation.

$$N_2(g) + O_2(g) \rightleftarrows 2NO(g)$$

If the temperature remains constant and the pressure increases, the number of moles of $NO(g)$ will
(1) decrease
(2) increase
(3) remain the same

34 Which two fundamental tendencies favor a chemical reaction occurring spontaneously?
(1) toward higher energy and less randomness
(2) toward higher energy and greater randomness
(3) toward lower energy and less randomness
(4) toward lower energy and greater randomness

Parts B–2 and C

Base your answers to questions 35 through 37 on the information below.

At 550°C, 1.00 mole of $CO_2(g)$ and 1.00 mole of $H_2(g)$ are placed in a 1.00-liter reaction vessel. The substances react to form $CO(g)$ and $H_2O(g)$. The balanced equation for this process is shown below along with a graph showing the changes in the concentrations of the reactants and the products.

$$CO_2(g) + H_2(g) \rightarrow CO(g) + H_2O(g)$$

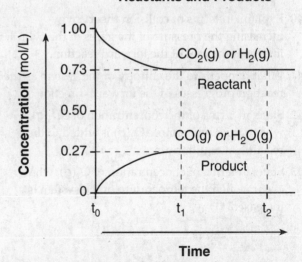

Concentrations of Reactants and Products

35 What effect would increasing the pressure of the system have on the equilibrium concentrations of $CO(g)$ and $H_2O(g)$?

36 Determine the change in concentration of $CO_2(g)$ between time t_0 and time t_1.

37 What can be concluded from the graph about the concentrations of the reactants and the concentrations of the products between time t_1 and t_2?

Base your answers to questions 38 and 39 on the following information.

When soda pop, such as Coke or Pepsi, is manufactured, CO_2 gas is dissolved in it forming a solution.

38 A capped bottle of cola contains $CO_2(g)$ under high pressure. When the cap is removed, how does pressure affect the solubility of the dissolved $CO_2(g)$?

39 A glass of cold cola is left to stand at room temperature for 5 minutes. How does temperature affect the solubility of the $CO_2(g)$?

Base your answers to questions 40 through 43 on the information below.

Several steps are involved in the industrial production of sulfuric acid. One step involves the oxidation of sulfur dioxide gas to form sulfur trioxide gas. In a rigid cylinder with a movable piston, this reaction reaches equilibrium, as represented by the equation below.

$$2SO_2(g) + O_2(g) \rightleftarrows 2SO_3(g) + 392 \text{ kJ}$$

40 Explain, in terms of collision theory, why increasing the pressure of the gases in the cylinder increases the rate of the forward reaction.

41 What happens to the entropy of the system as the reaction progresses in the forward direction.

42 State, in terms of the concentration of $SO_3(g)$, what occurs when more $O_2(g)$ is added to the reaction at equilibrium.

43 State, in terms of concentration of $O_2(g)$, what occurs when the temperature of the system is increased.

Base your answers to questions 44 through 46 on the potential energy diagram shown below.

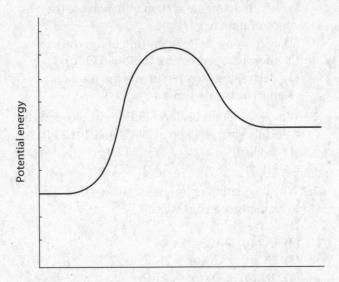

44 Is the forward reaction endothermic or exothermic?

45 Compare the activation energy of the forward reaction to the activation energy of the reverse reaction.

46 Draw a dotted line on the graph to illustrate the potential energy diagram as it would be altered by the action of a catalyst added to the system.

Base your answers to questions 47 through 49 on the following information.

The Haber process is the main industrial procedure for the production of ammonia today. The process converts atmospheric nitrogen, $N_2(g)$, to ammonia $NH_3(g)$, by a reaction with hydrogen $H_2(g)$. In a closed system, the reaction will reach equilibrium as illustrated in the balanced equation:

$$N_2(g) + 3H_2(g) \rightleftarrows 2NH_3(g) + 92.4 \text{ kJ/mol}$$

47 In terms of the concentration of $NH_3(g)$, what would be the effect of increasing the pressure of the system?

48 Describe, in terms of a shift in equilibrium, the effect of an increased temperature on the system.

Oxidation–Reduction

How Scientists Study Oxidation–Reduction

? *Will we all drive electric cars in the future?* **?**

It's a re-volt-olution!! After 100 years of using the internal combustion engine to run our cars and trucks, a new era is emerging—the age of the electric car.

Today, we see hybrid cars that make use of both combustion engines and batteries to power vehicles. Car companies have successfully introduced an all-electric car. The future will see more and more cars using electric motors powered by batteries.

In this topic you will learn the essentials of changing chemical energy into electrical energy.

Oxidation–Reduction

Vocabulary

anode	electrolytic cell	redox
cathode	half-reaction	reduction
electrochemical cell	oxidation	salt bridge
electrode	oxidation number (state)	voltaic cell
electrolysis		

Topic Overview

Oxidation and reduction are important chemical reactions. They work both for our benefit, in forms such as batteries, and against us, in ways such as the corrosion of important metals. Originally, the term *oxidation* meant the combination of a substance with oxygen. *Reduction* was the opposite, the loss of oxygen. Today, both terms have a wider interpretation. They are also recognized as interdependent—one cannot occur without the other.

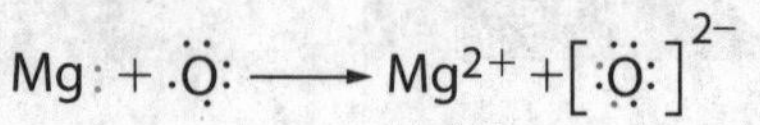

$$Mg: + \cdot \ddot{O}: \longrightarrow Mg^{2+} + \left[:\ddot{O}: \right]^{2-}$$

$$Mg + \frac{1}{2}O_2 \longrightarrow MgO$$

Figure 9-1. Chemical reaction between magnesium and oxygen: In the reaction between magnesium and oxygen, a magnesium atom transfers two electrons to an oxygen atom.

Oxidation and Reduction

When magnesium is burned in oxygen, the octet rule allows us to understand the transfer of electrons. Each magnesium atom loses two electrons as each oxygen atom gains two electrons. Both atoms acquire a stable octet, as shown in Figure 9-1.

The same electron transfer occurs as magnesium reacts with chlorine, as shown in Figure 9-2. Again the magnesium atom loses two electrons, while the two chlorine atoms each accept an electron, acquiring a stable octet.

In both of the equations, while the magnesium atom was losing electrons, other atoms were gaining them. **Oxidation** is defined as the loss of electrons by an atom or ion. **Reduction** is the gain of electrons by an atom or ion.

Redox Whenever one atom loses an electron, there must be another atom available to gain the electron. Neither reduction nor oxidation can ever occur alone. Whenever one occurs, the other must occur at the same time. Because these reactions must accompany each other, the two terms are often combined, and reactions in which both reduction and oxidation occur are called **redox** reactions.

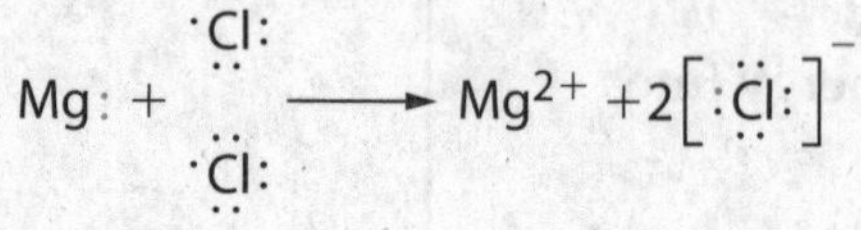

$$Mg: + \begin{matrix} \cdot \ddot{C}l: \\ \cdot \ddot{C}l: \end{matrix} \longrightarrow Mg^{2+} + 2 \left[:\ddot{C}l: \right]^{-}$$

$$Mg + Cl_2 \longrightarrow MgCl_2$$

Figure 9-2. Chemical reaction between magnesium and chlorine: In the reaction between magnesium and chlorine, a magnesium atom transfers one electron to each of two chlorine atoms.

Oxidation Numbers

It is not always possible to simply read an equation and determine whether atoms have exchanged electrons. However, chemists have devised a system that makes it easy to keep track of the number of electrons lost or gained by an atom in a reaction. Positive, negative, or neutral values known as **oxidation numbers (states)** can be assigned to atoms. Changes in oxidation states identify how many electrons are either gained or lost by an atom or ion. The use of these oxidation numbers also provides a more complete way to define oxidation and reduction.

- Oxidation is defined as the loss of electrons and a gain in oxidation number.
- Reduction is defined as the gain of electrons and a loss in oxidation number.

Oxidation numbers are used to identify the path of electrons in redox reactions. A simple device may help in remembering the definitions.

> **LEO** says **GER**
> **LEO** = **L**oss of **E**lectrons is **O**xidation
> **GER** = **G**ain of **E**lectrons is **R**eduction

Oxidation numbers are written differently than ionic charges. The charge on the magnesium ion is 2+, while the oxidation number is written as +2. The periodic table in the *Reference Tables for Physical Setting/Chemistry* supplies some common oxidation numbers for elements in compounds.

It is important to learn the rules for assigning oxidation states to atoms in an equation. These numbers are used to identify what has been oxidized and what has been reduced. Here are some rules for assigning oxidation numbers.

1. Every uncombined element has an oxidation number of zero. In the chemical equation $2Na + Cl_2 \rightarrow 2NaCl$, both the uncombined Na and Cl_2 have oxidation numbers of 0.

2. Monatomic ions have an oxidation number equal to the ionic charge. In the equation $2Na + Cl_2 \rightarrow 2NaCl$, the sodium in the product NaCl has a charge of 1+ and an oxidation number of +1. The chlorine in NaCl has a charge of 1− and an oxidation number of −1.

3. The metals of Group 1 always have an oxidation number of +1 in compounds, and the metals of Group 2 always have an oxidation number of +2 in compounds.

4. Fluorine is always −1 in compounds. The other halogens are also −1 when they are the most electronegative element in the compound.

5. Hydrogen is +1 in compounds unless it is combined with a metal, in which case it is −1. Hydrogen is +1 in HCl but −1 in LiH.

6. Oxygen is usually −2 in compounds. When it is combined with fluorine, which is more electronegative, it is +2. Oxygen is −2 in H_2O, and +2 in OF_2. In the peroxide ion (O_2^{2-}), oxygen is −1.

    These six rules can be used to assign oxidation numbers to many atoms in equations. They can be used with the following two additional rules to calculate oxidation numbers for other elements in compounds or polyatomic ions.

7. The sum of the oxidation numbers in all compounds must be zero.

8. The sum of the oxidation numbers in polyatomic ions must be equal to the charge on the ion.

What are the oxidation numbers of the atoms in HNO_3?

SOLUTION: Identify the known and unknown values.

Known	*Unknown*
formula HNO_3	oxidation number of H = ?
	oxidation number of N = ?
	oxidation number of O = ?

Use as many of the first six rules as possible.

Hydrogen has an oxidation number of +1 (Rule 5). Each oxygen atom has an oxidation number of −2 (Rule 6), making the total for three oxygen atoms −6.

The sum of all oxidation numbers is zero.

oxidation number of N + (+1) + (−6) = 0
oxidation number of N = +5

The oxidation number for H is +1; for N, +5; and for O, −2.

SAMPLE PROBLEM

What is the oxidation number of chromium in the dichromate ion ($Cr_2O_7^{2-}$)?

SOLUTION: Identify the known and unknown values.

Known	*Unknown*
formula $Cr_2O_7^{2-}$	oxidation number of Cr = ?

Use as many of the first six rules as possible. O has an oxidation number of −2, producing a total of −14 for the seven O atoms.

The sum of the atoms in a polyatomic ion must equal the charge on the ion.

$$2(\text{oxidation number of Cr}) + (-14) = -2$$

$$\text{oxidation number of Cr} = \frac{+12}{2}$$

$$\text{oxidation number of Cr} = +6$$

Review Questions
Set 9.1

1. What is the sum of the oxidation numbers in the compound CO_2?
   (1) 0   (2) −2   (3) −4   (4) +4

2. The oxidation number of nitrogen in N_2 is
   (1) +1   (2) 0   (3) +3   (4) −3

3. What is the oxidation number of Pt in K_2PtCl_6?
   (1) −2   (2) +2   (3) −4   (4) +4

4. In which substance does phosphorus have a +3 oxidation state?
   (1) P_4O_{10} (3) $Ca_3(PO_4)_2$
   (2) PCl_5 (4) KH_2PO_3

5. What is the oxidation number of sulfur in H_2SO_4?
   (1) 0   (2) −2   (3) +6   (4) +4

6. What is the oxidation number of iodine in KIO_4?

(1) +1　　　　　(3) +7
(2) −1　　　　　(4) −7

7. What is the oxidation number of manganese in $KMnO_4$?

(1) +2　(2) +3　(3) +4　(4) +7

8. Oxygen has an oxidation number of −2 in

(1) O_2　(2) NO_2　(3) Na_2O_2　(4) OF_2

9. Oxygen will have a positive oxidation number when combined with

(1) fluorine　　　(3) bromine
(2) chlorine　　　(4) iodine

10. In which compound does hydrogen have an oxidation number of −1?

(1) NH_3　　　　(3) HCl
(2) KH　　　　　(4) H_2O

Examining Redox Reactions

Sometimes it's important to know whether a reaction is redox or not. Once it has been determined that a reaction is redox, it is important to know what is oxidized, what is reduced, and what brings about oxidation and reduction.

Recognizing Redox Reactions

Not all reactions are redox reactions. To determine whether or not a reaction is redox, assign oxidation numbers to each atom, both on the reactant and product side. If there is a change in oxidation number for a particular type of atom, the reaction is redox.

Sometimes it is easy to spot a redox reaction. If an uncombined element appears on one side of an equation and is in a compound on the other side, the reaction must be a redox reaction. If you recognize a reaction as a double replacement reaction, it is not redox.

For example:

Redox: $Zn + HCl \rightarrow ZnCl_2 + H_2$

Not Redox: $NaCl + AgNO_3 \Rightarrow AgCl + NaNO_3$

Identifying Oxidation and Reduction

Once oxidation numbers are assigned, the atom that has shown an increase can be identified as the one that has undergone oxidation. The atom that has a decrease in oxidation number has undergone reduction.

Consider the following reaction.

$$MnO_2 + 4HCl \rightarrow MnCl_2 + Cl_2 + 2H_2O$$

In the equation, chlorine has an oxidation number of −1 as a reactant in HCl. On the product side, some chlorine ions are still −1, but others have an oxidation state of 0 in Cl_2. Because the chloride ion (Cl^-) changes from a lower oxidation number to a higher one, it has been oxidized. Manganese changes from +4 as a reactant to +2 as a product. Because it changed from a higher oxidation number to a lower one, Mn^{4+} has undergone reduction.

Oxidizing Agents and Reducing Agents

In the previous reaction, Mn^{+4} underwent reduction, having received electrons from the Cl^-. The Cl^- caused the reduction of the Mn^{+4} and is called the <u>reducing agent.</u> By accepting electrons from Cl^-, the Mn^{+4}

caused the Cl^- to be oxidized. The Mn^{+4} is the <u>oxidizing agent.</u>
In summary,

- the substance oxidized is the reducing agent.
- the substance reduced is the oxidizing agent.

Review Questions
Set 9.2

11. Which equation represents an oxidation-reduction reaction?

   (1) $HCl + KOH \rightarrow KCl + H_2O$
   (2) $4HCl + MnO_2 \rightarrow MnCl_2 + 2H_2O + Cl_2$
   (3) $2HCl + CaCO_3 \rightarrow CaCl_2 + H_2O + CO_2$
   (4) $2HCl + FeS \rightarrow FeCl_2 + H_2S$

12. Which equation represents an oxidation-reduction reaction?

   (1) $Zn + 2HCl \rightarrow ZnCl_2 + H_2$
   (2) $Zn(OH)_2 + 2HCl \rightarrow ZnCl_2 + 2H_2O$
   (3) $H_2O + NH_3 \rightarrow NH^{4+} + OH^-$
   (4) $H_2O + H_2O \rightarrow H_3O^+ + OH^-$

13. Which balanced equation represents an oxidation-reduction reaction?

   (1) $Ba(NO_3)_2 + Na_2SO_4 \rightarrow BaSO_4 + 2NaNO_3$
   (2) $Fe(s) + S(s) \rightarrow FeS(s)$
   (3) $H_3PO_4 + 3KOH \rightarrow K_3PO_4 + 3H_2O$
   (4) $NH_3(g) + HCl(g) \rightarrow NH_4Cl(s)$

14. Oxidation-reduction reactions occur because of the competition between particles for

   (1) neutrons   (3) protons
   (2) electrons   (4) positrons

15. Which statement correctly describes a redox reaction?

   (1) Oxidation and reduction occur simultaneously.
   (2) Oxidation occurs before reduction.
   (3) Oxidation occurs after reduction.
   (4) Oxidation occurs, but reduction does not.

16. A redox reaction is a reaction in which

   (1) only reduction occurs
   (2) only oxidation occurs
   (3) reduction and oxidation occur at the same time
   (4) reduction occurs first and then oxidation occurs

17. All redox reactions involve

   (1) the gain of electrons only
   (2) the loss of electrons only
   (3) both the gain and the loss of electrons
   (4) neither the gain nor the loss of electrons

18. Consider the following equation.

   $$Zn(s) + Cu^{2+}(aq) \rightarrow Zn^{2+}(aq) + Cu(s)$$

   Which particles must be transferred from one reactant to the other reactant?

   (1) ions
   (2) neutrons
   (3) protons
   (4) electrons

19. What occurs during the reaction below?

   $$4HCl + MnO_2 \rightarrow MnCl_2 + 2H_2O + Cl_2$$

   (1) The manganese is reduced and its oxidation number changes from +4 to +2.
   (2) The manganese is oxidized and its oxidation number changes from +4 to +2.
   (3) The manganese is reduced and its oxidation number changes from +2 to +4.
   (4) The manganese is oxidized and its oxidation number changes from +2 to +4.

20. What occurs when an atom is oxidized in a chemical reaction?

   (1) a loss of electrons and a decrease in oxidation number
   (2) a loss of electrons and an increase in oxidation number
   (3) a gain of electrons and a decrease in oxidation number
   (4) a gain of electrons and an increase in oxidation number

21. When a substance is oxidized, it

   (1) loses protons
   (2) gains protons
   (3) acts as an oxidizing agent
   (4) acts as a reducing agent

22. Consider the following redox reaction.

   $$Co(s) + PbCl_2(aq) \rightarrow CoCl_2(aq) + Pb(s)$$

   Which statement correctly describes the oxidation and reduction that occur?

   (1) $Co(s)$ is oxidized and $Cl^-(aq)$ is reduced.
   (2) $Co(s)$ is oxidized and $Pb^{2+}(aq)$ is reduced.
   (3) $Co(s)$ is reduced and $Cl^-(aq)$ is oxidized.
   (4) $Co(s)$ is reduced and $Pb^{2+}(aq)$ is oxidized.

23. Consider the following equation.

$$MnO_2(s) + 4H^+(aq) + 2Fe^{2+}(aq) \rightarrow Mn^{2+}(aq) + 2Fe^{3+}(aq) + 2H_2O(\ell)$$

Which species is oxidized?

(1) $H^+(aq)$ (3) $Fe^{2+}(aq)$
(2) $H_2O(\ell)$ (4) $MnO_2(s)$

24. Consider the following equation.

$$Zn(s) + 2HCl(aq) \rightarrow ZnCl_2(aq) + H_2(g)$$

Which substance is oxidized?

(1) $Zn(s)$ (3) $Cl^-(aq)$
(2) $HCl(aq)$ (4) $H^+(aq)$

25. Consider the following redox reaction.

$$Ni + Sn^{4+} \rightarrow Ni^{2+} + Sn^{2+}$$

Which species undergoes reduction?

(1) Ni   (2) Sn^{4+} (3) Ni^{2+} (4) Sn^{2+}

26. Consider the following equation.

$$2Fe^{3+} + Sn^{2+} \rightarrow 2Fe^{2+} + Sn^{4+}$$

Which species is the oxidizing agent?

(1) Fe^{3+} (3) Fe^{2+}
(2) Sn^{2+} (4) Sn^{4+}

27. Consider the following equation.

$$Pb^0(s) + Cu^{2+}(aq) \rightarrow Pb^{2+}(aq) + Cu^0(s)$$

What is the reducing agent?

(1) $Pb^{2+}(aq)$ (3) $Pb^0(s)$
(2) $Cu^{2+}(aq)$ (4) $Cu^0(s)$

28. Consider the following equation.

$$Mg(s) + CuSO_4(aq) \rightarrow MgSO_4(aq) + Cu(s)$$

Which species acts as the oxidizing agent?

(1) $Cu(s)$ (3) $Mg(s)$
(2) $Cu^{2+}(aq)$ (4) $Mg^{2+}(aq)$

29. In the reaction $2H_2S + 3O_2 \rightarrow 2SO_2 + 2H_2O$, the oxidizing agent is

(1) oxygen   (3) sulfur dioxide
(2) water   (4) hydrogen sulfide

30. In the reaction $Cu + 2Ag^+ \rightarrow Cu^{2+} + 2Ag$, the oxidizing agent is

(1) Cu   (2) Cu^{2+} (3) Ag^+ (4) Ag

31. In a redox reaction, the reducing agent will

(1) lose electrons and be reduced
(2) lose electrons and be oxidized
(3) gain electrons and be reduced
(4) gain electrons and be oxidized

Half-Reactions

Chemical equations show the formulas of reactants and products, but they do not show the exchange of electrons. A **half-reaction** shows either the oxidation or reduction portion of a redox reaction, including the electrons gained or lost.

A reduction half-reaction shows an atom or ion gaining one or more electrons while its oxidation number decreases.

$$Fe^{3+}(aq) + 3e^- \rightarrow Fe(s)$$

An oxidation half-reaction shows an atom or an ion losing one or more electrons while its oxidation number increases.

$$Fe(s) \rightarrow Fe^{3+}(aq) + 3e^-$$

Like other chemical equations, half-reactions follow the law of conservation of matter; that is, there must be the same number of atoms on both sides of the arrow. Generally, in a half reaction there will only be one type of atom or ion shown on both reactant and product side of the equation.

In addition to conservation of mass, there must also be a conservation of charge. In molecular equations, because no charges are shown, the net charge is zero on both reactant and product side. In half-reactions, the net charge must be the same on both sides of the equation, but it does not necessarily equal zero. Several examples of balanced half-reactions follow.

$$\text{Fe}^{3+}(aq) + 3e^- \rightarrow \text{Fe}(s) \qquad \text{Net charge/side} = 0$$
$$\text{Fe}(s) \rightarrow \text{Fe}^{3+}(aq) + 3e^- \qquad \text{Net charge/side} = 0$$
$$\text{Sn}^{4+}(aq) + 2e^- \rightarrow \text{Sn}^{2+}(aq) \qquad \text{Net charge/side} = 2+$$
$$\text{Sn}^{2+}(aq) \rightarrow \text{Sn}^{4+}(aq) + 2e^- \qquad \text{Net charge/side} = 2+$$

To write a half-reaction from an equation, first assign an oxidation number to each element.

$$\overset{0}{\text{Cu}} + \overset{+1\,+5\,-2}{\text{AgNO}_3} \rightarrow \overset{+2\,+5\,-2}{\text{Cu(NO}_3)_2} + \overset{0}{\text{Ag}}$$

Then write a partial half-reaction to show the change in oxidation state.

$$\text{Oxidation: } \text{Cu} \rightarrow \text{Cu}^{2+}$$
$$\text{Reduction: } \text{Ag}^+ \rightarrow \text{Ag}$$

Then show the number of electrons needed to explain how the oxidation number changed, and to achieve a conservation of charge. Check to see that the net charge is the same on both sides of these equations.

$$\text{Oxidation: } \text{Cu} \rightarrow \text{Cu}^{2+} + 2e^- \qquad \text{Net charge/side} = 0$$
$$\text{Reduction: } \text{Ag}^+ + e^- \rightarrow \text{Ag} \qquad \text{Net charge/side} = 0$$

In all redox reactions, there must be a balance between the number of electrons lost and gained. In the previous example,

$$\text{Oxidation: } \text{Cu} \rightarrow \text{Cu}^{2+} + 2e^-$$
$$\text{Reduction: } \text{Ag}^+ + e^- \rightarrow \text{Ag}$$

balance can be achieved by multiplying the reduction equation by two. Thus, there are two electrons lost and two electrons gained. $2\text{Ag}^+ + 2e^- \rightarrow 2\text{Ag}$. Since the number of electrons lost and gained are equal, we can cancel them and add the two half-reactions:

$$\text{Cu} \rightarrow \text{Cu}^{2+} + 2e^-$$
$$2\,\text{Ag}^+ + 2e^- \rightarrow 2\text{Ag}$$
$$2\text{Ag}^+ + \text{Cu} \rightarrow \text{Cu}^{2+} + 2\text{Ag}$$

Redox equations can be balanced by first balancing the number of electrons lost and gained. After balancing the redox portion of the equation, the remainder can be balanced by inspection.

Review Questions
Set 9.3

32. Which half-reaction correctly represents reduction?

(1) $\text{Fe}^{2+} + 2e^- \rightarrow \text{Fe}$ (3) $\text{Fe} + 2e^- \rightarrow \text{Fe}^{2+}$

(2) $\text{Fe}^{2+} + e^- \rightarrow \text{Fe}^{3+}$ (4) $\text{Fe} + e^- \rightarrow \text{Fe}^{3+}$

33. Consider the following oxidation reduction equation.

$$\text{Hg}^{2+} + 2\text{I}^- \rightarrow \text{Hg} + \text{I}_2$$

Which equation correctly represents the half-reaction for the oxidation that occurs?

(1) $\text{Hg}^{2+} \rightarrow \text{Hg} + 2e^-$ (3) $2\text{I}^- \rightarrow \text{I}_2 + 2e^-$

(2) $\text{Hg}^{2+} + 2e^- \rightarrow \text{Hg}$ (4) $2\text{I}^- + 2e^- \rightarrow \text{I}_2$

34. Which statement describes what occurs in the following redox reaction?

$$\text{Cu}(s) + 2\text{Ag}^+(aq) \rightarrow \text{Cu}^{2+}(aq) + 2\text{Ag}(s)$$

(1) Only mass is conserved.

(2) Only charge is conserved.

(3) Both mass and charge are conserved.

(4) Neither mass nor charge is conserved.

35. Which equation is correctly balanced?

(1) $Fe^{3+} + 2Ni \rightarrow Fe^{2+} + 2Ni^{2+}$
(2) $2Fe^{3+} + Ni \rightarrow 2Fe^{2+} + Ni^{2+}$
(3) $Fe^{3+} + Ni \rightarrow Fe^{2+} + Ni^{2+}$
(4) $2Fe^{2+} + 2Ni \rightarrow 2Fe^{2+} + 2Ni^{2+}$

36. Which equation is correctly balanced?

(1) $Cr^{3+} + Mg \rightarrow Cr + Mg^{2+}$
(2) $Al^{3+} + K \rightarrow Al + K^+$
(3) $Sn^{4+} + H_2 \rightarrow Sn + 2H^+$
(4) $Br_2 + Hg \rightarrow Hg^{2+} + 2Br^-$

Electrochemical Cells

In redox reactions there is a chemical reaction and an exchange of electrons between the particles being oxidized and reduced. One practical use of such a reaction is in an electrochemical cell. An **electrochemical cell** involves a chemical reaction and a flow of electrons.

There are two common types of electrochemical cells. A **voltaic cell** is an electrochemical cell in which a spontaneous chemical reaction produces a flow of electrons. An **electrolytic cell** requires an electric current to force a nonspontaneous chemical reaction to occur.

Electrochemical cells have two surfaces called electrodes that can conduct electricity. An **electrode** is the site at which oxidation or reduction occurs. The electrode at which oxidation occurs is called the **anode**. The electrode at which reduction occurs is called the **cathode**.

Spontaneous Reactions—Voltaic Cells

If a strip of zinc is placed into a solution of lead nitrate, the zinc will be oxidized and the copper ions will be reduced according to the following equation.

$$Zn(s) + Cu^{2+}(aq) \rightarrow Cu(s) + Zn^{2+}(aq)$$

The exchange of electrons takes place on the surface of the zinc, as shown by equations for the two half-reactions.

$$Zn(s) \rightarrow Zn^{2+}(aq) + 2e^-$$
$$Cu^{2+}(aq) + 2e^- \rightarrow Cu(s)$$

It is also possible to have these materials separated into two containers, so the electrons travel through a wire connecting them. In a voltaic cell, a **salt bridge** connects the two containers and provides a path for a flow of ions between the two beakers. This makes a complete circuit and allows the reaction to proceed. The diagram in Figure 9-3 shows a voltaic cell. In a voltaic cell, chemical energy is spontaneously converted to electrical energy.

In such a voltaic cell, when a strip of zinc metal is located in one beaker and copper ions are in solution in another beaker, the reaction can occur as if the solutions were in the same beaker. An electrical current is produced by separating the solutions into two beakers and forcing electrons to flow through the wire to complete the circuit.

When electrons are lost during oxidation at the anode, they travel through the wire to the cathode. At this electrode, the material being reduced gains

Memory Jogger

A metal will react with the ion of another metal found below it on the table. For example, zinc metal will react with lead nitrate, but not with aluminum nitrate.

$$Zn + Pb(NO_3)_2 \rightarrow Pb + Zn(NO_3)_2$$
$$Zn + Al(NO_3)_3 \rightarrow \text{no reaction}$$

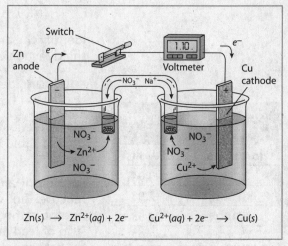

Figure 9-3. A typical voltaic cell

electrons. As with all redox reactions, the substance being oxidized loses electrons, and the substance being reduced gains them. The number of electrons lost must be equal to the number of electrons gained.

Ⓡ The Activity series in *Reference Tables for Physical Setting/Chemistry* can be used to identify the anode and cathode in a voltaic cell. Identify the two metals shown in the cell, and locate them on the table. The metal that is higher on the chart will be oxidized, and is thus the anode. The lower metal is the site of reduction and will be the cathode. Notice that the cathode itself is not reduced; it is the place where the reduction occurs. Ions in solution are reduced. To help you identify the anode and cathode, remember **RED CAT** and **AN OX**.

REDuction occurs at the **CAT**hode.
ANode is the site of **OX**idation.

SAMPLE PROBLEM

Consider the following equation.

$$Zn^0(s) + Pb^{2+}(aq) \rightarrow Zn^{2+}(aq) + Pb^0(s)$$

Identify the anode and the cathode, and give the direction of electron flow.

SOLUTION: Identify the known and unknown values.

Known	*Unknown*
reaction equation	anode = ?
Data in Table J	cathode = ?
	direction of electron flow

Locate zinc and lead on Table J. Zinc is higher on the table. Thus, it is more reactive. Zinc will undergo oxidation and is the anode. The Pb^{2+} ions are not the cathode, but they will be reduced at the cathode. If the cell has a strip of lead metal in the beaker with the Pb^{2+} ions, the lead metal will be the cathode.

The zinc is oxidized and is losing electrons. The electrons will flow from the zinc to the lead, which is from anode to cathode. Electrons always flow from the anode to the cathode.

Table 9-1. Reduction Potentials	
Ion/Metal	**E^0 (Volts)**
Li^+/Li	−3.04
Rb^+/Rb	−2.98
K^+/K	−2.93
Cs^+/Cs	−2.92
Ba^{2+}/Ba	−2.91
Sr^{2+}/Sr	−2.89
Ca^{2+}/Ca	−2.87
Na^+/Na	−2.71
Mg^{2+}/Mg	−2.37
Al^{3+}/Al	−1.66
Mn^{2+}/Mn	−1.19
Zn^{2+}/Zn	−0.76
Cr^{3+}/Cr	−0.74
Co^{2+}/Co	−0.28
Ni^{2+}/Ni	−0.26
Pb^{2+}/Pb	−0.13
H^+/H_2	0.00
Cu^{2+}/Cu	+0.34
Ag^+/Ag	+0.80
Au^{3+}/Au	+1.50

When a voltaic cell begins to react, the electrons flow from the anode to the cathode. A voltmeter placed in the circuit measures the electric potential between the metals in the electrodes in units of volts. Table 9-1 shows a series of reduction pairs as ions are reduced to the atomic state. The voltage for each pair is the voltage obtained when the given pair is compared to the standard hydrogen cell, which is assigned a value of 0.00 V.

The reductions at the top of the table are the least likely to occur. The more positive the E^0 value, the more likely the reduction. Thus, when Zn^{2+}/Zn and Cu^{2+}/Cu are in a voltaic cell, the reduction of Cu^{2+} to Cu will occur, while the oxidation of Zn to Zn^{2+} will supply the electrons. The voltage between the two can be calculated using the following relationship.

$$E^0_{cell} = E^0_{reduction} - E^0_{oxidation}$$
$$= E^0_{Cu^{2+}} - E^0_{Zn^{2+}}$$
$$= +0.34V - (-0.76V)$$
$$= +1.10V$$

Nonspontaneous Reactions—Electrolytic Cells

In a voltaic cell, the electrons flow spontaneously from the anode to the cathode. In the example given, electrons from the oxidation of zinc travel through the wire to reduce lead ions. Can the reverse take place? Can the electrons travel from the lead to the zinc causing the lead metal to be oxidized and the zinc ions to be reduced? The answer is yes, but the reaction cannot occur spontaneously. There must be some electrical generator placed into the circuit to force the electrons to flow from the anode to the cathode. When electricity is used to force a chemical reaction to occur, the process is called **electrolysis.** In an automobile, both spontaneous and nonspontaneous redox reactions occur. When the car is started, a spontaneous chemical reaction occurs in the battery, providing electricity to start the car. Once the car has been started, the alternator, in a nonspontaneous reaction, recharges the battery.

Electrolysis can be used to obtain active elements such as sodium and chlorine by the electrolysis of fused (molten) salts.

$$2NaCl(\ell) \rightarrow 2Na(s) + Cl_2(g)$$

Electrolysis can also be used to electroplate metals onto a surface. The material to be plated with a metal is the cathode. The anode is made of the metal used for the plating. The electrolyte contains ions of the desired metal. Figure 9-4 shows the diagram of an apparatus used to plate silver. The anode is itself a piece of silver. As silver ions are produced by oxidation, they travel through the solution to the cathode. At the cathode, they are reduced back to silver atoms and adhere to the metal being plated.

Notice that the positive silver ions migrate away from the anode. Because like charges repel, the anode is positive in an electrolytic cell. The positive silver ions migrate through the solution toward the cathode, which must have a negative charge. The external power source forces the electrons in the wire to travel from the anode to the cathode.

Although there are distinct differences in voltaic and electrolytic cells, they also have several things in common.

- Both use redox reactions.
- The anode is the site of oxidation.
- The cathode is the site of reduction.
- The electrons flow through the wire from anode to cathode.

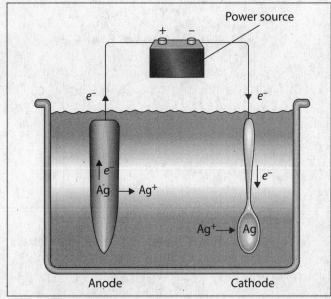

Figure 9-4. An electroplating apparatus

Differences between voltaic and electrolytic cells include the following.

- The redox reaction in a voltaic cell is spontaneous, but it is nonspontaneous in an electrolytic cell.
- In a voltaic cell the anode is negative and the cathode is positive. In an electrolytic cell, the anode is positive and the cathode is negative.

Review Questions   Set 9.4

37. The type of reaction in a voltaic cell is best described as

(1) spontaneous oxidation reaction only
(2) nonspontaneous oxidation reaction only
(3) spontaneous oxidation-reduction reaction
(4) nonspontaneous oxidation-reduction reaction

38. An electrochemical cell is made up of two half-cells connected by a salt bridge and an external conductor. What is the function of the salt bridge?

(1) to permit the migration of ions
(2) to prevent the migration of ions
(3) to permit the mixing of solutions
(4) to prevent the flow of electrons

39. Which energy conversion must occur in an operating electrolytic cell?

(1) chemical energy to electrical energy
(2) chemical energy to nuclear energy
(3) electrical energy to chemical energy
(4) electrical energy to nuclear energy

40. The diagram below shows an electrochemical cell.

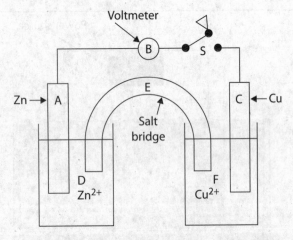

When the switch is closed, which series of letters shows the path and direction of electron flow?

(1) ABC   (2) CBA   (3) DEF   (4) FED

41. Consider the following equation.

$$2H_2O + electricity \rightarrow 2H_2 + O_2$$

In which type of cell would this reaction most likely occur?

(1) a voltaic cell, because it releases energy
(2) an electrolytic cell, because it releases energy
(3) a voltaic cell, because it absorbs energy
(4) an electrolytic cell, because it absorbs energy

42. Which process occurs in an operating voltaic cell?

(1) Electrical energy is converted to chemical energy.
(2) Chemical energy is converted to electrical energy.
(3) Oxidation takes place at the cathode.
(4) Reduction takes place at the anode.

43. The overall reaction in a chemical cell is

$$Zn(s) + Cu^{2+}(aq) \rightarrow Zn^{2+}(aq) + Cu(s)$$

As the reaction takes place the

(1) mass of the Zn(s) electrode decreases
(2) mass of the Cu(s) electrode decreases
(3) Cu^{2+} (aq) concentration stays the same
(4) Zn^{2+} (aq) concentration stays the same

44. In an operating voltaic cell, reduction occurs

(1) in the salt bridge
(2) in the wire
(3) at the anode
(4) at the cathode

45. In the electrolysis of fused (molten) silver chloride, the Ag+ ions are

(1) reduced at the negative electrode
(2) reduced at the positive electrode
(3) oxidized at the negative electrode
(4) oxidized at the positive electrode

46. In an electrolytic cell, to which electrode will a positive ion migrate and undergo reduction?

(1) The anode, which is negatively charged
(2) The anode, which is positively charged
(3) The cathode, which is negatively charged
(4) The cathode, which is positively charged

Directions

Review the Test-Taking Strategies section of this book. Then answer the following questions. Read each question carefully and answer with a correct choice or response.

Part A

1 The oxidation number of an uncombined Group 2 metal is
   (1) +1   (2) +2   (3) −2   (4) 0

2 In all oxidation-reduction reactions there is conservation of
   (1) charge, but not mass
   (2) mass, but not charge
   (3) neither mass nor charge
   (4) both mass and charge

3 During a reduction reaction there is a
   (1) loss of electrons and a loss of oxidation number
   (2) loss of electrons and a gain of oxidation number
   (3) gain of electrons and a loss of oxidation number
   (4) gain of electrons and a gain of oxidation number

4 As an atom is oxidized, the number of protons in the nucleus
   (1) decreases
   (2) increases
   (3) remains the same
   (4) depends on the atom

5 In a redox reaction, the species reduced
   (1) gains electrons
   (2) gains oxidation number
   (3) loses electrons and is the oxidizing agent
   (4) loses electrons and is the reducing agent

6 In an oxidation-reduction reaction, the total number of electrons lost is
   (1) equal to the total number of electrons gained.
   (2) equal to the total number of protons gained.
   (3) less than the total number of electrons gained.
   (4) less than the total number of protons gained.

7 The function of a salt bridge in a voltaic cell is to
   (1) allow the flow of electrons
   (2) allow the flow of protons
   (3) allow the flow of ions
   (4) provide a site for electron transfer

8 Which of the following occurs in an electrolytic cell?
   (1) A chemical reaction produces an electric current.
   (2) An electric current produces a chemical reaction.
   (3) An oxidation reaction takes place at the cathode.
   (4) A reduction reaction takes place at the anode.

9 Hydrogen has an oxidation number of
   (1) 0 only   (3) −1 only
   (2) +1 only   (4) 0, +1, or −1

10 Voltaic cells differ from electrolytic cells because in a voltaic cell
   (1) the cathode is positively charged
   (2) the anode is positively charged
   (3) electrons flow from anode to cathode
   (4) electrons flow from cathode to anode

11 In a half-reaction
   (1) mass only is conserved
   (2) charge only is conserved
   (3) both mass and charge are conserved
   (4) neither mass nor charge is conserved

12 Which reaction occurs at the anode in voltaic and electrolytic cells?
   (1) reduction only
   (2) oxidation only
   (3) both reduction and oxidation
   (4) neither reduction nor oxidation

Part B–1

13 What is the oxidation number of carbon in $NaHCO_3$?
   (1) −2   (2) +2   (3) −4   (4) +4

14 Chlorine has an oxidation state of +3 in the compound
   (1) $HClO$ (2) $HClO_2$ (3) $HClO_3$ (4) $HClO_4$

15 What are the two oxidation states of nitrogen in the compound NH_4NO_3?
   (1) −3 and +5   (3) +3 and +5
   (2) −3 and −5   (4) +3 and −5

16 Which equation represents a redox reaction?

(1) $NaCl + AgNO_3 \rightarrow AgCl + NaNO_3$

(2) $HCl + KOH \rightarrow H_2O + KCl$

(3) $2KClO_3 \rightarrow 2KCl + 3O_2$

(4) $H_2CO_3 \rightarrow H_2O + CO_2$

17 Consider the equations A, B, C, and D.

(A) $AgNO_3 + NaCl \rightarrow AgCl + NaNO_3$

(B) $Cl_2 + H_2O \rightarrow HClO + HCl$

(C) $CuO + CO \rightarrow CO_2 + Cu$

(D) $NaOH + HCl \rightarrow NaCl + H_2O$

Which two reactions are redox equations?

(1) A and C   (3) C and D

(2) B and C   (4) A and D

18 In the reaction $AgNO_3(aq) + NaCl(aq) \rightarrow$ $NaNO_3(aq) + AgCl(s)$, the reactants

(1) gain electrons only

(2) lose electrons only

(3) both gain and lose electrons

(4) neither gain nor lose electrons

19 In the reaction $Cl_2 + H_2O \rightarrow HClO + HCl$, hydrogen is

(1) oxidized only

(2) reduced only

(3) both oxidized and reduced

(4) neither oxidized nor reduced

20 In the reaction $2KCl(\ell) \rightarrow 2K(s) + Cl_2(g)$, the K^+ ions are

(1) reduced by losing electrons

(2) reduced by gaining electrons

(3) oxidized by losing electrons

(4) oxidized by gaining electrons

21 Which equation correctly represents a reduction half-reaction?

(1) $Sn^0 + 2e^- \rightarrow Sn^{2+}$ (3) $Li^0 + e^- \rightarrow Li^+$

(2) $Na^0 + e^- \rightarrow Na^+$ (4) $Br_2^0 + 2e^- \rightarrow 2Br^-$

22 In the reaction $Mg + Cl_2 \rightarrow MgCl_2$, the correct half-reaction for the oxidation that occurs is

(1) $Mg + 2e^- \rightarrow Mg^{2+}$

(2) $Cl_2 + 2e^- \rightarrow 2Cl^-$

(3) $Mg \rightarrow Mg^{2+} + 2e^-$

(4) $Cl_2 \rightarrow 2Cl^- + 2e^-$

23 In an electrolytic cell, which ion would migrate through the solution to the negative electrode?

(1) a chloride ion   (3) a bromide ion

(2) a silver ion   (4) a fluoride ion

24 Which statement describes where the oxidation and reduction half-reactions occur in the operating electrochemical cell below?

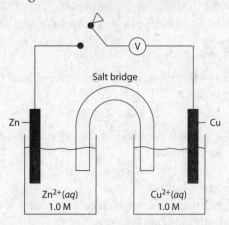

(1) Oxidation and reduction both occur at the Zn anode.

(2) Oxidation and reduction both occur at the Zn cathode.

(3) Oxidation occurs at the Cu cathode, and reduction occurs at the Zn anode.

(4) Oxidation occurs at the Zn anode, and reduction occurs at the Cu cathode.

25 The diagram below shows a spoon that will be electroplated with nickel metal. What will occur when switch S is closed?

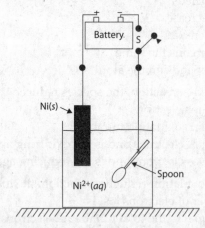

(1) The spoon will lose mass, and the Ni(s) will be reduced.

(2) The spoon will lose mass, and the Ni(s) will be oxidized.

(3) The spoon will gain mass, and the Ni(s) will be reduced.

(4) The spoon will gain mass, and the Ni(s) will be oxidized.

26 The diagram below represents a chemical cell.

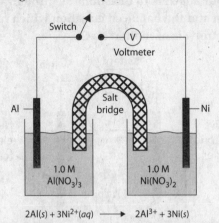

$$2Al(s) + 3Ni^{2+}(aq) \longrightarrow 2Al^{3+} + 3Ni(s)$$

When the switch is closed, electrons flow from
(1) $Al(s)$ to $Ni(s)$
(2) $Ni(s)$ to $Al(s)$
(3) $Al^{3+}(aq)$ to $Ni^{2+}(aq)$
(4) $Ni^{2+}(aq)$ to $Al^{3+}(aq)$

27 The diagram below represents a voltaic cell.

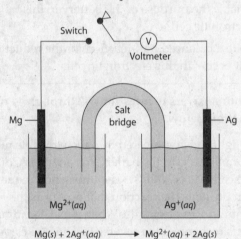

$$Mg(s) + 2Ag^{+}(aq) \longrightarrow Mg^{2+}(aq) + 2Ag(s)$$

Which species is oxidized when the switch is closed?
(1) $Mg(s)$
(2) $Mg^{2+}(aq)$
(3) $Ag(s)$
(4) $Ag^{+}(aq)$

28 The overall reaction in an electrochemical cell is $Zn(s) + Cu^{2+}(aq) \rightarrow Cu(s) + Zn^{2+}$. As the reaction in this cell takes place,
(1) oxidation occurs at the cathode
(2) the Cu^{2+} is oxidized
(3) the concentration of Zn^{2+} increases
(4) the concentration of Cu^{2+} increases

29 The diagram below represents an electrochemical cell.

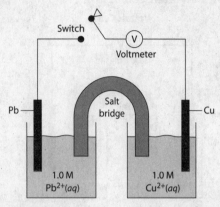

$$Pb(s) + Cu^{2+}(aq) \longrightarrow Pb^{2+}(aq) + Cu(s)$$

Which change occurs when the switch is closed?
(1) Pb is oxidized, and electrons flow to the Cu electrode.
(2) Pb is reduced, and electrons flow to the Cu electrode.
(3) Cu is oxidized, and electrons flow to the Pb electrode.
(4) Cu is reduced, and electrons flow to the Pb electrode.

30 Consider the following equation.

$$2Cr(s) + 3Cu^{2+}(aq) \rightarrow 2Cr^{3+}(aq) + 3Cu(s)$$

Which reaction occurs at the cathode in this voltaic cell?
(1) reduction of $Cu^{2+}(aq)$
(2) reduction of $Cu(s)$
(3) oxidation of $Cr^{3+}(aq)$
(4) oxidation of $Cr(s)$

Parts B–2 and C

Use the following balanced equation for questions 31 and 32.

Given the reaction: $4Al(s) + 3O_2(g) \rightarrow 2Al_2O_3(s)$

31 Write the balanced oxidation half-reaction for this oxidation-reduction reaction.

32 What is the oxidation number of oxygen in Al_2O_3?

Base your answers to questions 33 through 35 on the diagram of the voltaic cell below.

Voltaic Cell

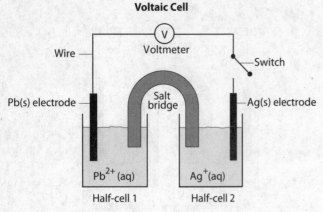

$$2 \, Ag^+(aq) + Pb(s) \longrightarrow Pb^{2+}(aq) + 2 \, Ag(s)$$

33 What is the direction of the electron flow through the wire?

34 Write an equation for the half-reaction that occurs at the silver electrode.

35 Explain the function of the salt bridge.

Base your answers to questions 36 through 38 on the diagram of a voltaic cell below.

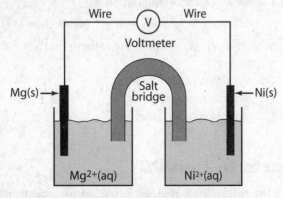

$$Mg(s) + Ni^{2+}(aq) \longrightarrow Mg^{2+}(aq) + Ni(s)$$

36 What is the total number of moles of electrons needed to completely reduce 6.0 moles of $Ni^{2+}(aq)$ ions?

37 Identify one metal from Reference Table J that is more easily oxidized than $Mg(s)$.

38 As the cell operates, the mass of the $Mg(s)$ decreases. Explain, in terms of particles, why this decrease occurs.

Base your answers to questions 39 through 41 on the diagram and the balanced equation which represent the electrolysis of molten NaCl.

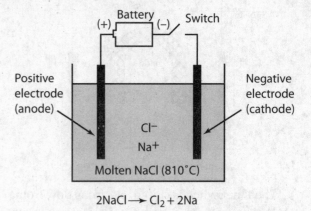

$$2NaCl \longrightarrow Cl_2 + 2Na$$

39 When the switch is closed, which electrode will attract the sodium ion?

40 What is the purpose of the battery in this electrolytic cell?

41 Write a balanced half-reaction for the reduction that occurs in this electrolytic cell.

Base your answers to questions 42 through 44 on the information below.

A flashlight can be powered by a rechargeable nickel-cadmium battery. In the battery, the anode is $Cd(s)$ and the cathode is $NiO_2(s)$. The unbalanced equation below represents the reaction that occurs as the battery produces electricity. When a nickel-cadmium battery is recharged, the reverse reaction takes place.

$$Cd(s) + NiO_2(s) + H_2O(\ell) \rightarrow Cd(OH)_2(s) + Ni(OH)_2(s)$$

42 Balance the equation for the reaction that produces electricity using the smallest whole-number coefficients.

43 Determine the change in oxidation number for the element that makes up the anode in the reaction that produces electricity.

44 Explain why Cd would be above Ni if placed on Table J.

Acids, Bases, and Salts

How Scientists Study Acids, Bases, and Salts

What makes an acid strong or weak?

Why is HCl a strong acid and CH₃COOH a weak acid? Does it need more time at the gym to build molecules?

Quite the opposite. HCl has learned to relax and completely ionize its molecules into hydrogen and chloride ions. Acetic acid has many molecules and only a few ions. It's the number of hydrogen ions that determines if an acid is strong or weak.

10 Acids, Bases, and Salts

Vocabulary

acidity	electrolyte	neutralization
alkalinity	hydrogen ion	pH scale
Arrhenius acid	hydronium ion	salt
Arrhenius base	indicator	titration

Topic Overview

(R) Common Acids and Common Bases in the *Reference Tables for Physical Setting/Chemistry* list a few of the most common acids and bases. But what exactly are acids and bases? Acids and bases are classes of compounds that can be recognized by their easily observed properties. In this topic you will learn about these properties, the definitions that are used to explain these properties, and the important reactions that occur between acids and bases.

Properties of Acids and Bases

Certain observable properties can be used to identify both acids and bases. Although these properties can indicate whether or not a substance is an acid or a base, they do not explain why acids and bases behave the way they do.

Characteristic Properties of Acids

- *Dilute solutions of acids have a sour taste.* It would be foolish to taste a substance to see if it is an acid. However, there are acids in many of the foods that we eat. You have probably noticed the sour taste of lemons; the sour taste is due to the presence of citric acid. Vinegar contains acetic acid, and carbonated drinks have carbonic acid as one of the ingredients.

- *Aqueous solutions of acids conduct an electric current.* Substances that conduct an electric current are called **electrolytes.** The ability of a solution to conduct an electric current is dependent on the concentration (number) of ions in solution. That is, the greater the concentration of ions in solution, the greater the electrical conductivity. If a solution of an acid is a good conductor of electricity, it is called a strong acid. If such a solution is a poor conductor, it is termed a weak acid.

- *Acids react with bases to form water and a salt.* This type of reaction is called a **neutralization** reaction. Neutralization reactions are in fact a type of double replacement reaction. The **salt** that is formed as a product of a neutralization reaction is an ionic substance composed of a positively charged metallic or polyatomic ion and a negative ion other than the hydroxide ion.

- *Acids react with certain metals to produce hydrogen gas.* The metals listed in Table J of the *Reference Tables for Physical Setting/Chemistry* that are ⓡ above hydrogen (H_2) will react with acids to produce hydrogen gas and a salt. Thus, magnesium will react with hydrochloric acid, whereas copper will not.
- *Acids cause acid-base indicators to change color.* Indicators are substances that have different colors when mixed in acidic and basic solutions. Table M of the *Reference Tables for Physical Setting/Chemistry* lists several ⓡ common indicators and the color changes that they undergo.

Characteristic Properties of Bases
- *Bases have a bitter taste.*
- *Bases have a slippery or soapy feeling.*
- *Bases conduct an electric current.* Note that the terminology used to describe the strength of a base is the same as that used for acids. Thus, a solution of a base with a high concentration of ions that conducts electricity is called a strong base. Weak bases are poor conductors of electricity and are not highly ionized.
- *Bases react with acids to produce water and a salt.*
- *Bases cause acid-base indicators to change color.*

Arrhenius Theory

There have been several attempts to develop explanations for the observable properties of acids and bases. Svante Arrhenius, a Swedish chemist, proposed a commonality of all acids to explain their similar properties. An **Arrhenius acid** is defined as a substance whose water solution contains the hydrogen ion as the only positive ion. For example, hydrochloric acid ionizes in water to form hydrogen and chloride ions.

$$HCl \rightarrow H^+ + Cl^-$$

Not all substances that contain hydrogen are acids. Methane (CH_4) is an organic compound containing hydrogen, yet it is not an acid. The hydrogen atoms in methane are bonded to the carbon by covalent bonds. These hydrogen atoms do not ionize in solution: rather, they remain attached to the molecule. Because the hydrogen atoms do not form ions, methane is neither an electrolyte nor an acid.

The Nature of the Hydrogen Ion

A hydrogen atom consists of a single electron orbiting a nucleus that contains a single proton. As shown in Figure 10-1, when the hydrogen atom becomes a positive ion, the electron is lost, leaving behind the proton. Thus, a positive **hydrogen ion** is a proton.

Chemists believe that this proton cannot exist in a water solution as an isolated proton. The positively charged proton is attracted to an unshared pair of electrons in the water molecule. See Figure 10-2. The proton covalently bonds with

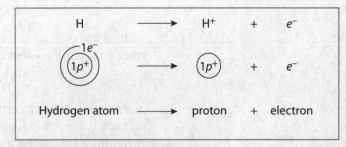

Figure 10-1. An H⁺ ion is a proton.

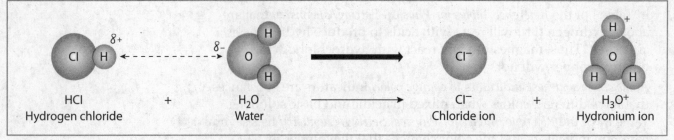

Figure 10-2. Acids react with water to produce the hydronium ion.

the water forming H_3O^+, the **hydronium ion.** Acids dissolve in water and react to produce hydronium and negative ions.

$$HCl + H_2O \rightarrow H_3O^+ + Cl^-$$

$$H^+ + H_2O \rightarrow H_3O^+$$

According to the Arrhenius theory, the properties of acids are properties of the hydrogen (hydronium) ion.

As shown in the first equation above, each molecule of hydrochloric acid (HCl) that ionizes in water produces a single hydrogen ion. Hydrochloric acid and other acids that produce a single hydrogen ion are called monoprotic acids. Sulfuric acid (H_2SO_4), however, ionizes in two steps.

$$H_2SO_4 \rightarrow H^+ + HSO_4^-$$

$$HSO_4^- \rightarrow H^+ + SO_4^{2-}$$

Each molecule of H_2SO_4 that ionizes produces two hydrogen ions. Sulfuric acid and other acids that produce two hydrogen ions are called diprotic acids. Similarly, an H_3PO_4 molecule ionizes to yield three hydrogen ions and is called a triprotic acid.

The Nature of the Hydroxide Ion

In a parallel manner to acids, the properties of bases are explained as properties of the hydroxide ion (OH^-) in solution. Each **Arrhenius base** produces hydroxide ions when dissolved in water. The presence of the hydroxide ion makes the base an electrolyte. It is also the presence of the hydroxide ion that produces the slippery feel and bitter taste common to Arrhenius bases.

Ammonia (NH_3) and organic compounds called amines are bases, though at first glance their chemical formulas do not show the presence of hydroxide ions. However, ammonia reacts with water to form the ammonium and hydroxide ions.

$$NH_3 + H_2O \rightarrow NH_4^+ + OH^-$$

Amines are compounds containing carbon and nitrogen that are related to ammonia. Amines also react with water to produce hydroxide ions.

$$CH_3NH_2 + H_2O \rightarrow CH_3NH_3^+ + OH^-$$

There are also other compounds whose formulas do contain an –OH group but which are not bases. The hydroxyl group is composed of an oxygen atom and a hydrogen atom covalently bonded to a carbon chain. This group of organic compounds, called alcohols, are not bases as they do not

---

Digging Deeper

Some organic compounds that are acids have chemical formulas that are somewhat misleading. These compounds contain a carboxyl group (–COOH) that gives them the appearance of a base. However, the hydrogen atom in the carboxyl group does ionize in water, thus defining these compounds as acids.

$$CH_3COOH \rightarrow H^+ + CH_3COO^-$$

ionize in water. Thus, they are nonelectrolytes and do not have the characteristics of bases. CH_3OH and CH_3CH_2OH are examples of alcohols, and they do not ionize to produce the hydroxide ion.

Strength of Acids and Bases

Hydrochloric acid is a dangerous acid that can cause severe injury to your skin. Citric acid is present in citrus and other fruits that we commonly eat. Even more surprising, boric acid is used as an eye-washing solution. How can we explain that these substances are all acids, yet have such different effects? The answer involves the strength of each acid.

When one hundred molecules of hydrochloric acid dissolve in water, all one hundred molecules ionize and form ions. When an acid completely ionizes, it is called a strong acid. Other acids ionize to a much smaller degree. Perhaps only one molecule out of one hundred ionizes. Acids that ionize only slightly are called weak acids.

The degree of ionization is a function of the number of ions that are produced. Highly ionized (strong) acids and bases produce large numbers of ions. These strong acids and bases are strong electrolytes, and hence good conductors of electricity.

Naming Acids and Bases

Binary acids are composed of hydrogen and one other element. Hydrogen chloride (HCl) is a molecular gas, but becomes an Arrhenius acid when it reacts with water to produce hydrogen ions. The names of binary acids begin with *hydro-* followed by the name of the other element modified to end with *−ic.* Thus, hydrogen chloride gas becomes hydrochloric acid when dissolved in water. Other binary acids are named in the same fashion.

Ternary acids are also molecular substances that produce hydrogen ions when dissolved in water. They consist of a polyatomic ion containing oxygen such as nitrate (NO_3^-) or sulfate (SO_4^{2-}). To name a ternary acid, the anion suffixes *−ate* and *−ite* usually are replaced by the suffixes *−ic* and *−ous* respectively. For example, HNO_3 is nitric acid. Sometimes the names are modified slightly, as in H_2SO_4, sulfuric acid. Table 10-1 lists the names of several common acids.

Bases are quite simple to name. The name of the positive ion is not modified, and the name of the base ends with hydroxide. For example, $Ca(OH)_2$ is named calcium hydroxide.

Memory Jogger

Electrolytes are substances whose water solutions conduct an electric current. When there are many ions in solution, the substance is termed a strong electrolyte and is a good conductor. Weak electrolytes have relatively few ions in solution, and are poor conductors or nonconductors.

Table 10-1. Names of Several Acids and Their Ions

Acid Name	Formula of Acid	Anion Name
Hydrochloric	HCl	chloride
Sulfuric	H_2SO_4	sulfate
Sulfurous	H_2SO_3	sulfite
Nitric	HNO_3	nitrate
Nitrous	HNO_2	nitrite

Review Questions
Set 10.1

1. According to the Arrhenius theory, when an acidic substance is dissolved in water it will produce a solution containing only one kind of positive ion. To which ion does the theory refer?

   (1) acetate   (3) chloride
   (2) hydrogen   (4) sodium

2. When an Arrhenius base is dissolved in H_2O, the only negative ion present in the solution is

   (1) OH^- (3) H^-
   (2) H_3O^- (4) O^{2-}

3. Which type of substance yields hydrogen ions, H^+, in an aqueous solution?

   (1) an Arrhenius acid
   (2) an Arrhenius base
   (3) a saturated hydrocarbon
   (4) an unsaturated hydrocarbon

4. In an aqueous solution, which substance yields hydrogen ions as the only positive ion?

   (1) C_2H_5OH (3) KH
   (2) CH_3COOH (4) KOH

5. Which compound is an electrolyte?

   (1) $C_6H_{12}O_6$ (3) CH_3CH_2OH
   (2) $C_{12}H_{22}O_{11}$ (4) CH_3COOH

6. If 1 mol of each of the following substances were dissolved in 1 L of water, which solution would contain the highest concentration of OH^- ions?

   (1) H_2SO_4 (2) NH_4Cl (3) KNO_3 (4) NaOH

7. If 1 mol of each of the following substances were dissolved in 1 L of water, which solution would contain the highest concentration of H_3O^+ ions?

   (1) CH_3COOH (3) KBr
   (2) NaCl   (4) $Ba(OH)_2$

8. Which compound yields H^+ ions as the only positive ions in an aqueous solution?

   (1) KOH   (3) CH_3COOH
   (2) NaOH   (4) CH_3OH

9. Which species is classified as an Arrhenius base?

   (1) CH_3OH (2) LiOH   (3) PO_4^{3-} (4) CO_3^{2-}

10. As 1 g of sodium hydroxide dissolves in 100 g of water, the conductivity of the water

    (1) decreases   (3) remains the same
    (2) increases

11. Which compounds are classified as Arrhenius acids?

    (1) HCl and NaOH
    (2) HNO_3 and NaCl
    (3) NH_3 and H_2CO_3
    (4) HBr and H_2SO_4

12. A solution of hydrochloric acid is a stronger acid than a solution of acetic acid of the same concentration because

    (1) it has more hydrogen ions in solution
    (2) it has more hydroxide ions in solution
    (3) it has fewer hydrogen ions in solution
    (4) it has fewer hydroxide ions in solution.

13. What can be explained by the Arrhenius theory?

    (1) the behavior of many acids and bases
    (2) the effect of stress on a phase equilibrium
    (3) the operation of an electrochemical cell
    (4) the spontaneous decay of some nuclei

14. Potassium hydroxide is classified as an Arrhenius base because KOH contains

    (1) OH^- ions.   (3) K^+ ions.
    (2) O^{2-} ions.   (4) H^+ ions.

15. Name the following acids and bases.

    (a) H_2S (c) LiOH
    (b) HBr   (d) $Mg(OH)_2$

16. A student tests the conductivity of an unknown substance and determines it to be a good conductor of electricity. Based on this he decides that it is an acid. Criticize the student's conclusion. Is there enough evidence to warrant the conclusion? What additional test or tests could be performed to confirm the conclusion? For each test, indicate the result that would verify the substance to be an acid.

Reactions Involving Acids and Bases

Chemical reactions involving acids and bases are common in industrial and consumer applications, natural processes, and in classroom experiments. Acids and bases undergo many reactions because they are able to react with each other as well as with other compounds and elements.

Reactions of Acids with Metals

You may recall that any element in the Activity Series of the *Reference*
Ⓡ *Tables for Physical Setting/Chemistry* will react with the ion of any element

below it. Note that hydrogen (H_2) is found near the bottom of the table. Thus, any metal above hydrogen in the table will react with the hydrogen ions in acids to produce H_2 and a salt. The reaction between zinc and hydrochloric acid is an example.

$$Zn(s) + 2HCl(aq) \rightarrow H_2(g) + ZnCl_2(aq)$$

Copper, which is below hydrogen in the table, will not react with hydrogen ions in acids.

Neutralization Reactions

In a neutralization reaction, an Arrhenius acid reacts with an Arrhenius base to produce water and a salt. There are several ways that these reactions can be expressed. For example, consider the neutralization reaction between hydrochloric acid (HCl) and sodium hydroxide (NaOH).

This reaction can be expressed as a word equation:

Hydrochloric acid + Sodium hydroxide → Water + Sodium chloride

Substituting the chemical formulas for words yields the formula equation:

$$HCl(aq) + NaOH(aq) \rightarrow H_2O(\ell) + NaCl(aq)$$

Writing the equation to take the ions in solution into account yields the ionic equation:

$$H^+(aq) + Cl^-(aq) + Na^+(aq) + OH^-(aq) \rightarrow H_2O(\ell) + Na^+(aq) + Cl^-(aq)$$

Note that the sodium and chloride ions are present on both sides of the reaction arrow. Because they have not taken part in the reaction, they are called spectator ions and can be omitted.

$$H^+(aq) + \cancel{Cl^-(aq)} + \cancel{Na^+(aq)} + OH^-(aq) \rightarrow H_2O(\ell) + \cancel{Na^+(aq)} + \cancel{Cl^-(aq)}$$

Omitting the spectator ions yields the net ionic equation:

$$H^+(aq) + OH^-(aq) \rightarrow H_2O(\ell)$$

Because hydrogen ions exist in solution as hydronium ions (H_3O^+), this equation can also be written as the reaction between hydronium and hydroxide ions.

$$H_3O^+(aq) + OH^-(aq) \rightarrow 2H_2O(\ell)$$

All neutralization reactions have the same net equation. The Arrhenius definition is able to explain the process of neutralization as a reaction between hydrogen (hydronium) ions and hydroxide ions to form water with the spectator ions forming a salt.

Writing Neutralization Reactions Writing neutralization reactions is not a difficult task, as shown in the following Sample Problem.

Memory Jogger

Single-replacement reactions have the general formula:

$$A + BC \rightarrow AC + B$$

Memory Jogger

When writing equations, first write correct formulas using charges and subscripts. Then, balance the equation using coefficients.

Memory Jogger

When writing the formula of the salt in a neutralization reaction, check the charge on both ions. If the ionic charges are not equal and opposite, write the charge of one ion as the subscript of the other.

SAMPLE PROBLEM

Write the equation for the neutralization reaction between dilute nitric acid and potassium hydroxide.

SOLUTION: Identify the known and unknown values.

Known
reactant 1 = nitric acid (HNO_3)

reactant 2 = potassium hydroxide (KOH)

Unknown
neutralization equation = ?

1. Write a simple word equation for the neutralization reaction.

   acid + base → water + salt

2. Substitute the known compounds into the general word equation.

   HNO_3 + KOH → water + salt

3. Picture a box enclosing the hydroxide (OH^-) of the base and the hydrogen (H^+) of the acid. These particles combine to form water (H_2O).

   HNO_3 + KOH → H_2O + salt

The remaining K^+ and NO_3^- ions combine to form the salt KNO_3.

HNO_3 + KOH → H_2O + KNO_3

4. Now check to see that the equation is balanced. Because the hydroxide and hydrogen ions combine in a 1:1 ratio to form water molecules, they must be present in equal numbers. If needed, the coefficients of the acid and the base are adjusted to balance these ions. In this example, there is one hydroxide ion and one hydrogen ion, so the coefficients are both 1. A coefficient of 1 is not written; the above equation is balanced. Note that the spectator ions form the salt.

Digging Deeper

Because salts are produced by neutralization, it would seem logical that a salt would be neutral, that is, neither acidic nor basic. There are, however, acidic, basic, and neutral salts. Salts that were formed from a strong acid and a strong base are neutral salts. If the salt was formed by the reaction of a strong acid and a weak base, it will be acidic. If the opposite is the case, that is, a salt formed from a strong base and a weak acid, the salt will be basic. The acidity or basicity of a salt formed from a weak acid and a weak base must be evaluated on a case-by-case basis.

When a diprotic acid reacts with a dihydroxy base, there are two hydrogen ions and two hydroxide ions. These will combine to form two molecules of water. The remaining ions will form the salt.

$$Ca(OH)_2 + H_2SO_4 → 2H_2O + CaSO_4$$

Combinations of acids and bases that do not have an equal number of hydroxide and hydrogen ions are also easy to balance. Consider the following unbalanced equation:

$$Mg(OH)_2 + HCl → H_2O + MgCl_2$$

Note that there are two hydroxide ions but only one hydrogen ion. Placing a 2 in front of the HCl balances the hydroxide and hydrogen ions that form two molecules of water. The 2 coefficient also supplies the two chloride ions needed to form the salt. The equation is now balanced:

$$Mg(OH)_2 + 2HCl → 2H_2O + MgCl_2$$

Salts

As you learned earlier, when a metal reacts with an acid, hydrogen gas and a salt are formed. In a neutralization reaction, an acid and a base react to form water and a salt. The salts in these reactions are ionic substances composed of positively charged metallic or polyatomic ions, and negative ions other than hydroxide ions. Sodium chloride (NaCl) and ammonium phosphate (($NH_4)_3PO_4$) are examples of salts. Salts are named by using the name of the positive ion of the base, and the negative ion of the acid.

17. According to the *Reference Tables for Physical Setting/Chemistry,* which metal would react spontaneously with hydrochloric acid?

(1) gold   (2) silver   (3) copper   (4) zinc

18. According to the *Reference Tables for Physical Setting/Chemistry,* which of the following metals will react most readily with HCl to release hydrogen gas?

(1) aluminum   (3) silver
(2) copper   (4) gold

19. Which solution reacts with LiOH(*aq*) to produce a salt and water?

(1) KCl(*aq*)   (3) NaOH(*aq*)
(2) H_2SO_4(*aq*)   (4) CaO(*aq*)

20. The reaction between one mole of hydrogen ions and one mole of hydroxide ions is called

(1) oxidation   (3) hydrolysis
(2) reduction   (4) neutralization

21. Which type of reaction occurs when equal volumes of 0.1M HCl and 0.1M NaOH are mixed?

(1) neutralization   (3) electrolysis
(2) ionization   (4) hydrolysis

22. Which type of reaction occurs when 50-mL quantities of 1 M Ba(OH)$_2$(*aq*) and H_2SO_4(*aq*) are combined?

(1) hydrolysis   (3) hydrogenation
(2) ionization   (4) neutralization

23. Which compound reacts with an acid to produce water and a salt?

(1) CH_3Cl (3) KCl
(2) CH_3COOH (4) KOH

24. Which compound reacts with an acid to form salt and water?

(1) LiOH   (2) LiCl   (3) CH_3F (4) C_2H_5COOH

25. What are the products when potassium hydroxide reacts with hydrochloric acid?

(1) K(*s*), Cl_2(*g*), and H_2O(ℓ)
(2) KH(*s*), Cl^+(*aq*), and OH^-(*aq*)
(3) KOH(*aq*) and Cl_2(ℓ)
(4) KCl(*aq*) and H_2O(ℓ)

26. Which is the net ionic equation for a neutralization?

(1) $H^+ + H_2O \rightarrow H_3O^+$ (3) $2H^+ + 2O^{2-} \rightarrow 2OH^-$
(2) $H^+ + NH_3 \rightarrow NH_4^+$ (4) $H^+ + OH^- \rightarrow H_2O$

27. Which substance is always produced by a neutralization reaction?

(1) water
(2) acid
(3) ester
(4) base

28. Which products are formed when an acid reacts with a base?

(1) an alcohol and carbon dioxide
(2) an ester and water
(3) a soap and glycerin
(4) a salt and water

29. Which compound is a salt?

(1) Na_3PO_4
(2) H_3PO_4
(3) CH_3COOH
(4) $Ca(OH)_2$

30. Which compound is classified as a salt?

(1) CH_3COOH
(2) C_2H_5OH
(3) NaOH
(4) $NaC_2H_3O_2$

31. Which formula represents a salt?

(1) KOH
(2) KCl
(3) CH_3OH
(4) CH_3COOH

32. The diagram below shows an acid being added to a base.

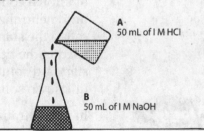

A
50 mL of l M HCl

B
50 mL of l M NaOH

As the acid in beaker A is added to the base in flask B, the number of OH^- ions in flask B

(1) decreases and the number of Na^+ ions decreases
(2) increases and the number of Na^+ ions decreases
(3) decreases and the number of Na^+ ions remains the same
(4) increases and the number of Na^+ ions remains the same

33. The diagram below illustrates an apparatus used to test the conductivity of various solutions.

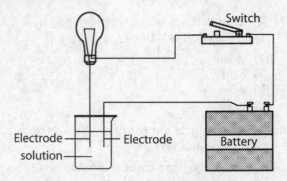

When the switch is closed, which of the following 1-molar solutions would cause the bulb to glow most brightly?

(1) ammonia   (3) carbonic acid
(2) acetic acid   (4) sulfuric acid

34. Which salt is formed when hydrochloric acid is neutralized by a potassium hydroxide solution?

(1) potassium chloride
(2) potassium chlorate
(3) potassium chlorite
(4) potassium perchlorate

35. In the neutralization reaction between hydrochloric acid and sodium hydroxide, the spectator ions are

(1) H^+ and OH^- (3) Na^+ and H^+
(2) Cl^- and OH^- (4) Na^+ and Cl^-

36. When NaOH(*aq*) reacts completely with HCl(*aq*) and the resulting solution is evaporated to dryness, the solid remaining is

(1) an ester   (3) a salt
(2) an alcohol   (4) a metal

37. Name each of the following.

(a) HF
(b) H_2Se
(c) HI

38. Consult the Activity Series in the *Reference Tables for Physical Setting/Chemistry* to determine if the following reactions actually occur. If a reaction does occur, write the correctly balanced equation. If the reaction does not occur, write "No reaction."

(a) calcium and hydrochloric acid
(b) zinc and dilute nitric acid
(c) lead and carbonic acid
(d) aluminum and acetic acid
(e) copper and phosphoric acid

39. Write the balanced equation for each of the following neutralization reactions, and write the name of the salt formed.

(a) nitric acid and sodium hydroxide
(b) nitric acid and magnesium hydroxide
(c) sulfuric acid and magnesium hydroxide
(d) sulfuric acid and potassium hydroxide
(e) phosphoric acid and lithium hydroxide
(f) phosphoric acid and calcium hydroxide

Acid–Base Titration

Titration is the process of adding measured volumes of an acid or a base of known concentration to an acid or a base of unknown concentration until neutralization occurs. The solution of known concentration is called the standard solution. Knowing the volumes of acid and base used in the titration, together with the known concentration of the standard solution, it is possible to calculate the concentration of the unknown solution.

In all neutralization reactions there must be a 1:1 ratio between the moles of hydrogen ions (H^+) and the moles of hydroxide ions (OH^-). The equation for concentration shows the relationship among number of moles, volume in liters, and molarity.

$$\text{molarity} = \frac{\text{moles}}{\text{volume}}$$

or

$$\text{moles} = \text{molarity} \times \text{volume}$$

Square brackets [ ] are used to indicate concentration of a particle in units of moles per liter, molarity (M). For example, [OH^-] stands for the concentration of OH^- ions in units of moles of OH^- per liter of solution.

Since the number of moles of H^+ ions must equal the number of moles of OH^- ions, equating mol H^+ and mol OH^- yields the following equation.

$$\text{molarity } H^+ \times \text{volume}_{acid} = \text{molarity } OH^- \times \text{volume}_{base}$$

or

$$M_A \times V_A = M_B \times V_B$$

In the above equation, M_A = molarity of H^+, V_A = volume of acid in milliliters, M_B = molarity of OH^-, and V_B = volume of base in milliliters.

To solve any titration problem, the molarity of the acid and base must be expressed as the molarity of the hydrogen ion (H^+) and the molarity of the hydroxide ion (OH^-), respectively. In the case of monoprotic acids such as HCl, the molarity of the H^+ is the same as the molarity of the acid. Thus, a 2.0 M HCl solution has a 2.0 M H^+ concentration. The same applies to monohydroxy bases. That is, a 2.5 M NaOH solution has a 2.5 M OH^- concentration.

The case is different for diprotic and triprotic acids. Consider the complete ionization of a 1.0 M solution of sulfuric acid (H_2SO_4).

$$H_2SO_4(aq) \rightarrow 2H^+(aq) + SO_4{}^{2-}(aq)$$

One liter of 1.0 M solution of H_2SO_4 yields 2 mol of H^+ ions. The molarity of the H^+ ions will be twice the molarity of the acid solution. Similarly, a triprotic acid produces an H^+ ion molarity three times that of the molarity of the acid solution.

The following examples summarize the relationships between the concentration of an acid or base and the resulting concentration of hydrogen ions (H^+) or hydroxide ions (OH^-) in solution for mono-, di-, and triprotic acids and mono- and dihydroxy bases.

Monoprotic Acids The H^+ molarity equals the molarity of the acid solution. Hydrochloric acid is an example.

$$2.5 \text{ M HCl} = 2.5 \text{ M } H^+$$

Diprotic Acids The H^+ molarity is twice the molarity of the acid solution. Sulfuric acid is an example.

$$2.5 \text{ M } H_2SO_4 = 5.0 \text{ M } H^+$$

Triprotic Acids The H^+ molarity is three times the molarity of the acid solution. Phosphoric acid is an example.

$$2.0 \text{ M } H_3PO_4 = 6.0 \text{ M } H^+$$

Monohydroxy Bases The OH^- molarity equals the molarity of the base solution. Sodium hydroxide is an example.

$$3.0 \text{ M NaOH} = 3.0 \text{ M } OH^-$$

Dihydroxy Bases The OH^- molarity is twice the molarity of the base solution. Barium hydroxide is an example.

$$0.5 \text{ M } Ba(OH)_2 = 1.0 \text{ M } OH^-$$

SAMPLE PROBLEM

What is the concentration of a hydrochloric acid solution if 50.0 mL of a 0.250 M KOH are needed to neutralize 20.0 mL of the HCl solution of unknown concentration?

SOLUTION: Identify the known and unknown values.

Known
molarity of KOH = 0.250 M
V_B = volume of KOH = 50.0 mL
V_A = volume of HCl = 20.0 mL

Unknown
M_A = molarity of HCl = ? M

1. Write the balanced equation for the neutralization reaction

$KOH + HCl \rightarrow H_2O + KCl$

2. Determine the molarity of the hydroxide ion. Because KOH is a monohydroxy base, the molarity of the hydroxide ion is the same as the molarity of the base solution.

M_B = molarity KOH = 0.250 M

3. Solve the neutralization reaction equation for M_A, substitute the known values, and solve.

$M_A \times V_A = M_B \times V_B$

$M_A = (M_B \times V_B)/ V_A$

$M_A = \dfrac{(0.250 \text{ M}) (50.0 \text{ mL})}{20.0 \text{ mL}}$

M_A = 0.625 M

The molarity of the hydrogen ion is 0.625 M. Because HCl is a monprotic acid, the molarity of the acid is also 0.625 M.

SAMPLE PROBLEM

What is the concentration of a sulfuric acid solution if 50. mL of a 0.25 M KOH are needed to neutralize 20. mL of the H_2SO_4 solution of unknown concentration?

SOLUTION: Identify the known and unknown values.

Known
molarity of KOH = 0.25 M
V_B = volume of KOH = 50. mL
V_A = volume of H_2SO_4 = 20. mL

Unknown
M_A = molarity of H_2SO_4 = ? M

1. Write the balanced equation for the neutralization reaction.

$2KOH + H_2SO_4 \rightarrow 2H_2O + K_2SO_4$

2. Determine the molarity of the hydroxide ion. Because KOH is a monohydroxy base, the molarity of the hydroxide ion is the same as the molarity of base solution.

M_B = molarity KOH = 0.25 M

3. Solve the neutralization reaction equation for M_A, substitute the known values, and solve.

$M_A \times V_A = M_B \times V_B$

$M_A = (M_B \times V_B)/ V_A$

$M_A = \dfrac{(0.250 \text{ M}) (50.0 \text{ mL})}{20.0 \text{ mL}}$

M_A = 0.625 M

4. To determine the molarity of the H_2SO_4, adjust for the fact that the acid is diprotic. That is, the molarity of the acid is only half that of the hydrogen ion.

$\text{molarity } H_2SO_4 = \dfrac{[H^+]}{2} = \dfrac{0.625 \text{ M}}{2} = 0.31 \text{ M}$

40. What is the volume of 0.30 M NaOH(aq) needed to completely neutralize 15.0 mL of 0.80 M HCl(aq)?

(1) 3.6 mL (2) 5.6 mL (3) 20. mL (4) 40. mL

41. To neutralize 1 mol of sulfuric acid, 2 mol of sodium hydroxide are required. How many liters of 1 M NaOH are needed to exactly neutralize 1 L of 1 M H_2SO_4?

(1) 1 (2) 2 (3) 0.5 (4) 4

42. How many moles of sodium hydroxide (NaOH) are required to completely neutralize 2 mol of nitric acid (HNO_3)?

(1) 1 (2) 2 (3) 40 (4) 60

43. During an acid-base neutralization, how many moles of hydroxide ions will react with one mole of hydrogen ions?

(1) 1.0 mol   (3) 17.0 mol
(2) 0.5 mol   (4) 22.4 mol

44. How many moles of KOH are needed to exactly neutralize 500. mL of 1.0 M HCl?

(1) 1.0 mol   (3) 0.25 mol
(2) 2.0 mol   (4) 0.50 mol

45. One liter of 1 M NaOH will completely neutralize one liter of

(1) 1 M H_2SO_4 (3) 2 M H_2SO_4
(2) 0.5 M H_2SO_4 (4) 1.5 M H_2SO_4

For questions 46–54, show all of your work.

46. Consider the following reaction.

$$KOH + HCl \rightarrow H_2O + HOH$$

How many milliliters of 2.0 M KOH are necessary to neutralize 50. mL of 1.0 M HCl?

47. How many milliliters of 2.5 M HCl are required to exactly neutralize 1.5 L of 5.0 M NaOH?

48. How many milliliters of 0.20 M H_2SO_4 are required to completely neutralize 40. mL of 0.10 M $Ca(OH)_2$?

49. How many milliliters of 0.200 M NaOH are needed to neutralize 100. mL of 0.100 M HCl?

50. A 2.0-mL sample of NaOH solution is exactly neutralized by 4.0 mL of 3.0 M HCl solution. What is the concentration of the NaOH solution?

51. A 10.-mL sample of hydrochloric acid neutralizes 15 mL of a 0.40 M solution of NaOH. What is the molarity of the hydrochloric acid?

52. How many mL of 0.20 M hydrochloric acid is required to neutralize 100. mL of 0.80 M potassium hydroxide?

53. A 3.0-mL sample of HNO_3 solution is exactly neutralized by 6.0 mL of 0.50 M KOH. What is the molarity of the HNO_3 solution?

54. What is the molarity of hydrogen ions in a 2.7 M solution of the strong acid HCl?

55. Write the electron dot diagram of a hydrogen chloride molecule.

56. Write the electron dot diagram for the hydronium ion (H_3O^+).

57. Write the electron dot diagram for the hydroxide ion (OH^-).

58. Write the word equation form of the net ionic equation for all neutralization equations.

59. Write the electron dot diagram for the net ionic equation for a neutralization reaction. Be sure to include the charge on any ionic substance.

60. Phosphoric acid is neutralized by a solution of sodium hydroxide. What is the name of the salt formed from the neutralization?

Acidity and Alkalinity of Solutions

Although water is a covalently bonded substance, it does ionize to a very small extent as shown by the equation below.

$$HOH \leftrightarrow H^+ + OH^-$$

It can be seen that in pure water $[H^+] = [OH^-]$. Le Châtelier's principle tells us that if one of these factors increases, the other decreases. When HCl is added to pure water, the concentration of the hydrogen ion increases, and the concentration of the hydroxide ion decreases. When $[H^+] > [OH^-]$, the solution is acidic. If the reverse is true, and the concentration of OH^- is greater than the concentration of the H^+, the solution is alkaline, or basic. The terms **acidity** and **alkalinity** (or basicity) refer to the relative strength of the acid or base in terms of their H^+ and OH^- concentrations.

pH Scale

A scale, called the **pH scale**, has been developed to express $[H^+]$ as a number from 0 to 14. A pH of 0 is strongly acidic, a pH of 7 is neutral, and a pH of 14 is strongly basic. The pH scale is logarithmic. Each change of a single pH unit signifies a tenfold change in the concentration of the hydrogen ion. Thus the $[H^+]$ is ten times greater in a solution with a pH of 5 as in a solution with a pH of 6.

Because $[H^+]$ and $[OH^-]$ are directly related, a pH change of one unit represents a tenfold increase or decrease of both the hydrogen ion and hydroxide ion concentration. As the concentration of the hydrogen ion increases, the concentration of the hydroxide ion decreases.

$$HIn \longrightarrow H^+ + In^-$$
(colorless)   (pink)

Figure 10-3. Color change in phenolphthalein: Indicators are weak acids that have different colors depending on the presence or absence of hydrogen. In the diagram above, HIn represents the indicator phenolphthalein.

Acid-Base Indicators

An **indicator** is a substance that changes its color when it gains or loses a proton. Phenolphthalein is a common indicator that is colorless when it is protonated, that is, when it contains a hydrogen atom. When a base is gradually added to an acid containing phenolphthalein, the solution is initially colorless. Once the acid has been neutralized by the addition of the base, the base then reacts with the hydrogen atom of the indicator. As the phenolphthalein loses its hydrogen (proton), it turns pink. This color change is why phenolphthalein is an indicator; the color change in the phenolphthalein shows (indicates) when a titration has reached an end point.

Other indicators react in a similar way to phenolphthalein, but each has a unique color change that occurs over a specific pH range. Common Acid-Base Indicators in the *Reference Tables for Physical Setting/Chemistry* lists several common indicators, the color changes they undergo, and the pH range over which the color change occurs.

Another example of an indicator is methyl orange. An acid solution with a pH of 2.0 containing methyl orange is red in color. As a base is added to the acid solution, the pH slowly increases. Between pH 3.2 and 4.4, the solution contains both the red and the yellow forms of the indicator, resulting in an orange color. When a pH of 4.4 is achieved, there is no longer an appreciable number of red molecules present, and the solution appears yellow. This same process occurs in other indicators as well. That is, indicators tend to have a distinct color at each end of their useful pH range and pass through an intermediate color region that is a mixture of these two colors.

61. Which pH value indicates the most basic solution?

(1) 7   (2) 8   (3) 3   (4) 11

62. Which pH value represents a solution with the lowest OH^- ion concentration?

(1) 1   (2) 7   (3) 10   (4) 14

63. When tested, a solution turns red litmus to blue. This indicates that the solution contains more

(1) H^+ ions than OH^- ions
(2) H_3O^+ ions than OH^- ions
(3) OH^- ions than H_3O^+ ions
(4) H^+ and OH^- ions than H_2O molecules

64. Pure water at 25°C has a pH of

(1) 1   (2) 5   (3) 7   (4) 14

65. The acidity or alkalinity of an unknown aqueous solution is indicated by its

(1) electronegativity value
(2) percent by mass
(3) pH value
(4) percent by volume

66. The pH of a 0.1 M CH_3COOH solution is

(1) less than 1
(2) greater than 1, but less than 7
(3) equal to 7
(4) greater than 7 but less than 14

67. What is the color of the indicator thymol blue in a solution with a pH of 11?

(1) blue
(2) red
(3) pink
(4) yellow

68. As a strong acid is added to a beaker containing NaOH, the number of OH^- ions in the beaker

(1) decreases and the number of Na^+ ions decreases
(2) decreases and the number of Na^+ ions remains the same
(3) increases and the number of Na^+ ions decreases
(4) increases and the number of Na^+ ions remains the same

69. A water solution is tested with phenolphthalein and reveals a pink color. Which is a possible pH of this solution?

(1) 1   (2) 4   (3) 7   (4) 10

70. When the pH of an aqueous solution is changed from 1 to 2, the concentration of hydronium ions in the solution is?

(1) decreased by a factor of 2
(2) decreased by a factor of 10
(3) increased by a factor of 2
(4) increased by a factor of 10

Answer questions 71–72 using complete sentences.

71. A blue solution containing an acid-base indicator was tested with a pH meter and found to have a pH of 5.5. Which of the indicators on Common Acid-Base Indicators in the *Reference Tables for Physical Setting/Chemistry* could be this indicator?

72. A solution was yellow in bromthymol blue and blue in bromcresol green. According to Common Acid-Base Indicators in the *Reference Tables for Physical Setting/Chemistry*, what could be the pH of the solution?

Brønsted-Lowry Acids and Bases

There are other acid-base definitions that expand upon the Arrhenius definition of acids and bases. One of these, the Brønsted-Lowry theory, defines an acid as any substance that donates a hydrogen ion (H^+). As you know, a hydrogen ion is a hydrogen atom without an electron, that is, it is simply a proton. Thus, a Brønsted-Lowry acid is defined as a proton donor. All Arrhenius acids are also Brønsted-Lowry acids. Brønsted-Lowry theory expands upon the Arrhenius concept by including proton donors that are not in aqueous solution.

The Brønsted-Lowry theory defines a base as any substance that accepts a proton (H^+). Like the Arrhenius definition, the Brønsted-Lowry definition treats the hydroxide ion (OH^-) as a base. Compared with the Arrhenius definition, however, the Brønsted-Lowry definition greatly expands the number of substances that are considered bases.

Conjugate Acid-Base Pairs When an acid loses a proton, the remaining portion of the acid has an unshared pair of electrons that can act as a base. Consider the following reaction.

$$HNO_3 + H_2O \rightarrow H_3O^+ + NO_3^-$$

The HNO_3 acts as an acid, donating its proton to the water (which acts as a base) producing the hydronium and nitrate ions. If the reaction is reversed, the hydronium ion acts as an acid, donating its proton to the nitrate ion (which acts as a base) to produce nitric acid and water. Note that HNO_3 and NO_3^- differ only by a hydrogen ion (H^+). A pair of chemical formulas that differ only by the presence of a hydrogen ion are known as a <u>conjugate acid-base pair</u>. HNO_3 cannot donate a proton unless there is a proton acceptor (base) available to accept that proton. In this reaction, water serves the role of a base. As you can see, H_2O and H_3O^+ differ only by a hydrogen ion as well. The water and hydronium ion are also a conjugate acid-base pair in this reaction.

The reaction between HNO_3 and water illustrates the reaction between a Brønsted acid and a Brønsted base.

```
|———————— Conjugate pair ————————|
        |- Conjugate pair -|
   HNO₃   +   H₂O    →    H₃O⁺   +   NO₃⁻
   acid       base        acid       base
```

Review Questions Set 10.5

73. According to one acid-base theory, a base is an

(1) H^+ acceptor (3) Na^+ acceptor
(2) H^+ donor (4) Na^+ donor

74. Given the balanced equation representing a reaction:

$HSO_4^-(aq) + H_2O(l) \rightarrow H_3O^+(aq) + SO_4^{2-}(aq)$

According to one acid-base theory, the $H_2O(l)$ molecules act as

(1) a base because they accept H^+ ions
(2) a base because they donate H^+ ions
(3) an acid because they accept H^+ ions
(4) an acid because they donate H^+ ions

75. Given the balanced equation representing a reaction:

$H_2PO_4^-(aq) + H_2O(l) \rightarrow H_3PO_4(aq) + OH^-(aq)$

According to one acid-base theory, the $H_2O(l)$ molecules act as

(1) a base because it accepts an H^+
(2) a base because it donates an H^+
(3) an acid because it accepts an H^+
(4) an acid because it donates an H^+

76. According to one acid-base theory, a water molecule acts as a base when it accepts

(1) an OH^-
(2) a neutron
(3) an H^+ ion
(4) an electron

Directions

Review the Test–Taking Strategies section of this book. Then answer the following questions. Read each question carefully and answer with a correct choice or response.

Part A

1 According to the Arrhenius theory, the only negative ions in an aqueous solution of a base are
   (1) OH^- ions
   (2) HS^- ions
   (3) H^- ions
   (4) HCO_3^- ions

2 Which statement best describes the solution produced when an Arrhenius acid is dissolved in water?
   (1) The only negative ion in solution is OH^-.
   (2) The only negative ion in solution is HCO_3^-.
   (3) The only positive ion in solution is H^+.
   (4) The only positive ion in solution is NH_4^+.

3 Which substance can act as an Arrhenius acid in aqueous solution?
   (1) NaI
   (2) HI
   (3) LiH
   (4) NH_3

4 Unlike an acid, an aqueous solution of a base
   (1) causes some indicators to change color
   (2) conducts electricity
   (3) contains more H^+ than OH^-
   (4) contains more OH^- than H^+

5 According to one acid-base theory, a water molecule acts as an acid when the molecule
   (1) accepts an H^+ ion
   (2) donates an H^+ ion
   (3) accepts an OH^- ion
   (4) donates an OH^- ion

6 Which compounds yield hydrogen ions as the only positive ions in an aqueous solution?
   (1) NH_3 and $HC_2H_3O_2$
   (2) H_2CO_3 and $NaHCO_3$
   (3) H_2CO_3 and $HC_2H_3O_2$
   (4) NH_3 and $NaHCO_3$

7 What are the relative ion concentrations in an acid solution?
   (1) more H^+ ions than OH^- ions
   (2) fewer H^+ ions than OH^- ions
   (3) an equal number of H^+ ions and OH^- ions
   (4) H^+ ions, but no OH^- ions

8 What color is phenolphthalein in a basic solution?
   (1) blue   (2) pink   (3) yellow   (4) colorless

9 Given the balanced equation representing a reaction:

   $$H_2O(\ell) + HCl(g) \rightarrow H_3O^+(aq) + Cl^-(aq)$$

   According to one acid-base theory, the $H_2O(\ell)$ molecules
   (1) accept H^+ ions
   (2) accept OH^- ions
   (3) donate H^+ ions
   (4) donate OH^- ions

10 According to one acid-base theory, an acid is an
   (1) OH^- acceptor.
   (2) OH^- donor.
   (3) H^+ acceptor.
   (4) H^+ donor.

11 Pure water has a pH of
   (1) 1   (2) 7   (3) 10   (4) 4

Part B–1

12 Which substance is classified as a salt?
   (1) $Ca(OH)_2$
   (2) C_2H_4OH
   (3) CCl_4
   (4) $CaCl_2$

13 Consider this neutralization reaction.
   $$H_2SO_4 + 2KOH \rightarrow K_2SO_4 + 2HOH$$

   Which compound is the salt produced in this reaction?
   (1) KOH
   (2) H_2SO4
   (3) K_2SO_4
   (4) HOH

14 An aqueous solution turns litmus red. The pH of the solution could be
(1) 14
(2) 11
(3) 8
(4) 4

15 If equal volumes of 0.1 M NaOH and 0.1 M HCl are mixed, the resulting solution will contain a salt and
(1) HCl
(2) NaOH
(3) H_2O
(4) NaCl

16 If equal volumes of 0.1 M NaOH and 0.1 M H_2SO_4 are mixed, the resulting solution will contain water,
(1) H_2SO_4 and Na_2SO_4
(2) H_2SO_4 and NaOH
(3) NaOH and Na_2SO_4
(4) and Na_2SO_4

17 A sample of a solution with a pH of 10 is tested separately with litmus and phenolphthalein. The colors of the indicators are as follows:
(1) litmus is blue; phenolphthalein is pink
(2) litmus is red; phenolphthalein is pink
(3) litmus is blue; phenolphthalein is colorless
(4) litmus is red; phenolphthalein is colorless

18 A student observes that an unknown solution conducts electricity and turns blue litmus red. The student should be able to conclude that the unknown solution is most likely
(1) an acid
(2) a base
(3) an ester
(4) an alcohol

19 An aqueous solution of an ionic compound turns red litmus blue, conducts electricity, and reacts with an acid to form a salt and water. This compound could be
(1) HCl
(2) NaI
(3) KNO_3
(4) LiOH

20 What will be the concentration of 150. mL of a 2.4 M NaOH solution if it is diluted to form 200. mL of solution?
(1) 1.6 M
(2) 1.8 M
(3) 2.0 M
(4) 3.2 M

21 Both HNO_3 and CH_3COOH can be classified as
(1) Arrhenius acids that turn blue litmus red
(2) Arrhenius bases that turn blue litmus red
(3) Arrhenius acids that turn red litmus blue
(4) Arrhenius bases that turn red litmus blue

22 When the pH value of a solution is changed from 2 to 1, the concentration of the hydronium ions
(1) decreases by a factor of 2.
(2) increases by a factor of 2.
(3) increases by a factor of 10.
(4) decreases by a factor of 10.

23 Given the equation representing a reversible reaction:

$$NH_3(g) + H_2O(\ell) \rightleftarrows NH_4^+(aq) + OH^-(aq)$$

According to one acid-base theory, the reactant that donates an H^+ ion in the forward reaction is
(1) $H_2O(\ell)$
(2) $NH_3(g)$
(3) $NH_4^+(aq)$
(4) $OH^-(aq)$

24 Which volume of 2.0 M NaOH(aq) is needed to completely neutralize 24 milliliters of 1.0 M HCl(aq)?
(1) 6.0 mL
(2) 12 mL
(3) 24 mL
(4) 48 mL

25 Sulfuric acid, $H_2SO_4(aq)$ can be used to neutralize barium hydroxide, $Ba(OH)_2(aq)$. What is the formula of the salt produced by this neutralization?
(1) BaS
(2) $BaSO_2$
(3) $BaSO_3$
(4) $BaSO_4$

Parts B–2 and C

Use the following information to answer questions 26 through 30.

 (A)
 (B)
 (C)
 (D)

(A) KCl
(B) CH_3OH
(C) $Ba(OH)_2$
(D) CH_3COOH

Four flasks each contain 100 milliliters of aqueous solutions of equal concentrations at 25°C and 1 atm.

26 Which solutions contain electrolytes?

27 Which solution has the lowest pH?

28 Which solution has a solute that is classified as a salt?

29 Which solution is most likely to react with an acid to form salt and water?

30 Which solution has the lowest freezing point?

Base your answers to questions 31 through 33 on the information below.

Some carbonated beverages are made by forcing carbon dioxide gas into a beverage solution. When a bottle of one kind of carbonated beverage is first opened, the beverage has a pH value of 3.

31 State, in terms of the pH scale, why this beverage is classified as acidic.

32 Using Table M, identify *one* indicator that is yellow in a solution that has the same pH value as this beverage.

33 After the beverage bottle is left open for several hours, the hydronium ion concentration in the beverage solution decreases to 1/1000 of the original concentration. Determine the new pH of the beverage solution.

Use the following information to answer questions 34 and 35.

A student titrates 60.0 mL of $HNO_3(aq)$ with 0.30 M NaOH. Phenolphthalein is used as the indicator. After adding 42.2 mL of $NaOH(aq)$ a color change remains for 25 seconds, and the student stops the titration.

34 What color change does the phenolphthalein undergo during this titration?

35 What is the molarity of the HNO_3?

Base your answers to questions 36 and 37 on the information below.

In a titration experiment, a student use a 1.4 M $HBr(aq)$ solution and the indicator phenolphthalein to determine the concentration of a $KOH(aq)$ solution. The data for trial 1 is recorded in the table below.

Trial 1 Data		
Buret readings	HBr(aq)	KOH(aq)
Initial volume (mL)	7.50	11.00
Final volume (mL)	22.90	33.10
Volume used (mL)	15.40	22.10

36 Calculate the molarity of the KOH.

37 Why is it better to use several trials of a titration rather than one trial to determine the concentration of a solution of unknown concentration?

Use the information below to answer questions 38 and 39.

Using burets, a student titrated a sodium hydroxide solution of unknown concentration with a standard solution of 0.10 M hydrochloric acid. The data are recorded in the table below.

Titration Data		
Solution	HCl(aq)	NaOH(aq)
Initial buret reading (mL)	15.50	5.00
Final buret reading (mL)	25.00	8.80

38 Determine both the total volume of $HCl(aq)$ and the total volume of $NaOH(aq)$.

39 What is the molarity of the NaOH solution?

Base your answers to questions 40–42 on the following information.

Two samples of the same rainwater are tested using two indicators at an environmental lab. The first indicator, Methyl Orange, reveals a distinct yellow color when added to the sample. The second indicator, Litmus, turns red when placed in contact with the water sample.

40 Identify a possible pH value for the rainwater.

41 Explain, in terms of hydronium ions and hydroxide ion concentrations, the pH value of the rainwater.

42 If the rainwater were tested with Bromthymol Blue, what color would be observed?

Base your answers to questions 43 through 45 on the following information.

In a titration, a few drops of an indicator are added to a flask containing 35.0 milliliters of $HNO_3(aq)$ of unknown concentration. After 30.0 milliliters of 0.15 M $NaOH(aq)$ solution is slowly added to the flask, the indicator changes color, showing the acid is neutralized.

43 The volume of the $NaOH(aq)$ solution is expressed to what number of significant figures?

44 Complete the equation for this neutralization reaction by writing the formula of *each* product in the spaces below.

$$HNO_3(aq) + NaOH(aq) \rightarrow \underline{\hspace{1cm}} + \underline{\hspace{1cm}}$$

45 Show a correct numerical setup for calculating the concentration of the $HNO_3(aq)$ solution.

Base your answers to questions 46 through 49 on the information below.

In one trial of an investigation, 50.0 milliliters of $HCl(aq)$ of an unknown concentration is titrated with 0.10 M $NaOH(aq)$. During the titration, the total volume of $NaOH(aq)$ added and the corresponding pH value of the reaction mixture are measured and recorded in the table below.

Titration Data	
Total Volume of NaOH(*aq*) Added (mL)	pH Value of Reaction Mixture
10.0	1.6
20.0	2.2
24.0	2.9
24.9	3.9
25.1	10.1
26.0	11.1
30.0	11.8

46 On the grid below, plot the data from the table. Circle and connect the points.

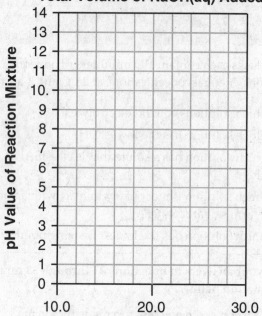

pH Value of Reaction Mixture Versus Total Volume of NaOH(aq) Added

Total Volume of NaOH(aq) Added (mL)

47 Determine the total volume of $NaOH(aq)$ added when the reaction mixture has a pH value of 7.0.

48 Write a balanced equation that represents this neutralization reaction.

49 In another trial, 40.0 milliliters of $HCl(aq)$ is completely neutralized by 20.0 milliliters of this 0.10 M $NaOH(aq)$. Calculate the molarity of the titrated acid in this trial.

Organic Chemistry

What You Know About Organic Chemistry

?

What does organic mean?

?

Although your grocery store might have a special "organic section" with specially grown foods, chances are more than just the food is organic! To chemists, *organic* refers to substances containing the element carbon. So in this picture the plastic racks, rubber hose, polyester shirt, and even the man are organic as well! Look around your classroom to see how many organic substances you can identify.

PRODUCE

11 Organic Chemistry

Vocabulary

addition reaction	esterification	organic acid
alcohol	ester	organic halide
aldehyde	ether	polymer
alkane	fermentation	polymerization
alkene	functional group	saponification
alkyne	hydrocarbon	saturated
amide	isomer	substitution reaction
amine	ketone	unsaturated
amino acid		

Topic Overview

Organic chemistry is the study of carbon and most carbon compounds. The name *organic* is a remnant of a time when it was thought that carbon compounds could only be made by living things; hence the term *organic*. Today it is widely recognized that organic chemistry contains far more compounds than only those made by living things. The number of organic compounds is enormous. Tens of thousands of new organic compounds are discovered every year, and there seems to be no end in sight to future discoveries.

The number of carbon compounds far exceeds the number of inorganic compounds. Why can carbon form so many compounds? The answer lies in the ability of carbon atoms to bond with other carbon atoms to form chains, rings, and networks. In this topic you will be introduced to the wide variety of organic compounds and the types of reactions that they undergo.

Bonding of Carbon Atoms

The ability of carbon to form many different compounds is based, to a large extent, on the tendency of carbon atoms to covalently bond with other carbon atoms and form chains. This process can be continued indefinitely, leading to chains of thousands of carbon atoms. Figure 11-1 shows electron dot diagrams of the ground state and the bonded state of a carbon atom and a three-dimensional representation of a tetrahedron with a carbon atom at its center. Note that when carbon bonds, the formerly paired electrons occupy separate orbitals, enabling carbon atoms to form four covalent bonds.

Study the diagram of carbon in Figure 11-1. Note that when carbon is in the bonded state it has four potential sites for covalent bonds. Although the

Memory Jogger

Substances that are covalently bonded form molecules. They generally have low melting and boiling points, and are poor conductors of heat and electricity. They are generally nonpolar and tend to dissolve in nonpolar solvents. Covalently bonded substances tend to react more slowly than ionic compounds.

angle between adjacent electrons appears to be 90°, the atom is actually three dimensional, and the electrons are located at the corners of a tetrahedron with an angle of 109.5° between each pair of electrons.

Figure 11-2 shows carbon atoms sharing electrons to form a chain. In such diagrams, a single line is often used to represent the pair of shared electrons (C–C). When one pair of electrons is shared between two carbon atoms, the bond is called a <u>single covalent bond</u> (Figure 11-2A). Organic compounds containing only single bonds are said to be **saturated.**

Sometimes carbon atoms can share two pairs of electrons, forming a <u>double covalent bond</u> (Figure 11-2B) or even three pairs of electrons in a <u>triple covalent bond</u> (Figure 11-2C). Compounds containing one or more double or triple covalent bonds are called **unsaturated** compounds. In Figure 11-2, double and triple covalent bonds are represented by double and triple lines, respectively.

The chains of carbon atoms can be open or closed. Figure 11-3 shows six carbon atoms in both an open chain and a closed chain.

Carbon atoms can also bond with other carbon atoms forming three-dimensional networks. Diamonds are made of networks of carbon atoms in which each carbon atom is bonded to four other carbon atoms in a characteristic network structure. As recent discoveries have shown, carbon atoms can be arranged in large networks in which each carbon atom is bonded with a single bond to two other carbon atoms and with a double bond to one other carbon atom. The most common of these forms is buckminsterfullerene, also called a buckyball, which contains 60 carbon atoms forming a pattern similar to that on a soccer ball. The carbon atoms form a framework, and the inside of the network is empty space.

Structural Formulas The molecular formula shows the kind and number of atoms in a compound. For example, the molecular formula C_3H_8 tells the reader that the compound contains three carbon atoms and eight hydrogen atoms. Structural formulas attempt to show not only the kinds and numbers of atoms but also the bonding patterns and approximate shapes of molecules. Figure 11-4 shows the molecular formulas and structural formulas for two organic compounds. It is important to remember that these structural formulas are two-dimensional representations of three-dimensional molecules. Each carbon atom can be pictured as the center of a tetrahedron, and a short line can represent each of its covalent bonds.

Hydrocarbons

Although there exists an extremely large number of organic compounds, the study of these compounds is simplified because they can be classified into groups called homologous series, the members of which have related

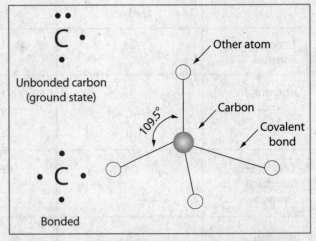

Figure 11-1. Lewis diagrams of carbon and bonded carbon: Carbon forms four equivalent covalent bonds. The tetrahedral molecular shape allows for equal spacing between these bonds.

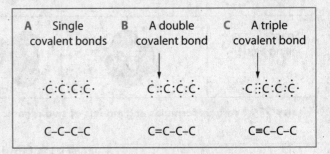

Figure 11-2. Carbon atoms share electrons in covalent bonds to form chains

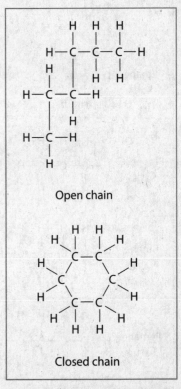

Figure 11-3: Open and closed carbon chains

	Methane	Ethane
Molecular Formula	CH_4	C_2H_6
Structural Formula	H | H–C–H | H	H H | | H–C–C–H | | H H
Condensed Structural Formula	CH_4	CH_3CH_3
Ball-and-Stick Model		
Space-Filling Model		

Figure 11-4. Various formulas and models of two organic compounds

structures and properties. A homologous series of compounds is a group of related compounds in which each member differs from the one before it by the same additional unit.

Hydrocarbons are organic compounds that contain only atoms of hydrogen and carbon. These compounds are the parent compounds from which many other organic compounds are derived. Alkanes, alkenes, and alkynes are three important homologous series of hydrocarbons. By studying these series you will more easily understand other organic series closely related to them.

Alkanes

The **alkanes** are a homologous series of saturated hydrocarbons that release energy when burned. Methane (CH_4), the first member of the series, comprises about 90% of natural gas, which is used to heat many homes. The second member, ethane (C_2H_6), accounts for most of the rest of natural gas. Propane (C_3H_8) is familiar as a home heating fuel and is also used for outdoor grills and camping equipment. The fourth alkane, butane (C_4H_{10}), is found in disposable lighters.

As the number of carbons increases in the alkane series, the boiling point increases. Chains of five to 12 carbon atoms are found in gasoline. Home heating oils contain 10 to 16 carbon atoms in chains. Paraffin wax, common in candles, contains 20 or more carbon atoms per chain, while road tar (asphalt) may contain 40 carbons in a chain. The names and molecular and structural formulas of the first five members of this series are found in Figure 11-5.

Study the formulas for the members of the alkane series shown in Figure 11-5. Notice that there is a constant relationship between each succeeding member. Ethane has one more carbon atom and two more hydrogen atoms than the preceding member, methane. The same relationship exists between propane and ethane, and butane and propane. This relationship, in which each successive member differs by one carbon atom and two hydrogen atoms (CH_2), from the previous member, defines the nature of a homologous series.

Alkenes

The same relationship between successive members can be found in the homologous series of alkenes. Each member of the **alkene** series contains one double covalent bond.

Because there must be at least two carbon atoms to form a double bond, there is no alkene corresponding to methane of the alkane

Methane CH_4

Ethane C_2H_6

Propane C_3H_8

Butane C_4H_{10}

Pentane C_5H_{12}

Figure 11-5. The first five members of the alkane family

series. Ethene, the first member of the alkene series, has the formula C_2H_4. The addition of CH_2 to ethene produces propene (C_3H_6), the second member of the series. Note that the names of the members of the alkene series are derived from the names of the alkane chains with the same number of carbon atoms. The alkenes are named from the corresponding alkane by replacing the *-ane* of the alkane name to *-ene*. For example, the four carbon chain of the alkane series is butane, while butene is the four carbon chain of the alkene series. The first two alkenes are shown in Figure 11-6.

Alkenes provide chemists with starting materials to make other organic compounds. Probably the most important of these is ethene, whose common name is ethylene. When ethylene units are attached to each other to make very long chains, the product is polyethylene, a common plastic.

Alkynes

The **alkynes** are a homologous series of unsaturated hydrocarbons that contain one triple bond. The naming of the alkyne series repeats the pattern observed in the alkenes. To find the alkyne name, use the corresponding name from the alkane series, and change the *-ane* ending to *-yne*. Thus the first member of the series is ethyne (C_2H_2), as shown in Figure 11-6.

The alkynes, like the alkenes, provide chemists with starting materials to make other organic compounds. The first member of the series, ethyne, is commonly known as acetylene, used as a fuel in welding torches.

General Formulas

In every homologous series there is a definite relationship between the number of carbon and hydrogen atoms. Note that in the alkene series, there are always twice as many hydrogen atoms as carbon atoms. Hence it is possible to show this by writing C_nH_{2n}, the general formula of alkenes. If it is known that a certain alkene contains 10 carbon atoms, then it will contain 20 hydrogen atoms.

Each corresponding member of the alkane series has two more hydrogen atoms than found in the alkenes. C_4H_8 is the formula of butene, but C_4H_{10} is the formula of butane. The general formula of the alkanes shows this change by adding two hydrogen atoms to the general formula, C_nH_{2n+2}. Ethyne (C_2H_2) has two fewer hydrogens than are present in ethene (C_2H_4). In a similar way, all alkynes have two fewer hydrogen atoms than the corresponding alkenes. This is shown in the general formula of the alkynes, C_nH_{2n-2}. These relationships are summarized in Table Q of the *Reference Tables for Physical Setting/Chemistry.*

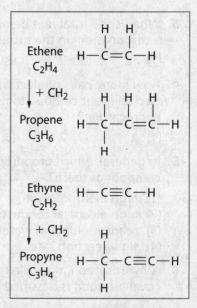

Figure 11-6. Some members of the alkene and alkyne families

Review Questions

Set 11.1

1. Which element is present in all organic compounds?

  (1) nitrogen   (3) carbon

  (2) oxygen   (4) sulfur

2. Hydrocarbons are composed of the elements

  (1) carbon, nitrogen, and oxygen

  (2) carbon, hydrogen, and oxygen

  (3) carbon and hydrogen, only

  (4) carbon and oxygen, only

3. What is the total number of valence electrons in a carbon atom in the ground state?

(1) 12   (2) 2   (3) 6   (4) 4

4. How many pairs of electrons are shared between two adjacent carbon atoms in a saturated hydrocarbon?

(1) 1   (2) 2   (3) 3   (4) 4

5. In general, which property do organic compounds share?

(1) high melting point
(2) high electrical conductivity
(3) readily soluble in water
(4) slow reaction rate

6. A hydrocarbon molecule containing one triple covalent bond is classified as an

(1) alkene   (3) alkyne
(2) alkane   (4) alkadiene

7. What is the total number of hydrogen atoms in a molecule of butene?

(1) 10   (2) 6   (3) 8   (4) 4

8. By how many carbon atoms does each member of a homologous series differ from the previous member?

(1) 1   (2) 2   (3) 3   (4) 4

9. Which formula represents an unsaturated hydrocarbon?

(1) C_5H_{12} (3) C_3H_8
(2) C_4H_{10} (4) C_2H_4

10. What is the total number of pairs of electrons shared between the two adjacent carbon atoms in an ethyne molecule?

(1) 1   (2) 2   (3) 3   (4) 4

11. Which compound is a member of the same homologous series as C_3H_6?

(1) C_2H_4 (3) C_3H_4
(2) C_2H_6 (4) C_3H_8

12. Which hydrocarbon is a member of the series with the general formula C_nH_{2n-2}?

(1) ethyne   (3) butane
(2) ethene   (4) benzene

13. Which compound belongs to the alkene series?

(1) C_2H_2 (3) C_6H_6
(2) C_2H_4 (4) C_6H_{14}

14. What is the number of electrons shared between the carbon atoms in a molecule of propyne?

(1) 6   (3) 8
(2) 2   (4) 4

15. Which type of bonds and solids are characteristic of organic compounds?

(1) ionic bonds and ionic solids
(2) ionic bonds and molecular solids
(3) covalent bonds and ionic solids
(4) covalent bonds and molecular solids

16. Which of the following organic compounds is a member of the alkene homologous series?

(1) C_4H_8 (3) C_5H_{12}
(2) C_4H_6 (4) C_5H_8

17. In which group could the hydrocarbons all belong to the same homologous series?

(1) C_2H_2, C_2H_4, C_2H_6 (3) C_2H_4, C_2H_6, C_3H_6
(2) C_2H_4, C_3H_4, C_4H_8 (4) C_2H_4, C_3H_6, C_4H_8

18. Which formula represents butane?

(1) CH_3CH_3 (3) $CH_3CH_2CH_2CH_3$
(2) $CH_3CH_2CH_3$ (4) $CH_3CH_2CH_2CH_2CH_3$

Isomers

Each of the alkanes listed on Figure 11-5 is composed of a continuous chain of carbon atoms. However, beginning with butane there is more than one way of combining the carbon and hydrogen atoms. In Figure 11-7, structural formulas show two different ways in which four carbon atoms and 10 hydrogen atoms can be combined. Not only can the carbon atoms be attached to each other in a continuous chain of four atoms, but they can also be arranged in a chain of three carbon atoms, with the fourth attached to the middle carbon. When a molecular formula can be represented by more than one structural arrangement, the compounds are called **isomers**. Isomers, while having the same molecular formula, have different chemical and physical properties. The boiling point of *n*-butane is 0.5°C, while its isomer boils at −10°C.

As the number of carbon atoms increases, so does the number of possible isomers. While butane has two isomers, octane (C_8H_{18}) has 18, and decane ($C_{10}H_{22}$) has 75. It is this ability to form isomers that is largely responsible for the large number of organic compounds.

Naming Organic Compounds

When carbon atoms are attached to each other in one continuous chain, the compounds are called straight-chain hydrocarbons. This arrangement is called the normal form, and the letter *n-* precedes the name (*n*-butane). Compounds with branched chains must be given names that are different from the straight-chain name because they have different chemical and physical properties. The rules for naming organic compounds are governed by the International Union of Pure and Applied Chemistry (IUPAC). The following rules will produce names of branched compounds that are approved by the IUPAC.

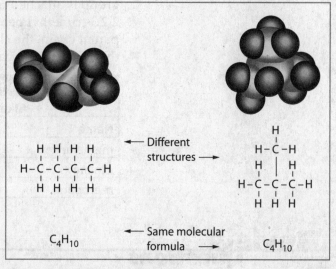

Figure 11-7. **Isomers of butane**

1. Each compound is named by finding the longest continuous chain of carbon atoms. In the structure on the top in Figure 11-8, the longest chain consists of three carbon atoms, and, hence the compound is named as a derivative of propane, the third alkane. In the second example, the longest continuous chain consists of six carbon atoms, and the compound will be named as a hexane. Note that the chain does not have to appear as a straight chain, but it must be continuous.

2. While the name for the longest chain in the first example is propane, there is a CH_3 group attached to the chain. How should it be named? A group that contains one less hydrogen atom than an alkane with the same number of carbon atoms is classified as one of the <u>alkyl groups,</u> with a group name derived from the name of its corresponding alkane. Thus, the CH_3 that is attached to the propane belongs to the methyl group, so called because, like methane, it has one carbon atom. Table 11-1 shows the relationship between the alkanes and the common alkyl groups. The compound in the first example is called methyl propane. There is no need to identify the location of the methyl group because it can only be attached to the central carbon.

3. If necessary, the location of the alkyl group is shown by assigning numbers to the carbon atoms in the longest chain. The carbon chain must be numbered from the end that will give the lowest number for the attached group. In the second example, the compound should be named 2-methyl hexane rather than 5-methyl hexane.

4. There may be more than one of the same type of group attached to the parent chain. A prefix is used to indicate the number of attached groups of each type that are present. If two methyl groups are attached, the prefix *di-* will be used. *Tri-* will indicate three, and *tetra-*, four. In addition, commas are used to indicate the specific carbon to which each group is attached. For example, if two methyl groups are attached to the second carbon atom in a five-carbon chain, and another methyl

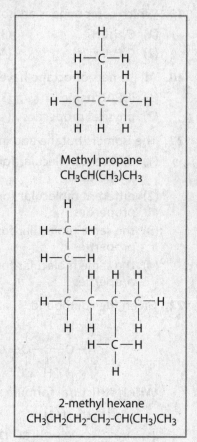

Methyl propane
$CH_3CH(CH_3)CH_3$

2-methyl hexane
$CH_3CH_2CH_2-CH_2-CH(CH_3)CH_3$

Figure 11-8. **Naming organic compounds**

group is attached to the third carbon atom, the compound would be 2,2,3-trimethyl pentane. When more than one group is attached to the parent chain, the chain must be numbered in such a way to produce the smaller total value of the attached chains.

Table 11-1. Relationship of Alkanes and Alkyl Groups

Alkane		Alkyl Group	
Name	Formula	Name	Formula
methane	CH_4	methyl	CH_3
ethane	C_2H_6	ethyl	C_2H_5
n-propane	C_3H_8	n-propyl	C_3H_7

Review Questions

Set 11.2

19. Which compound is an isomer of C_4H_9OH?

(1) $C_3H_7CH_3$

(2) $C_2H_5OC_2H_5$

(3) $C_2H_5COOC_2H_5$

(4) CH_3COOH

20. All isomers of octane have the same

(1) IUPAC name

(2) physical properties

(3) molecular formula

(4) structural formula

21. The isomers butane and methylpropane have

(1) different molecular formulas and the same properties

(2) different molecular formulas and different properties

(3) the same molecular formula and the same properties

(4) the same molecular formula and different properties

22. Given the compound:

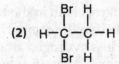

Which structural formula represents an isomer?

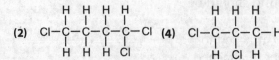

23. Which compounds are isomers?

(1) CH_3Br and CH_2Br_2

(2) CH_3OH and CH_3CH_2OH

(3) CH_3OH and CH_3CHO

(4) CH_3OCH_3 and CH_3CH_2OH

24. An –ol suffix indicates that an –OH group has been added to a hydrocarbon. Which formula represents 1,2-ethanediol?

(1) $C_2H_4(OH)_2$

(2) $C_3H_5(OH)_3$

(3) $Ca(OH)_2$

(4) $Co(OH)_3$

25. Which structural formula represents 1,1-dibromopropane?

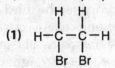
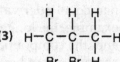

26. Given the formula representing a compound:

What is the most appropriate IUPAC name for this compound?

(1) 2-pentene

(2) 2-pentyne

(3) 3-pentene

(4) 3-pentyne

27. Which compound has the molecular formula C_5H_{12}?

(1) butane

(2) pentane

(3) 2,2-dimethyl butane

(4) 2,2-dimethyl pentane

28. Which is the correct IUPAC name for the hydrocarbon with the structural formula shown below?

```
        H
        |
   H—C—H      H
        |      |
   H—C————C—H
        |      |
        H    H—C—H
               |
             H—C—H
               |
               H
```

(1) 1-methyl-2-ethylenethane
(2) 1-propylethane
(3) *n*-propane
(4) *n*-pentane

29. Write the structural formula for 3-methyl pentane.

30. Write the structural formula for 2, 2-dimethyl hexane.

31. Write the structural formula for 2-methyl, 3-ethyl hexane.

32. Write the structural formula for 2,2,3-trimethyl heptane.

33. Write the structural formula for 3,3-dimethyl, 4-ethyl octane.

Functional Groups

Although hydrocarbons are the most basic organic compounds, many other organic compounds form when other atoms replace one or more hydrogen atoms in a hydrocarbon. These atoms or groups of atoms, called **functional groups,** replace hydrogen atoms in a hydrocarbon and give the compound distinctive physical and chemical properties. The naming of these compounds is made easy because they derive their names from the hydrocarbon with the corresponding number of carbon atoms.

Halides

When any of the halogens (F, Cl, Br, or I) replaces a hydrogen atom in an alkane, the compound is called an **organic halide,** or halocarbon. The functional group of an organic halide is the halogen that is attached to the chain. Organic halides are often used as organic solvents and are found in some pesticides. They are named by citing the location of the halogen attached to the chain. Figure 11-9 shows some examples of halocarbons and shows how the chain is numbered when necessary to show the location of the halogen.

Alcohols

Alcohols are organic compounds in which one or more hydrogen atoms of a hydrocarbon are replaced by an −OH group. The −OH group is called a <u>hydroxyl group</u> and is the functional group that gives alcohols their specific chemical and physical properties. Although the −OH group resembles the hydroxide ion of inorganic bases, it does not form an ion in water. Hence, alcohols are nonelectrolytes and do not turn indicators characteristic acid or basic colors. While these hydroxyl groups do not form ions in solution, they are quite polar. This polarity allows alcohols to be soluble in water, which is also polar.

There are several different types of alcohols. The type is dependent on the number of hydroxyl groups in the compound and on the position of each hydroxyl group on the main carbon chain.

Classification of Alcohols Alcohols are classified as primary, secondary, or tertiary based on whether the hydroxyl group is attached to a primary,

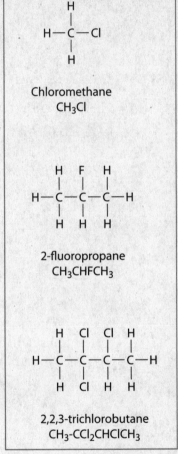

Chloromethane
CH_3Cl

2-fluoropropane
CH_3CHFCH_3

2,2,3-trichlorobutane
$CH_3\text{-}CCl_2CHClCH_3$

Figure 11-9. Some typical organic halides

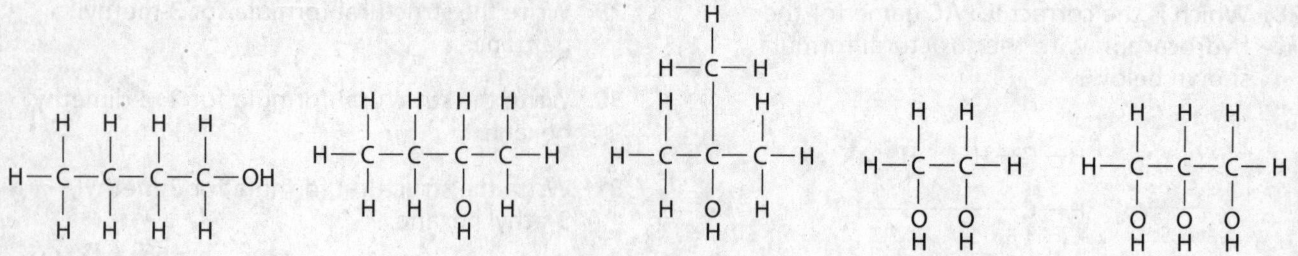

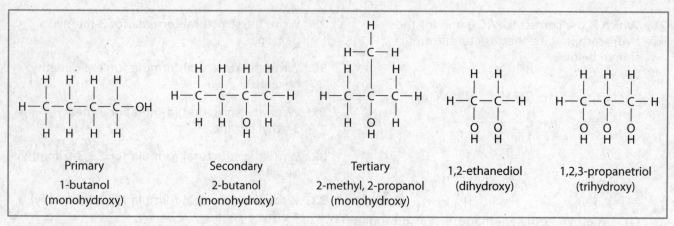

Figure 11-10. Some representative alcohols

secondary, or tertiary carbon atom. Primary carbon atoms are attached directly to only one other carbon atom and are located at the end of a chain or branch. Secondary carbon atoms are directly attached to two other carbon atoms. Tertiary carbon atoms are attached directly to three other carbon atoms.

Alcohols are classified according to the carbon atom to which the hydroxyl group is attached. A primary alcohol has a hydroxyl group attached to a primary carbon atom at the end of the chain. Primary alcohols are represented by *R*–OH or RCH_2OH, where the *R* represents a hydrocarbon chain in which a hydrogen atom is replaced by the functional group shown.

A secondary alcohol has a hydroxyl group attached to a secondary carbon atom. Secondary alcohols can be represented by *R*–CH(OH)–*R'*, where *R* and *R'* represent two hydrocarbon chains.

A tertiary alcohol has a hydroxyl group attached to a tertiary carbon atom. A tertiary alcohol can be represented by $R_1R_2R_3COH$.

Dihydroxy and Trihydroxy Alcohols Alcohols can also be classified by the number of hydroxyl groups that are attached to the carbon chain. In addition to alcohols that have one hydroxyl group (monohydroxy), there are families of alcohols with two or more attached groups. Ethylene glycol, also known as antifreeze, is the common name for a dihydroxy (two hydroxyl groups) alcohol. Its proper name is 1,2-ethanediol. 1,2,3-propanetriol is another common substance, glycerol, which is used as a moistening agent in cosmetics. Figure 11-10 shows examples of the various types of alcohols.

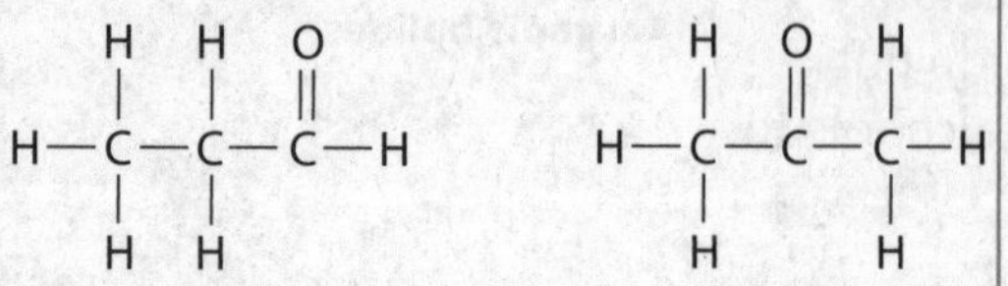

Figure 11-11. An aldehyde and a ketone: Both aldehydes and ketones contain the carbonyl group.

Other Substituted Hydrocarbons

Aldehydes When an oxygen atom is attached to a carbon chain by a double covalent bond, it is called a carbonyl group (–C=O). **Aldehydes** are organic compounds in which the carbonyl group is found on the end carbon (a primary carbon), as shown in Figure 11-11. Aldehydes are named by substituting –*al* in place of the final –*e* of the corresponding alkane name. The first member of the series has the IUPAC name methanal. Its common name is formaldehyde, and it is used as a preservative. An aldehyde can be recognized from

its structural formula by the presence of a double bonded oxygen atom together with a hydrogen atom attached to an end carbon.

Ketones A **ketone** is formed when the carbonyl group (–C=O) is found on an interior carbon atom that is attached to two other carbon atoms, as shown in Figure 11-11. Ketones are named by replacing the final –*e* from the corresponding alkane name with –*one*. The first ketone is formed by a carbonyl group attached to the central carbon atom of a chain of three carbon atoms. Its IUPAC name is propanone. The common name of propanone is acetone. Ketones are often used as solvents. The carbonyl group is quite polar, allowing the ketone to dissolve in water. The remainder of the molecule causes the ketone to be soluble in other organic compounds.

Ethers **Ethers** are a series of organic compounds in which two carbon chains are joined together by an oxygen atom bonded between two carbon atoms. The general formula is written *R*–O–*R'* to show the oxygen bridge between the two carbon chains. Structures and common and IUPAC names for some ethers are shown in Figure 11-12.

Organic Acids **Organic acids** are a homologous series of organic compounds whose functional group is a carboxyl group (–COOH). Organic acids derive their names from the corresponding hydrocarbons by replacing the –*e* with –*oic acid*. Thus the two-carbon hydrocarbon is ethane, while the corresponding acid is ethanoic acid. Ethanoic acid is commonly known as acetic acid, which is found in vinegar. Although most organic compounds are nonelectrolytes, organic acids are generally weak electrolytes.

Esters **Esters** are organic compounds whose type formula is *R*–CO–O*R'*. The *R*–CO–O– part of the formula comes from an organic acid, and the *R'* part of the formula comes from an alcohol. Esters have strong, fragrant aromas and are responsible for the odors of many foods and flavorings, such as pineapples, bananas, wintergreen, and oranges.

Amines Perhaps the easiest way to understand amines is as a derivative of ammonia. An **amine** is formed when one or more of the hydrogen atoms of ammonia are replaced by an alkyl group. To name an amine, the –*e* ending of the alkane name is changed to end in –*amine*, and the alkane chain is numbered to show the location of the amine group. Figure 11-13 shows the relation of amines to ammonia. Amines are important biological chemicals present in the B vitamins, hormones, and anesthetics. They are also used commercially in the preparation of dyes.

Amino Acids Like all organic acids, **amino acids** contain the carboxylic group (–COOH) but also contain an amine group. The amine group is attached to the carbon atom that is adjacent to the acid group (Figure 11-14). The remainder of the molecule is represented by *R*, which indicates the side chain. There are ten essential amino acids that the body must obtain through diet because it cannot synthesize them. The remaining amino acids can be synthesized. Amino acids are the building blocks of protein.

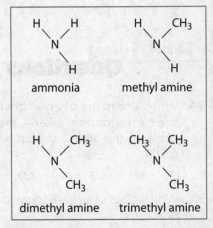

Common name: dimethyl ether
IUPAC name: methoxymethane

Common name: ethylmethyl ether
IUPAC name: methoxyethane

Common name: diethyl ether
IUPAC name: ethoxyethane

Figure 11-12. **Some common ethers**

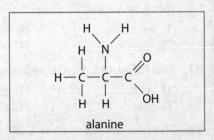

ammonia   methyl amine

dimethyl amine   trimethyl amine

Figure 11-13. **The relation of amines and ammonia**

alanine

Figure 11-14. **An amino acid:** Amino acids have both an acid group and an amine group.

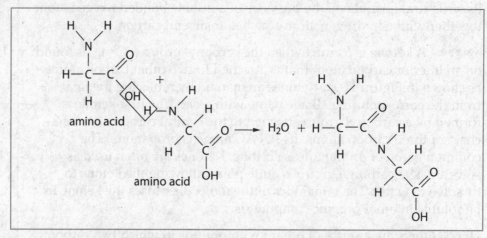

Figure 11-15. Formation of an amide: Two amino acids combine to form an amide (peptide).

Amides When one of the hydrogen atoms of the amino group reacts with the –OH of an organic acid, a condensation reaction occurs. This reaction produces water and an **amide**, which is a compound formed by the combination of the two amino acids. Look at Figure 11-15. Peptide bonding holds amino acid molecules together, forming long protein chains. While organic chemists call this linkage an amide, biologists refer to it as a peptide link. Additional condensation reactions occur, first producing a polypeptide. Eventually the chain is long enough to be a protein.

Review Questions

Set 11.3

34. When the name of an alcohol is derived from the corresponding alkane, the final –e of the name of the alkane should be replaced by the suffix

(1) –al   (2) –ol   (3) –one   (4) –ole

35. Which class of organic compounds contains nitrogen?

(1) ether   (3) alcohol
(2) amine   (4) aldehyde

36. Which class of compounds has the general formula R–O–R'?

(1) esters   (3) ethers
(2) alcohols   (4) aldehydes

37. The formula $C_5H_{11}OH$ represents an

(1) acid   (3) ether
(2) ester   (4) alcohol

38. The general formula R–COOH represents a class of compounds called

(1) alkanes   (3) acids
(2) alkenes   (4) alcohols

39. Which structural formula represents a secondary alcohol?

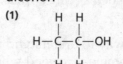

40. Which is the general formula for an aldehyde?

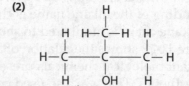
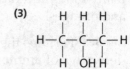

41. Which structural formula represents a tertiary alcohol?

(1)
```
      H   H   H
      |   |   |
  H — C — C — C — OH
      |   |   |
      H   H   H
```

(2)
```
      H   OH  H
      |   |   |
  H — C — C — C — H
      |   |   |
      H   H   H
```

(3)
```
      H   O   H
      |   ||  |
  H — C — C — C — H
      |       |
      H       H
```

(4)
```
      H   OH   H
      |   |    |
  H — C — C —— C — H
      |   |    |
      H  H—C—H H
          |
          H
```

42. Given a formula representing a compound:

```
  O   H   H   H
  ||  |   |   |
H—C — C — C — C — H
      |   |   |
      H   H   H
```

Which formula represents an isomer of this compound?

(1)
```
  H   H   H   O
  |   |   |   ||
H—C — C — C — C — H
  |   |   |
  H   H   H
```

(3)
```
  H   H   H   O
  |   |   |   ||
H—C — C — C — C — OH
  |   |   |
  H   H   H
```

(2)
```
  H   O   H   H
  |   ||  |   |
H—C — C — C — C — H
  |       |   |
  H       H   H
```

(4)
```
  H   H   O       H
  |   |   ||      |
H—C — C — C — O — C — H
  |   |           |
  H   H           H
```

43. Which functional group is found in all organic acids?

(1)
```
   H
   |
 — C — H
   |
   H
```

(3)
```
   H
   |
 — C = O
```

(2)
```
   H
   |
 — C — OH
   |
   H
```

(4)
```
       O
       ||
     — C
        \
         OH
```

44. Given the formula for a compound:

```
   H   H       H
   |   |       |
H— C — C — C — C — H
   |   |   ||  |
   H   H   O   H
```

A proper IUPAC name for this compound is

(1) butanone   (3) butanol
(2) butanoic acid   (4) butanal

45. Which atom is bonded to the carbon atom in the functional group of a ketone?

(1) fluorine   (3) oxygen
(2) hydrogen   (4) nitrogen

46. The molecule $CH_3—C—CH_3$ is a member of a class
```
              ||
              O
```
of organic compounds called

(1) ethers   (3) alcohols
(2) ketones   (4) aldehydes

47. Which is the structural formula for 2-propanol?

(1)
```
      H  H  H
      |  |  |
  H — C — C — C — OH
      |  |  |
      H  H  H
```

(3)
```
      H  H  H  H
      |  |  |  |
  H — C — C — C — C — OH
      |  |  |  |
      H  H  H  H
```

(2)
```
      H  H  H
      |  |  |
  H — C — C — C — H
      |  |  |
      H  OH H
```

(4)
```
      H  H  H  H
      |  |  |  |
  H — C — C — C — C — H
      |  |  |  |
      H  H  OH H
```

48. A hydrocarbon molecule has eight carbon atoms in a straight chain. There is a double bond between the third carbon and the fourth carbon atom in the chain. The IUPAC name for this hydrocarbon is

(1) 4-octene
(2) 3-octene
(3) 3-octyne
(4) 4-octyne

Organic Reactions

Organic reactions generally occur more slowly than inorganic reactions. When covalently bonded substances react, they must first break relatively strong existing bonds before making new bonds.

Combustion

Perhaps the most common type of organic reaction is <u>combustion</u>. Almost all organic compounds will burn. When sufficient oxygen is present, hydrocarbons will burn to produce water and carbon dioxide. Propane, commonly used in outdoor grills, burns according to the following equation.

$$C_3H_8(g) + 5O_2(g) \rightarrow 3CO_2(g) + 4H_2O(g)$$

When the supply of oxygen is limited, carbon monoxide may be produced instead of carbon dioxide.

$$2C_3H_8(g) + 7O_2(g) \rightarrow 6CO(g) + 8H_2O(g)$$

When carbon dioxide is produced the reaction is called complete combustion, while incomplete combustion describes the production of carbon monoxide and water.

Substitution

A **substitution reaction** involves the replacement of one or more of the hydrogen atoms in a saturated hydrocarbon with another atom or group. For example, halogen atoms can replace hydrogen atoms in saturated hydrocarbons. When ethane reacts with chlorine in a substitution reaction, the products of the reaction are chloroethane and hydrogen chloride.

$$C_2H_6 + Cl_2 \rightarrow C_2H_5Cl + HCl$$

Because all of the bonding sites on a saturated hydrocarbon are filled, chlorine must first remove a hydrogen atom from the hydrocarbon chain, forming hydrogen chloride. The removal of a hydrogen atom from the chain provides an open bond site where a chlorine atom can then attach itself.

Addition

Addition reactions involve adding one or more atoms at a double or triple bond. When ethene and chlorine react, the double bond of the ethene is opened and a chlorine atom is added to each carbon atom.

$$C_2H_4 + Cl_2 \rightarrow C_2H_4Cl_2$$

Unsaturated hydrocarbons can also react with hydrogen by addition reactions. In this case, the final product is a saturated hydrocarbon.

$$C_2H_4 + H_2 \rightarrow C_2H_6$$

Esterification

Esterification is the reaction between an organic acid and an alcohol to produce an ester plus water. An example of an esterification reaction between acetic acid and ethanol to produce the ester ethyl ethanoate is shown in Figure 11-16. Sulfuric acid is used as a dehydrating agent. It removes two hydrogen atoms and an oxygen atom to form water, with the remaining fragments combining to form the ester. Esters are named by using the alkyl name of the alcohol followed by the acid group modified to end in −oate. The ester produced by the reaction of methanol with ethanoic acid is methyl ethanoate.

Saponification

When an ester reacts with an inorganic base to produce an alcohol and a soap, the reaction is called a **saponification** reaction (Figure 11-17). One of the most common saponification reactions involves the reaction of a fat with a strong base such as sodium hydroxide. The products of this reaction are soap and glycerol.

Fermentation

Fermentation is a chemical process in which yeast cells secrete the enzyme zymase and break the six-carbon chain of sugars into carbon dioxide and two-carbon fragments of alcohol. The following equation shows what happens during fermentation.

$$C_6H_{12}O_6 \rightarrow 2C_2H_5OH + 2CO_2$$

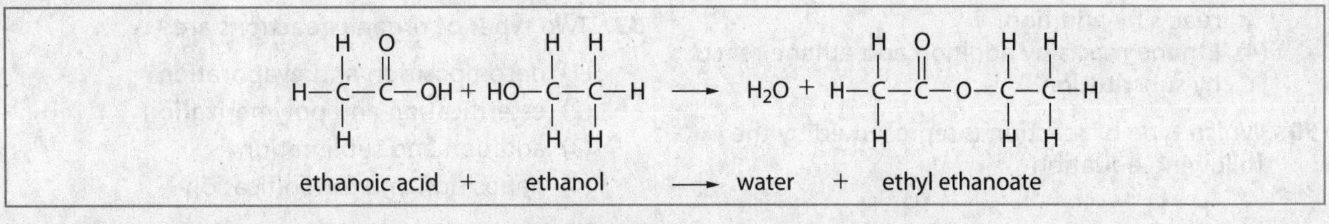

ethanoic acid + ethanol ⟶ water + ethyl ethanoate

Figure 11-16. **Esterification: An acid and an alcohol react to produce water and an ester.**

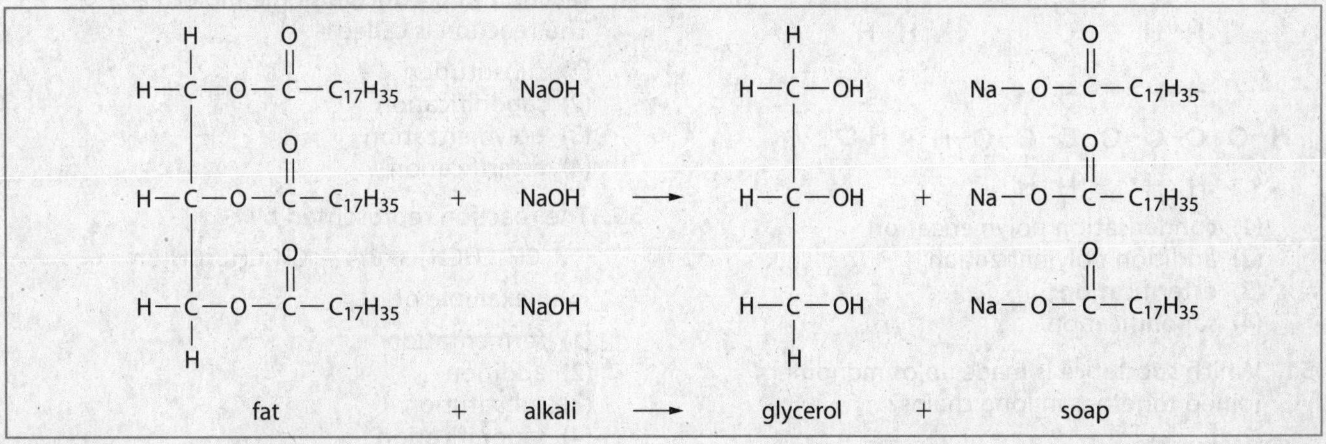

fat + alkali ⟶ glycerol + soap

Figure 11-17. **Saponification: A fat and an alkali react to produce glycerol and a soap, which is a salt of a fatty acid.**

Polymerization

Polymers are organic compounds made up of chains of smaller units covalently bonded together. The formation of these large polymer molecules is called **polymerization,** and each individual unit of a polymer is called a <u>monomer.</u> Synthetic plastics such as nylon, rayon, and polyethylene, are the best-known polymers. There are also many naturally occurring polymers, such as proteins, starches, and cellulose.

Addition Polymerization <u>Addition polymerization</u> reactions involve the joining of monomers of unsaturated compounds. When the double bond between the carbon atoms of ethene breaks, the resulting bond site is called a free radical because of the two unbonded electrons. These electrons can bond with similar open bonds of adjacent molecules to form long chains. A typical addition polymerization reaction can be shown as follows.

$$nC_2H_2 \rightarrow (C_2H_2)_n$$

Condensation Polymerization Condensation polymerization reactions result from the bonding of monomers by removing water from hydroxyl groups and joining the monomers by an ether or ester linkage.

Review Questions

49. Which type of reaction do ethane molecules and ethene molecules undergo when they react with chlorine?

(1) Ethane and ethene both react by addition.
(2) Ethane and ethene both react by substitution.
(3) Ethane reacts by substitution and ethene reacts by addition.
(4) Ethane reacts by addition and ethene reacts by substitution.

50. Which type of reaction is represented by the following equation?

(1) condensation polymerization
(2) addition polymerization
(3) esterification
(4) saponification

51. Which substance is made up of monomers joined together in long chains?

(1) ketone   (3) ester
(2) protein   (4) acid

52. Which equation represents a substitution reaction?

(1) $CH_4 + 2O_2 \rightarrow CO_2 + 2H_2O$
(2) $C_2H_4 + Br_2 \rightarrow C_2H_4Br_2$
(3) $C_3H_6 + H_2 \rightarrow C_3H_8$
(4) $C_4H_{10} + Cl_2 \rightarrow C_4H_9Cl + HCl$

53. Two types of organic reactions are

(1) decomposition and evaporation
(2) esterification and polymerization
(3) addition and sublimation
(4) deposition and saponification

54. Molecules of propene combine in a chemical reaction to produce a single molecule. The reaction is called

(1) substitution
(2) saponification
(3) polymerization
(4) esterification

55. The reaction represented by

$$CH_3CHCH_2 + Br_2 \rightarrow CH_3CHBrCH_2Br$$

is an example of

(1) fermentation
(2) addition
(3) substitution
(4) saponification

56. What are the products of a fermentation reaction?

    (1) an ester and water
    (2) a salt and water
    (3) an alcohol and carbon dioxide
    (4) a soap and glycerol

57. Which equation represents an addition reaction?

    (1) $CH_4 + O_2 \rightarrow CO_2 + 2H_2O$
    (2) $C_2H_6 + Br_2 \rightarrow C_2H_5Br + HBr$
    (3) $C_3H_6 + Cl_2 \rightarrow C_3H_6Cl_2$
    (4) $C_4H_{10} + Cl_2 \rightarrow C_4H_9Cl + HCl$

58. Which hydrocarbon will undergo a substitution reaction with chlorine?

    (1) methane
    (2) ethyne
    (3) propene
    (4) butene

59. The equation

$$CH_3OH + CH_3OH \rightarrow CH_3OCH_3 + H_2O$$

    illustrates the

    (1) oxidation of alcohols to form a ketone
    (2) oxidation of alcohols to form an acid
    (3) dehydration of alcohols to form a polymer
    (4) dehydration of alcohols to form an ether

60. Which type of reaction is represented by the following equation?

$$C_6H_{12}O_6 \rightarrow 2C_2H_5OH + 2CO_2$$

    (1) saponification
    (2) polymerization
    (3) esterification
    (4) fermentation

61. Which process usually produces water as one of the products?

    (1) cracking
    (2) hydrolysis
    (3) addition polymerization
    (4) condensation polymerization

62. Esterification is the reaction of an acid with

    (1) water
    (2) an alcohol
    (3) a base
    (4) a salt

63. Which reaction results in the production of ethanol?

    (1) combustion   (3) fermentation
    (2) esterification   (4) polymerization

64. Which term identifies a type of organic reaction?

    (1) esterification   (3) deposition
    (2) sublimation   (4) distillation

65. Two types of organic reactions are

    (1) fermentation and saponification
    (2) fermentation and transmutation
    (3) deposition and synthesis
    (4) deposition and esterification

For each substance in questions 66 through 70, write the number of the organic reaction, chosen from the list below, that will produce this substance.

Organic Reactions

    (1) esterification
    (2) saponification
    (3) polymerization
    (4) fermentation
    (5) substitution
    (6) halogen addition

66. ethanol

67. glycerol

68. methyl ethanoate

69. polyethylene

70. dichloromethane

Directions

Review the Test–Taking Strategies section of this book. Then answer the following questions. Read each question carefully and answer with a correct choice or response.

Part A

1 In the alkane series, each molecule contains
   (1) only one double bond
   (2) two double bonds
   (3) one triple bond
   (4) all single bonds

2 Which kind of bond is most common in organic compounds?
   (1) covalent   (3) hydrogen
   (2) ionic   (4) metallic

3 A carbon atom in an alkane has a total of
   (1) two covalent bonds (3) four covalent bonds
   (2) two ionic bonds   (4) four ionic bonds

4 What is the maximum number of covalent bonds that a carbon atom can form?
   (1) 1   (2) 2   (3) 3   (4) 4

5 A hydrocarbon molecule is saturated if the molecule contains
   (1) single covalent bonds only
   (2) only one double covalent bond
   (3) a triple covalent bond
   (4) single and double covalent bonds

6 Which statement explains why the element carbon forms so many compounds?
   (1) Carbon atoms combine readily with oxygen.
   (2) Carbon atoms have a high electronegativity value.
   (3) Carbon atoms readily form ionic bonds with other carbon atoms.
   (4) Carbon atoms readily form covalent bonds with other carbon atoms.

7 In the alkane family, each member differs from the preceding member by one carbon atom and two hydrogen atoms. Such a series of hydrocarbons is called
   (1) a homologous series
   (2) a periodic series
   (3) an actinide series
   (4) a lanthanide series

8 Which condensed structural formula represents an unsaturated compound?
   (1) $CH_3CH_2CH_3$ (3) CH_4
   (2) $CH_3CHCHCH_3$ (4) CH_3CH_3

9 The products of condensation polymerization are a polymer and
   (1) carbon dioxide   (3) ethanol
   (2) water   (4) glycerol

10 Which type of compound is represented by the structural formula shown below?

   (1) a ketone   (3) an ester
   (2) an aldehyde   (4) an ether

11 If a hydrocarbon molecule contains a triple bond, its IUPAC name ends in
   (1) -ane   (2) -ene   (3) -one   (4) -yne

12 Which compound is an organic acid?
   (1) CH_3OH (3) CH_3COOH
   (2) CH_3OCH_3 (4) CH_3COOCH_3

13 Which is the structural formula of an aldehyde?

14 Which general formula represents an ether?
   (1) $R–OH$ (3) $R–O–R'$
   (2) $R–CHO$ (4) $R–COOH$

15 What are the products of a fermentation reaction?
   (1) an alcohol and carbon monoxide
   (2) an alcohol and carbon dioxide
   (3) a salt and water
   (4) a salt and an acid

Part B–1

16 Which compounds are isomers?
(1) 1-propanol and 2-propanol
(2) methanoic acid and ethanoic acid
(3) methanol and methanal
(4) ethane and ethanol

17 Which is the correct structural formula for 2, 2-dimethylpropane?

(1)
```
          H
          |
      H — C — H
          |
      H   H   H   H
      |   |   |   |
  H — C — C — C — C — H
      |   |   |   |
      H   H   |   H
          H — C — H
              |
              H
```

(2)
```
      H   H   H   H
      |   |   |   |
  H — C — C — C — C — H
      |   |   |   |
      H   H   H   H
              |
          H — C — H
              |
              H
```

(3)
```
          H
          |
      H — C — H
      H   H   |
      |   |   |
  H — C — C — C — H
      |   |   |
      H   H   |
          H — C — H
              |
              H
```

(4)
```
          H
          |
      H — C — H
          |
      H   H   H
      |   |   |
  H — C — C — C — H
      |   |   |
      H   H   H
          |
      H — C — H
          |
          H
```

18 What is the chemical process illustrated by the following equation?

$$C_6H_{12}O_6 \rightarrow 2C_2H_5OH + 2CO_2$$

(1) fermentation   (3) esterification
(2) saponification   (4) polymerization

19 Which reaction is used to produce polyethylene $(C_2H_4)_n$ from ethylene?
(1) addition polymerization
(2) substitution
(3) condensation polymerization
(4) reduction

20 Which structural formula represents the product formed from the reaction of Cl_2 and C_2H_4?

(1)
```
      H   H
      |   |
  H — C — C — H
      |   |
      Cl  Cl
```

(2)
```
      Cl  Cl
      |   |
  H — C = C — H
```

(3)
```
  H — C ≡ C — Cl
```

(4)
```
      H   H
      |   |
  H — C — C — Cl
      |   |
      H   H
```

21 Methanol is classified as a
(1) monohydroxy alcohol
(2) secondary alcohol
(3) tertiary alcohol
(4) dihydroxy alcohol

22 What is the total number of pairs of electrons that one carbon atom shares with the other carbon atom in the molecule C_2H_4?
(1) 1   (3) 3
(2) 2   (4) 4

23 Which formula represents a hydrocarbon?
(1) CH_3CH_2F (3) CH_3CH_3
(2) CH_3NH_2 (4) CH_3CH_2OH

24 A student investigated four different substances in the solid phase. The table below is a record of the characteristics (marked with an *X*) exhibited by each substance. Which substance has characteristics most like those of an organic compound?

Characteristic Tested	Substance			
	A	B	C	D
High melting point	X		X	
Low melting point		X		X
Soluble in water	X			X
Insoluble in water		X	X	
Decomposed under high heat		X		
Stable under high heat	X		X	X
Electrolyte	X			X
Nonelectrolyte		X	X	

(1) A   (2) B   (3) C   (4) D

25 Which hydrocarbon is a member of the alkene family?
(1) C_2H_2
(2) C_3H_6
(3) C_4H_{10}
(4) C_5H_{12}

26 Given the balanced equation representing a reaction:

Which type of reaction is represented by this equation?
(1) substitution   (3) fermentation
(2) addition   (4) polymerization

27 Which organic compound will dissolve in water to produce a solution that will turn blue litmus red?

28 The compound 1,2-ethanediol is a
(1) monohydroxy alcohol
(2) dihydroxy alcohol
(3) primary alcohol
(4) secondary alcohol

29 Which formula represents a ketone?
(1) CH_3COOH
(2) C_2H_5OH
(3) CH_3COCH_3
(4) CH_3COOCH_3

30 The compounds CH_3OCH_3 and CH_3CH_2OH have different functional groups. Therefore, these compounds have different
(1) percent composition by mass.
(2) numbers of atoms per molecule.
(3) chemical properties.
(4) gram-formula masses.

Parts B–2 and C

Base your answers to questions 31 through 34 on the condensed structural formula below.

$$CH_3CH_2CHCH_2$$

31 Draw the structural formula for this compound.

32 State the IUPAC name for the compound you have drawn in question 31.

33 The formula below represents a product formed when HCl reacts with $CH_3CH_2CHCH_2$

What is the IUPAC name for this product?

34 In question 33, what type of organic reaction takes place to produce the organic product in the diagram?

Base your answers to questions 35 through 37 on the information below.

Given the reaction between 1-butene and chlorine gas:

$$C_4H_8 + Cl_2 \rightarrow C_4H_8Cl_2$$

35 Which type of chemical reaction is represented by this equation?

36 Draw the structural formula of the product, 1,2-dichlorobutane.

37 Identify the homologous series of hydrocarbons to which the organic reactant belongs.

Base your answers for questions 38 and 39 on the information below.

Given the balanced equation for an organic reaction between butane and chlorine:

$$C_4H_{10} + Cl_2 \rightarrow C_4H_9Cl + HCl$$

38 Identify the type of organic reaction shown.

39 Draw a structural formula for the organic product.

Base your answers to questions 40 and 41 on the information below.

Many esters have distinctive odors, which lead to their widespread use as artificial flavorings and fragrances. For example, methyl butanoate has an odor similar to pineapple and ethyl methanoate has an odor similar to raspberry.

40 Draw a structural formula for the ester that has an odor similar to pineapple.

41 What is the chemical name for the alcohol that reacts with methanoic acid to produce the ester that has an odor similar to raspberry?

Base your answers to questions 42 through 46 on the information below.

The incomplete equation below represents an esterification reaction. The alcohol is represented by X.

42 Circle only the acid functional group.

43 Write the IUPAC name for the reactant represented by its structural formula in this equation.

44 Draw the structural formula for the alcohol represented in this equation.

45 State the name of the alcohol represented by X.

46 Name the organic product of this reaction.

Base your answers to questions 47 and 48 on the following information.

Two hydrocarbons that are isomers of each other are represented by the structural formulas and molecular formulas below.

Hydrocarbon 1

$$H-C=C-C=C-C-H$$

C_5H_8

Hydrocarbon 2

$$H-C-C-C-C\equiv C-H$$

C_5H_8

47 Explain, in terms of bonds, why these hydrocarbons are unsaturated.

48 Explain, in terms of structural formulas and molecular formulas, why these hydrocarbons are isomers of each other.

Base your answers to questions 49 through 51 on the following information.

In one industrial organic reaction, C_3H_6 reacts with water in the presence of a catalyst. This reaction is represented by the balanced equation below.

$$H-C-C=C-H + H_2O \xrightarrow{\text{catalyst}} H-C-C-C-H$$
$$OH$$

49 Explain, in terms of bonding, why C_3H_6 is classified as an unsaturated hydrocarbon.

50 Write the IUPAC name for the organic reactant.

51 Identify the class of organic compound to which the product of the reaction belongs.

Nuclear Chemistry

What You Know About Nuclear Chemistry

?

Are you ready for a debate?

?

Danger! Danger! Nuclear radiation! Or is it so dangerous? In addition to generating power, scientists make daily use of nuclear energy in industry, medicine, and research. As you study this topic, think about the pros and cons of nuclear power.

- **What makes nuclear power unique?**

- **How are nuclear reactions different from ordinary chemical reactions?**

- **Is nuclear chemistry a natural or human-made phenomenon?**

- **What are the uses and dangers of nuclear chemistry?**

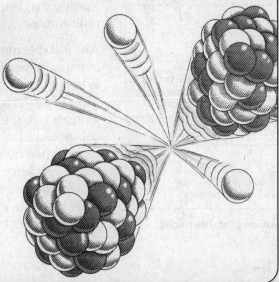

Nuclear Chemistry

Vocabulary

alpha particle	fusion	radioisotope
artificial transmutation	gamma ray	tracer
beta particle	half-life	transmutation
fission	natural transmutation	

Topic Overview

Most chemical reactions involve either the exchange or sharing of electrons between atoms. Nuclear chemistry is quite different in nature because it involves changes in the nucleus. When the atomic nucleus of one element is changed into the nucleus of a different element, the reaction is called a **transmutation.** In this topic you will study various types of transmutations and learn about properties of radioactive substances.

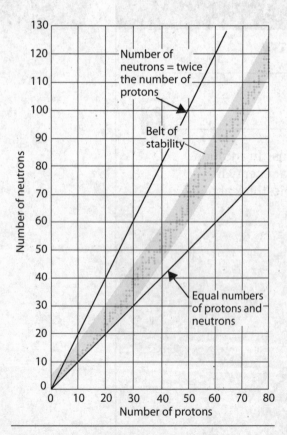

Figure 12-1. Composition of stable nuclei

Stability of Nuclei

Nuclei are composed of combinations of protons and neutrons. Hydrogen, with one proton, is the only element that does not contain one or more neutrons. Most nuclei are stable; that is, they are found within the "belt of stability" shown in Figure 12-1. It is the ratio of neutrons to protons that determines the stability of a given nucleus. The ratio in all nuclei with atomic numbers greater than 83 makes those nuclei unstable.

Because of this instability, all nuclei with atomic numbers greater than 83 are also radioactive, as explained in the next paragraph. For any element, an isotope that is unstable and thus radioactive is called a **radioisotope.**

An unstable nucleus decays in a series of steps which eventually produce a stable nucleus in the belt of stability. When an unstable nucleus decays, it emits radiation in the form of alpha particles, beta particles, positrons, and/or gamma radiation. An **alpha particle** is a helium nucleus composed of two protons and two neutrons. It is represented by the symbol $_2^4\text{He}$ or the symbol α, which is the Greek letter alpha. A **beta particle** (β^-) is an electron whose source is an atomic nucleus, while a positron (β^+) is identical to an electron except that it has a positive charge. Almost all nuclear decay also releases some energy in the form of **gamma rays** (γ), which are similar to X rays but have greater energy.

Figure 12-2 shows how alpha particles, beta particles and gamma rays react to an electric field. Table 12-1 summarizes information about each type of radiation.

Radiation can be harmful when it interacts with living things. Serious damage occurs when radioactivity causes ionization of normal tissue. When molecules in a cell are ionized, they may no longer carry on their normal functions and thus may cause the death of the cell. Other interactions of radioactivity with the DNA of a cell may cause mutations to occur. When these mutations occur in sperm or egg cells, they can cause mutations to be transmitted from generation to generation.

Alpha Decay

When an unstable nucleus emits an alpha particle, the nucleus is called an alpha emitter. Alpha emission is characteristic of heavy nuclei, especially of atoms with atomic numbers greater than 82. As a nucleus emits an alpha particle, its atomic number decreases by two (the two protons of the alpha particle), and its mass number decreases by four (the two protons and two neutrons of the alpha particle). For example, when radium-226 emits an alpha particle, its atomic number decreases by two, from 88 to 86. It is then no longer an atom of radium; it has become an atom of radon (atomic number 86). During the process, the nucleus has lost a total of 4 amu, and the new radon nucleus has a total mass of 222. The alpha decay of radium-226 is shown in Figure 12-3. The process is a transmutation because the atom undergoes a change in its atomic number and becomes a different element.

Alpha decay can be summarized as follows.

- atomic number decreases by two
- number of protons decreases by two
- number of neutrons decreases by two
- mass number decreases by four

Beta Decay

A nucleus that emits a beta particle as a result of nuclear disintegration is said to undergo beta decay and is called a beta emitter. Beta decay is interpreted as the emission of an

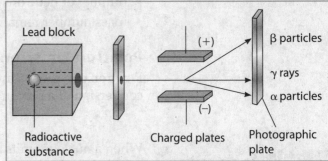

Lead block
β particles
γ rays
α particles
Radioactive substance
Charged plates
Photographic plate
(+)
(−)

Figure 12-2. **Separation of radioactive emissions:** Because they are positively charged, alpha particles are attracted to the negative plate. Because they are negatively charged, beta particles are attracted to the positively charged plate. Because they have no charge, gamma rays are undeflected in an electrical field. Alpha particles are not deflected as much as beta particles because alpha particles are more massive.

Table 12-1. Some Common Forms of Radiation

Particle	Mass	Charge	Symbol	Penetrating Power
Alpha	4 amu	2+	$^{4}_{2}He$, α	low
Beta	0 amu	1−	$^{0}_{-1}e$, β^-	moderate
Positron	0 amu	1+	$^{0}_{+1}e$, β^+	moderate
Gamma	0 amu	none	γ	high

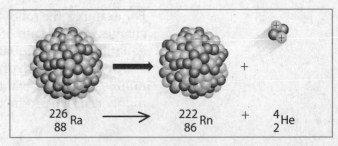

$^{226}_{88}Ra \longrightarrow {}^{222}_{86}Rn + {}^{4}_{2}He$

Figure 12-3. **Alpha decay:** In alpha decay, a nucleus ejects an alpha particle and becomes a smaller nucleus with less positive charge.

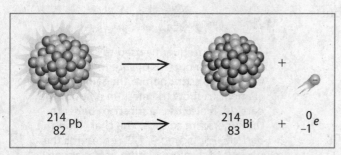

Figure 12-4. Beta decay: Beta decay has the effect of turning a neutron in the nucleus into a proton and an electron.

electron during the conversion of a neutron to a proton.

$$_0^1n \rightarrow \, _1^1p + \, _{-1}^0e$$

When a nucleus emits a beta particle, which has a charge of $1-$, the charge on the nucleus increases by one, which also means that the atomic number increases by one. The beta decay of lead-214 to bismuth-214 is shown in Figure 12-4.

Beta decay can be summarized as follows.

- atomic number increases by one
- number of protons increases by one
- number of neutrons decreases by one
- mass number remains the same

Positron Emission

Positron emission is interpreted as the production of a positron during the conversion of a proton to a neutron.

$$_1^1p \rightarrow \, _0^1n + \, _{+1}^0e$$

When a nucleus emits a positron, which has a charge of $1+$, the charge on the nucleus decreases by one, and thus the atomic number decreases by one. For example the positron emission of potassium-37 to argon-37 is represented by the following equation.

$$_{19}^{37}K \rightarrow \, _{18}^{37}Ar + \, _{+1}^0e$$

Positron emission can be summarized as follows.

- atomic number decreases by one
- number of protons decreases by one
- number of neutrons increases by one
- mass number remains the same

Nuclear Equations

As you have seen in this section, nuclear reactions can be represented by equations. As in chemical equations, mass and charge must balance on both sides of the equation.

For example, the following equation is balanced because the sum of charges and the sum of mass numbers are the same on both sides of the equation. For this equation, the sum of the charges of reactants equals 9 and so does the sum of the charges of the products. The sum of the mass numbers of the reactants is 18, which balances the sum of the mass numbers of the products.

$$_7^{14}N + \, _2^4He \rightarrow \, _8^{17}O + \, _1^1H$$

By using the concept of the conservation of charge and mass number, you can identify a missing particle in an equation.

Digging Deeper

Although positron emission is a natural type of transmutation, there is another reaction that will produce the same result. When a radioactive nucleus captures one of its least energetic electrons, the result is the same as a positron emission.

$$_{19}^{37}K + \, _{-1}^0e \rightarrow \, _{18}^{37}Ar$$

This capture of a low-energy electron is called a K-capture.

SAMPLE PROBLEM

What particle is represented by X in the following equation?

$$^{27}_{13}\text{Al} + ^{1}_{0}n \rightarrow ^{24}_{11}\text{Na} + X$$

SOLUTION: Identify the known and unknown values.

Known
charge and mass numbers
for Al, neutron, and Na

Unknown
identity of X = ?

1. Balance charge on both sides of the equation:

   The sum of the charges on the left is 13. Therefore, the sum on the right must also be 13. Na accounts for 11, so X must have a charge of 2.

2. Balance mass numbers on both sides of the equation:

   The sum of the mass numbers on the left is 28, so the sum on the right must also be 28. Na accounts for 24, so X must have a mass number of 4.

   The particle with an atomic number of 2 and a mass number of 4 is the alpha particle ($^{4}_{2}\text{He}$). X is an alpha particle.

Review Questions

Set 12.1

1. Which particle has the greatest mass?
   - (1) an alpha particle
   - (2) a beta particle
   - (3) an electron
   - (4) a neutron

2. In the following equation, which particle is represented by the letter X?

   $$^{14}_{6}\text{C} \rightarrow ^{14}_{7}\text{N} + X$$

   - (1) an alpha particle
   - (2) a beta particle
   - (3) a neutron
   - (4) a proton

3. Which radioactive emanations have a charge of 2+?
   - (1) alpha particles
   - (2) beta particles
   - (3) gamma rays
   - (4) neutrons

4. Which nuclear emission is negatively charged?
   - (1) a neutron
   - (2) a positron
   - (3) an alpha particle
   - (4) a beta particle

5. According to Reference Table N in the *Reference Tables for Physical Setting/Chemistry*, a product of the radioactive decay of Ra-226 is
   - (1) $^{4}_{2}\text{He}$
   - (2) $^{226}_{89}\text{U}$
   - (3) $^{0}_{-1}e$
   - (4) $^{230}_{90}\text{U}$

6. Which equation represents nuclear disintegration resulting in release of a beta particle?
   - (1) $^{220}_{87}\text{Fr} + ^{4}_{2}\text{He} \rightarrow ^{224}_{89}\text{Ac}$
   - (2) $^{239}_{94}\text{Pu} \rightarrow ^{235}_{92}\text{U} + ^{4}_{2}\text{He}$
   - (3) $^{32}_{15}\text{P} + ^{0}_{-1}e \rightarrow ^{32}_{14}\text{Si}$
   - (4) $^{198}_{79}\text{Au} \rightarrow ^{198}_{80}\text{Hg} + ^{0}_{-1}e$

7. In the nuclear equation $^{232}_{90}\text{Th} \rightarrow ^{228}_{88}\text{Ra} + X$, the letter X represents
   - (1) an alpha particle
   - (2) a beta particle
   - (3) a gamma ray
   - (4) a neutron

8. In the reaction $^{238}_{92}\text{U} \rightarrow X + ^{4}_{2}\text{He}$, the particle represented by X is
   - (1) $^{234}_{90}\text{Th}$
   - (2) $^{234}_{92}\text{U}$
   - (3) $^{238}_{93}\text{Np}$
   - (4) $^{242}_{94}\text{Pu}$

9. Positrons and beta particles have
   - (1) the same charge and the same mass
   - (2) the same charge and different masses
   - (3) different charges and the same mass
   - (4) different charges and different masses

10. In which reaction does the letter X represent an alpha particle?

(1) $^{226}_{88}\text{Ra} \rightarrow {}^{222}_{86}\text{Rn} + \text{X}$ (3) $^{230}_{90}\text{Th} \rightarrow {}^{230}_{88}\text{Ra} + \text{X}$

(2) $^{234}_{90}\text{Th} \rightarrow {}^{235}_{91}\text{Pa} + \text{X}$ (4) $^{234}_{92}\text{U} \rightarrow {}^{234}_{90}\text{Th} + \text{X}$

11. What does the X represent in the following reaction?

$$^{2}_{1}\text{H} + {}^{3}_{1}\text{H} \rightarrow {}^{4}_{2}\text{He} + {}^{1}_{0}n + \text{X}$$

(1) a released electron
(2) another neutron
(3) energy converted from mass
(4) mass converted from energy

12. Which of the following nuclear reactions is classified as positron decay?

(1) $^{37}_{19}\text{K} \rightarrow {}^{37}_{18}\text{Ar} + {}^{0}_{+1}e$ (3) $^{226}_{88}\text{Ra} \rightarrow {}^{222}_{86}\text{Rn} + {}^{4}_{2}\text{He}$

(2) $^{42}_{19}\text{K} \rightarrow {}^{42}_{20}\text{Ca} + {}^{0}_{-1}e$ (4) $^{3}_{1}\text{H} \rightarrow {}^{0}_{-1}e + {}^{4}_{2}\text{He}$

13. When an atom of the unstable isotope Na-24 decays, it becomes an atom of Mg-24 because the Na-24 atom spontaneously releases

(1) an alpha particle   (3) a positron
(2) a beta particle   (4) a neutron

14. Which element has no stable isotopes?

(1) $_{27}\text{Co}$ (2) $_{51}\text{Sb}$ (3) $_{90}\text{Th}$ (4) $_{82}\text{Pb}$

15. Write balanced nuclear equations for each of the following:

(a) beta decay of Pb-210
(b) beta decay of Cs-137
(c) alpha decay of Rn-222
(d) alpha decay of Au-185
(e) positron emission of Fe-53
(f) positron emission of Ca-37

Transmutations

Nuclear reactions can be either naturally occurring or artificial. Alpha, beta, and positron decay are **natural transmutations** that occur as a result of unstable neutron-to-proton ratios. When bombarding the nucleus with high-energy particles brings about the change, the process is given the name of **artificial transmutation.** Scientists in research and commercial settings perform artificial transmutations.

Types of Transmutations There are two types of artificial transmutations. The first type involves the collision of a charged particle with a target nucleus. If charged particles such as protons or alpha particles are to react with atomic nuclei, they must have sufficient energy to overcome the repulsive forces that exist between positively charged objects. Scientists can supply this energy by accelerating charged particles in devices called cyclotrons and synchrotrons, which use magnetic or electrostatic fields to speed up protons and other charged particles.

A second type of artificial transmutation occurs when a neutron collides with a target nucleus. Neutrons can be obtained as by-products of nuclear reactors similar to those used to generate electricity. Because the neutron does not possess a charge, it is not repelled by the target nucleus and can be captured by the "strong" force that holds protons and neutrons in the nucleus. These reactions are used to prepare radioactive nuclei from stable nuclei. Listed below are a few examples.

$$^{238}_{92}\text{U} + {}^{1}_{0}n \rightarrow {}^{239}_{92}\text{U}$$

$$^{59}_{27}\text{Co} + {}^{1}_{0}n \rightarrow {}^{60}_{27}\text{Co}$$

$$^{32}_{16}\text{S} + {}^{1}_{0}n \rightarrow {}^{32}_{15}\text{P} + {}^{1}_{1}\text{H}$$

It is easy to tell the difference between natural and artificial transmutation. Natural transmutation consists of a single nucleus undergoing decay. Artificial transmutation will have two reactants, a fast-moving particle and a target material.

16. Which term identifies a type of nuclear reaction?

(1) neutralization
(2) deposition
(3) reduction
(4) transmutation

17. Which particle is represented by X in the following transmutation?

$$^{234}_{90}\text{Th} \rightarrow {}^{234}_{91}\text{Pa} + \text{X}$$

(1) $_{-1}^{0}e$ (2) $_{2}^{4}\text{He}$ (3) $_{1}^{1}\text{H}$ (4) $_{+1}^{0}e$

18. Which equation represents a nuclear reaction that is an example of an artificial transmutation?

(1) $^{43}_{21}\text{Sc} \rightarrow {}^{43}_{20}\text{Ca} + {}_{+1}^{0}e$ (3) $^{10}_{4}\text{Be} \rightarrow {}^{10}_{5}\text{B} + {}_{-1}^{0}e$

(2) $^{14}_{7}\text{N} + {}_{2}^{4}\text{He} \rightarrow {}^{17}_{8}\text{O} + {}_{1}^{1}\text{H}$ (4) $^{14}_{6}\text{C} \rightarrow {}^{14}_{7}\text{N} + {}_{-1}^{0}e$

19. Which particle is represented by X in the following transmutation?

$$^{131}_{53}\text{I} \rightarrow {}^{131}_{54}\text{Xe} + \text{X}$$

(1) alpha   (2) beta   (3) neutron   (4) proton

20. What is the charge of the element represented by X in the following transmutation?

$$^{1}_{0}n + {}^{235}_{92}\text{U} \rightarrow {}^{141}_{56}\text{Ba} + \text{X} + 3{}_{0}^{1}n$$

(1) 36   (2) 89   (3) 92   (4) 93

21. Which species is represented by X in the following transmutation?

$$^{9}_{4}\text{Be} + {}_{1}^{1}\text{H} \rightarrow {}_{2}^{4}\text{He} + \text{X}$$

(1) $^{8}_{3}\text{Li}$ (2) $^{6}_{3}\text{Li}$ (3) $^{8}_{5}\text{B}$ (4) $^{10}_{5}\text{B}$

22. Which species is represented by X in the following transmutation?

$$^{7}_{3}\text{Li} + \text{X} \rightarrow {}^{8}_{4}\text{Be}$$

(1) $^{1}_{1}\text{H}$ (2) $^{2}_{1}\text{H}$ (3) $^{3}_{2}\text{He}$ (4) $^{4}_{2}\text{He}$

23. What is the identity of particle X in the following transmutation?

$$^{9}_{4}\text{Be} + \text{X} \rightarrow {}^{6}_{3}\text{Li} + {}_{2}^{4}\text{He}$$

(1) $^{1}_{1}\text{H}$ (2) $^{2}_{1}\text{H}$ (3) $_{-1}^{0}e$ (4) $_{0}^{1}n$

Fission and Fusion

A **fission** reaction involves the splitting of a heavy nucleus to produce lighter nuclei. A **fusion** reaction involves the combining of light nuclei to produce a heavier nucleus. In both types of reactions, the total mass of the products is less than the total nuclear mass of the reactants.

Conversion of Matter to Energy

At first glance this loss of mass seems to contradict our concept that matter (mass) can neither be created nor destroyed. Properly expressed, the law states that the total amount of matter and energy cannot be destroyed. The loss of mass in these nuclear reactions represents a conversion of some matter into energy. The relationship was expressed by Albert Einstein in his famous equation

$$E = mc^2$$

where E is energy, m is mass, and c is the speed of light, which is 3.00×10^8 m/s. Because the speed of light is such a large number, you can see that the conversion of a minute amount of matter produces an extremely large amount of energy.

The energy produced by nuclear reactions is far greater than that of ordinary chemical reactions. The conversion of 1.00 g of matter into energy yields 9.00×10^{13} J. When 1.00 g of methane is burned in an ordinary chemical reaction, there is a release of 5.56×10^4 J of energy.

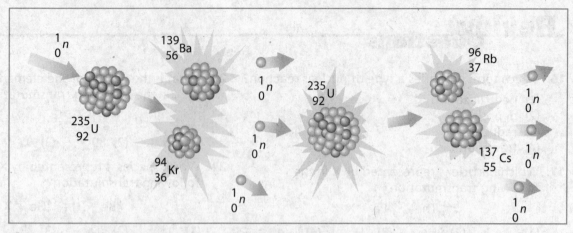

Figure 12-5. Fission: Fission involves the splitting of a large nucleus into middle-weight nuclei and neutrons.

Gram for gram, the nuclear reaction gives off over a billion times as much energy.

This conversion of matter into energy occurs when protons and neutrons are combined into nuclei. The total mass of the nucleus is less than the sum of the masses of the individual protons and neutrons. The matter that has been converted into energy is called the <u>mass defect.</u>

Fission Reactions

A fission reaction begins with the capture of a neutron by the nucleus of a heavy element such as uranium-235 or plutonium-239. The nucleus produced by the capture is unstable. It immediately splits, undergoing the process of fission. The products of fission are two middle-weight nuclei, one or more neutrons, and a large amount of energy. A small amount of matter from the original atom of uranium or plutonium is converted into energy.

$$\,_0^1n + \,_{92}^{235}U \rightarrow \,_{56}^{142}Ba + \,_{36}^{91}Kr + 3\,_0^1n + energy$$

The products shown in this equation are only two of more than 200 different radioactive products that may be produced by the fission process. Some other possible products are shown in Figure 12-5.

Fusion Reactions

Fusion reactions involve the combining of light nuclei to form heavier ones. The most common example of fusion occurs in the sun where hydrogen nuclei react in a series to produce helium nuclei. These fusion reactions produce the huge amounts of energy released by the sun. One of the possible series of reactions involving the fusion of hydrogen nuclei to form helium and release energy is given by the following sequence.

$$\,_1^1H + \,_1^1H \rightarrow \,_1^2H + \,_{+1}^0e$$

$$\,_1^1H + \,_1^2H \rightarrow \,_2^3He$$

$$\,_2^3He + \,_2^3He \rightarrow \,_2^4He + 2\,_1^1H$$

$$\,_2^3He + \,_1^1H \rightarrow \,_2^4He + \,_{+1}^0e$$

While these reactions produce the energy from the sun, they are not yet available to produce energy here on Earth. Extremely high temperatures and pressures are needed to allow the positively charged hydrogen nuclei to fuse into helium. When methods are developed that will contain a reaction such as these and make it practical, an important new energy source will have been developed. One major advantage of fusion as an energy source is that the products are not highly radioactive, like the products of fission reactions.

Review Questions

Set 12.3

24. High energy is a requirement for fusion reactions to occur because the nuclei involved

(1) attract each other because they have like charges
(2) attract each other because they have unlike charges
(3) repel each other because they have like charges
(4) repel each other because they have unlike charges

25. When a uranium nucleus breaks up into fragments, which type of nuclear reaction occurs?

(1) fusion   (3) replacement
(2) fission   (4) redox

26. Which pair of nuclei can undergo a fusion reaction?

(1) potassium-40 and cadmium-113
(2) zinc-64 and calcium-44
(3) uranium-238 and lead-208
(4) hydrogen-2 and hydrogen-3

27. Given the reaction:

$$^{27}_{13}Al + {}^{4}_{2}He \rightarrow X + {}^{1}_{0}n$$

Which particle is represented by X?

(1) $^{30}_{14}Si$ (3) $^{28}_{12}Mg$
(2) $^{30}_{15}P$ (4) $^{28}_{13}Al$

28. During a fission reaction, which type of particle is captured by a nucleus?

(1) deuteron   (3) neutron
(2) electron   (4) proton

29. What occurs in both fusion and fission reactions?

(1) Small amounts of matter are converted into large amounts of energy.
(2) Small amounts of energy are converted into large amounts of matter.
(3) Light nuclei are combined into heavier nuclei.
(4) Heavy nuclei are split into lighter nuclei.

30. Compared to an ordinary chemical reaction, a fission reaction will

(1) release smaller amounts of energy
(2) release larger amounts of energy
(3) absorb smaller amounts of energy
(4) absorb larger amounts of energy

31. Which type of reaction produces energy and intensely radioactive waste products?

(1) fusion of tritium and deuterium
(2) fission of uranium
(3) burning of heating oil
(4) burning of wood

32. Which process occurs in a controlled fusion reaction?

(1) Light nuclei collide to produce heavier nuclei.
(2) Heavy nuclei collide to produce lighter nuclei.
(3) Neutron bombardment splits light nuclei.
(4) Neutron bombardment splits heavy nuclei.

33. Consider this reaction.

$$^{235}_{92}U + {}^{1}_{0}n \rightarrow {}^{138}_{56}Ba + {}^{95}_{36}Kr + 3{}^{1}_{0}n + energy$$

This equation can best be described as

(1) fission   (3) natural decay
(2) fusion   (4) endothermic

Half-Life

Radioactive substances decay at a constant rate that is not dependent on factors such as temperature, pressure, or concentration. It is also a random event. That is, it is impossible to predict when a given unstable nucleus will decay. However, the number of unstable nuclei that will decay in a given time in a sample of the element can be predicted. The time it takes for half of the atoms in a given sample of an element to decay is called the **half-life** of the element. Each isotope has its own half-life. The shorter the half-life of an isotope, the less stable it is. Table N in *Reference Tables for Physical Setting/Chemistry* lists various isotopes together with their half-lives and the mode by which they decay. Figure 12-6 shows the decay of carbon-14.

If radioactive substance X has a half-life of 5 s, each five seconds will result in the amount of X present at the beginning of the time being reduced by half. If 20 g of X begins to decay, after 5 s only 10 g will remain. Five seconds later, only 5 g of the original 20 g will remain. $(1/2 \times 1/2 = 1/4)$. The fraction remaining after a given number of half-lives is calculated using the relationship

$$\text{fraction remaining} = (1/2)^n$$

where n is equal to the number of half-lives. The number of half-lives is calculated by dividing the total time that the substance has decayed by the half-life of the isotope.

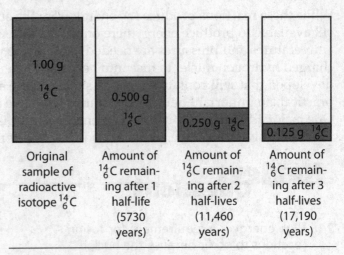

Figure 12-6. The half-life of C-14

SAMPLE PROBLEM

Most chromium atoms are stable, but Cr-51 is an unstable isotope with a half-life of 28 days.
(a) What fraction of a sample of Cr-51 will remain after 168 days?
(b) If a sample of Cr-51 has an original mass of 52.0 g, what mass will remain after 168 days?

SOLUTION: Identify the known and unknown values.

Known
half-life of Cr-51 = 28 days
time = 168 days
original mass = 52.0 g

Unknown
fraction of Cr-51 remaining after 168 days = ?
mass of Cr-51 remaining after 168 days = ? g

1. Determine how many half-lives elapse during 168 days.

$$\text{Number of half-lives} = \frac{\text{time elapsed (t)}}{\text{half-life (T)}}$$

$$= \frac{168 \text{ days}}{28 \text{ days/half-life}}$$

$$= 6 \text{ half-lives}$$

2. Calculate the fraction remaining.

$$\text{Fraction remaining} = (1/2)^{t/T}$$
$$= (1/2)^6$$
$$= 1/64$$

The fraction of Cr-51 remaining after 168 days will be 1/64 of the original.

3. Calculate the mass remaining.

$$\text{mass remaining} = \text{original mass} \times \text{fraction remaining}$$
$$= 52.0 \text{ g} \times 1/64 = 0.813 \text{ g}$$

Mass remaining can also be calculated by dividing the current mass by 2 at the end of each half-life.

After 1 half-life, mass = 52.0 g/2 = 26.0 g
After 2 half-lives, mass = 26.0 g/2 = 13.0 g
After 3 half-lives, mass = 13.0 g/2 = 6.50 g
After 4 half-lives, mass = 6.50 g/2 = 3.25 g
After 5 half-lives, mass = 3.25 g/2 = 1.63 g
After 6 half-lives, mass = 1.63 g/2 = 0.815 g

SAMPLE PROBLEM

How much was present originally in a sample of Cr-51 if 0.75 mg remains after 168 days?

SOLUTION: Identify the known and unknown values.

Known
half-life of Cr-51 = 28 days
time = 168 days
final mass = 0.75 mg

Unknown
original mass = ? g

From the previous sample problem, 168 days represents 6 half-life periods for Cr-51. The sample will double for each half-life period. Multiply the remaining amount by a factor of 2 for each half-life.

original mass = final mass $\times 2^n$

$= 0.75$ mg $\times 2^6$

$= 48$ mg

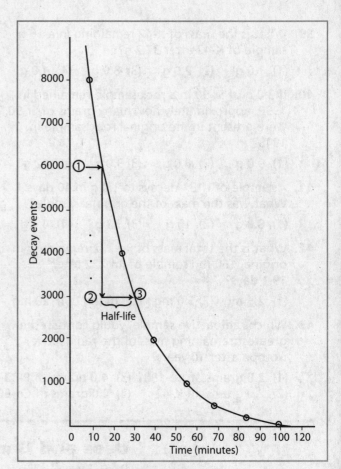

Figure 12-7. A hypothetical half-life

The initial amount of a substance can be determined from the half-life, the amount remaining, and the time passed. When determining an original amount, each half-life represents a doubling of the amount present.

Graphing Half-Life Data As a radioactive substance decays, a Geiger counter can be used to record the individual decay events. When this data is graphed, it provides a way to measure the half-life of an isotope. Figure 12-7 is a graph of the data of the decay of a hypothetical radioisotope. To determine the half-life, select a convenient count on the *y*-axis (1). Draw a vertical line to a value of half of the original (2). In this case the line extends from 6000 counts to 3000 counts. The half-life is represented by the time segment on the *x*-axis (2 to 3), or 15 minutes. It does not matter where you begin, the half-life will still be the same. Simply draw a line to reduce the count by half, and then read the half-life.

Review
Questions
Set 12.4

Refer to Table N in *Reference Tables for Physical Setting/Chemistry* for half-life values as needed.

34. After 62.0 hours, 1.0 g remains unchanged from a sample of ^{42}K. How much ^{42}K was in the original sample?

    (1) 8.0 g (2) 16 g (3) 32 g (4) 64 g

35. If 80 mg of a radioactive element decays to 10 mg in 30 min, what is the element's half-life in minutes?

    (1) 10 (2) 20 (3) 30 (4) 40

36. A radioactive isotope has a half-life of 2.5 years. Which fraction of the original mass remains unchanged after 10. years?

    (1) $\frac{1}{8}$ (2) $\frac{1}{16}$ (3) $\frac{1}{2}$ (4) $\frac{1}{4}$

37. Which of the following 10-g samples of a radioisotope will decay to the greatest extent in 28 days?

    (1) P-32 (2) Kr-85 (3) Fr-220 (4) I-131

38. How many hours are required for potassium-42 to undergo three half-life periods?

    (1) 6.2 h (2) 12.4 h (3) 24.8 h (4) 37.2 h

39. What is the mass of K-42 remaining in a 16-g sample of K-42 after 37.2 h?

(1) 1.0 g   (2) 2.0 g   (3) 8.0 g   (4) 4.0 g

40. If 3.0 g of Sr-90 in a rock sample remained in 1999, approximately how many grams of Sr-90 were present in the original rock sample in 1943?

(1) 9.0 g   (2) 6.0 g   (3) 3.0 g   (4) 12 g

41. A sample of I-131 decays to 1.0 g in 40 days. What was the mass of the original sample?

(1) 8.0 g   (2) 16 g   (3) 32 g   (4) 4.0 g

42. What is the total mass of Rn-222 remaining in an original 160-mg sample of Rn-222 after 19.1 days?

(1) 2.5 mg   (2) 5.0 mg   (3) 10 mg   (4) 20 mg

43. Which radioactive sample would contain the greatest remaining mass of the radioactive isotope after 10 years?

(1) 2.0 grams of Au-198   (3) 4.0 grams of P-32
(2) 2.0 grams of K-42   (4) 4.0 grams of Co-60

44. A radioactive element has a half-life of 2 days. Which fraction represents the amount of an original sample of this element remaining after 6 days?

(1) $\frac{1}{8}$ (3) $\frac{1}{3}$
(2) $\frac{1}{2}$ (4) $\frac{1}{4}$

45. What fraction of a Sr-90 sample remains unchanged after 87.3 years?

(1) $\frac{1}{2}$ (3) $\frac{1}{8}$
(2) $\frac{1}{4}$ (4) $\frac{1}{16}$

46. As the temperature of a sample of a radioactive element decreases, the half-life of the element

(1) decreases   (3) remains the same
(2) increases   (4) varies with the pressure

47. If one-eighth of the mass of the original sample of a radioisotope remains unchanged after 4800 years, the isotope could be

(1) H-3   (3) Sr-90
(2) K-42   (4) Ra-226

Uses and Dangers of Radioisotopes

Radioisotopes have many practical applications in industry, medicine, and research. They also have potential dangers because of harm that could be done by the radiation released.

Uses of Radioisotopes

The following applications represent just a few of the many uses of radioisotopes. Although they must be used with proper precautions, certain radioisotopes provide information that could not be determined from isotopes that are not radioactive.

Dating Carbon-14 is perhaps best known for its use in dating previously living materials. There is an extremely small amount of C-14 in the atmosphere. When an organism is alive, it uses this radioactive carbon in the same way as it uses stable C-12. When the organism dies, it no longer takes in any carbon.

Each gram of carbon in a living organism emits about 15 disintegrations per minute (dpm). After the organism dies and time passes, the radioactive C-14 continues to decay, but it is not replaced. Therefore the dpm decreases with time. Because the half-life of C-14 is 5730 years, after that time period there will only be about 7 dpm for each gram of carbon in the organism. Therefore, a reading of 7 dpm/g carbon indicates the remains are about 5700 years old, while a reading of 3.5 dpm would show a material to be about twice as old, about 11,000 years. After about four half-lives, C-14 becomes ineffective as a method for dating materials because too little C-14 remains to be accurately measured.

U-238 is a radioactive material that spontaneously decays through a series of steps until it forms stable Pb-206. As time passes, the amount of lead in the sample will increase as the amount of uranium decreases. Scientists can use the ratio of U-238/Pb-206 to date rocks and other geological formations.

Chemical Tracers The ability to detect radioactive materials and their decay products makes it possible to determine their presence or absence in a substance. Any radioisotope used to follow the path of a material in a system is called a **tracer.** If radioactive P-31 is present in fertilizer administered to a plant, the uptake of the phosphorus can be traced by detectors. Scientists can then determine the proper amounts and timing of fertilizer applications. C-14 is another tracer used to map the path of carbon in metabolic processes.

Industrial Applications Radioactive isotopes and gamma rays are absorbed in varying amounts by different materials. The thicker the material, the more radiation that will be absorbed. Thus, radiation products can be used to measure the thickness of materials such as a plastic wrap or aluminum foil or to test the strength of a weld.

Medical Applications Certain radioisotopes that are quickly eliminated from the body and have short half-lives are important as tracers in medical diagnosis. Many are also used in treatment of various disorders and diseases. Others might be used to make materials free from bacteria or other disease-causing organisms.

I-131 has uses both in the detection and treatment of thyroid conditions. Because iodine accumulates in the thyroid gland, small amounts of I-131 can be administered to a patient and a radiogram made of the thyroid to diagnose a disorder. When a person has an overactive thyroid (hyperthyroidism), I-131 can be given in large enough doses to destroy some of the thyroid and reduce its production of thyroxin.

Cobalt-60 emits large amounts of gamma radiation as it decays. These rays can be aimed at cancerous tumors. The rapidly growing cells of the tumor are more likely to be killed than normal cells by the gamma rays.

Intense beams of gamma radiation can be used to irradiate foods to kill bacteria. Certain types of foods, such as spices, are irradiated on a regular basis. Irradiation of produce and meats has also been approved in many locations. By killing the bacteria present, the food lasts longer without spoiling and causes fewer bacterial infections in those who consume it. Other destruction of bacteria by radiation is also important. Co-60 and Cs-137 are two of the sources of gamma radiation currently being used to destroy anthrax bacilli.

Technetium, atomic number 43, is a radioactive element that is rapidly absorbed by cancerous cells. When Tc-99 is given to patients with cancerous tumors, it accumulates in the tumor and can easily be detected by a scan. When radioisotopes are used for diagnostic purposes, it is advantageous if they have a short half-life and are quickly eliminated by the body so that they do not damage healthy tissue.

Radiation Risks

The uses of radiation are not without risks. While radioisotopes can be used to kill cancerous cells, they also have the potential of damaging normal tissue. High doses of radiation can cause serious illness and death. Radiation can cause mutations that could potentially be passed from generation to generation.

Nuclear power plants are a particular problem. After the fuel rods no longer have enough uranium to make them useful in the reactor, they contain many decay products, many with long half-lives. It is difficult to store and dispose of these waste products.

Of major concern to many people is the overall safety issue of nuclear power plants themselves. While the plants are designed to protect the public, there is still a danger of a nuclear accident that might release radioactivity into the air or water. The 1986 accident at Chernobyl in Ukraine destroyed farmland that will probably be unusable for generations.

Review Questions

Set 12.5

48. Which radioisotope is used for diagnosing thyroid disorders?

(1) cobalt-60   (3) lead-206
(2) uranium-238   (4) iodine-131

49. Which procedure is based on the half-life of a radioisotope?

(1) accelerating to increase kinetic energy
(2) radiation to kill cancer cells
(3) counting to determine a level of radioactivity
(4) dating to determine age

50. Radiated food can be safely stored for a longer time because radiation

(1) prevents air oxidation
(2) prevents air reduction
(3) kills bacteria
(4) causes bacteria to mutate

51. A radioactive-dating procedure to determine the age of a mineral compares the mineral's remaining amounts of U-238 and the isotope

(1) Pb-206   (3) Pb-214
(2) Bi-206   (4) Bi-214

52. Which isotopic ratio needs to be determined when the age of ancient wooden objects is investigated?

(1) U-235 to U-238   (3) N-16 to N-14
(2) H-2 to H-3   (4) C-14 to C-12

53. Which two characteristics do radioisotopes have that are useful in medical diagnosis?

(1) long half-lives and slow elimination from the body
(2) long half-lives and quick elimination from the body
(3) short half-lives and slow elimination from the body
(4) short half-lives and quick elimination from the body

54. One beneficial use of radioisotopes is

(1) decreasing dissolved $O_2(g)$ level in seawater
(2) increasing $CO_2(g)$ concentration in the atmosphere
(3) neutralization of an acid spill
(4) detection of disease

55. Which radioactive isotope is used in geological dating?

(1) U-238   (2) I-131   (3) Co-60   (4) Tc-99

56. Which isotope can be used as a tracer to study the age of organic material?

(1) C-12   (2) C-14   (3) Sr-88   (4) Sr-90

57. Brain tumors can be located by using an isotope of

(1) C-14   (2) I-131   (3) Tc-99   (4) U-238

Directions

Review the Test–Taking Strategies section of this book. Then answer the following questions. Read each question carefully and answer with a correct choice or response.

Part A

1 Samples of elements that are radioactive must contain atoms
   (1) with stable nuclei
   (2) with unstable nuclei
   (3) in the excited state
   (4) in the ground state

2 Organic molecules react to form a product. These reactions can be studied using
   (1) Sr-90   (2) Co-60   (3) N-16   (4) C-14

3 Radiation used in the processing of food is intended to
   (1) increase the rate of nutrient decomposition
   (2) kill microorganisms that are found in food
   (3) convert ordinary nutrients to more stable forms
   (4) replace chemical energy with nuclear energy

4 The age of certain minerals can be determined if they contain the nuclide
   (1) P-32   (3) U-238
   (2) Co-60   (4) Au-198

5 The course of a chemical reaction can be traced by using a
   (1) polar molecule   (3) stable isotope
   (2) diatomic molecule   (4) radioisotope

6 Bombarding a nucleus with high-energy particles that change it from one element into another is called
   (1) a half-reaction
   (2) a breeder reaction
   (3) artificial transmutation
   (4) natural transmutation

7 An alpha decay results in the formation of a new element with the atomic number
   (1) increased by two   (3) decreased by two
   (2) increased by four   (4) decreased by four

8 When a radioactive nucleus emits a beta particle, the atom's
   (1) mass number is increased by 1
   (2) mass number is decreased by 1
   (3) atomic number is increased by 1
   (4) atomic number is decreased by 1

9 As the temperature increases, pressure remaining constant, the half-life of a radioactive element
   (1) decreases   (3) remains the same
   (2) increases   (4) depends on the mass

10 Which of the following is not deflected by an electric field?
   (1) alpha   (3) positron
   (2) beta   (4) gamma ray

Part B–1

11 Which statement explains why fusion reactions are difficult to initiate?
   (1) Positive nuclei attract each other.
   (2) Positive nuclei repel each other.
   (3) Neutrons prevent nuclei from getting close enough to fuse.
   (4) Electrons prevent nuclei from getting close enough to fuse.

12 Which particle has the greatest chance of overcoming the electrostatic forces surrounding the nucleus of an atom?
   (1) an alpha particle   (3) a proton
   (2) a beta particle   (4) a neutron

13 The diagram below shows a nuclear reaction in which a neutron is captured by a heavy nucleus. Which type of reaction is illustrated by the diagram?

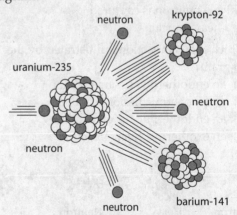

neutron   krypton-92

uranium-235

neutron

neutron

neutron   barium-141

   (1) an endothermic fission reaction
   (2) an exothermic fission reaction
   (3) an endothermic fusion reaction
   (4) an exothermic fusion reaction

14 Given the balanced equation representing a nuclear reaction:

$$_{1}^{2}H + _{1}^{3}H \rightarrow _{2}^{4}He + _{0}^{1}H$$

Which phrase identifies and describes this reaction?
(1) fission, mass converted to energy
(2) fission, energy converted to mass
(3) fusion, mass converted to energy
(4) fusion, energy converted to mass

15 Consider this reaction.

$$_{13}^{27}Al + _{2}^{4}He \rightarrow _{15}^{30}P + _{0}^{1}n$$

This reaction can best be described as
(1) beta decay
(2) artificial transmutation
(3) fission
(4) fusion

16 When I-131 undergoes radioactive decay, which element is formed?
(1) Te-132   (3) I-130
(2) Xe-131   (4) Sb-127

17 Which reaction releases the greatest amount of energy per mole of reactant?
(1) fission   (3) decomposition
(2) esterification   (4) fermentation

18 Which particle is represented by X in the following correctly balanced nuclear equation?

$$_{6}^{12}C + _{98}^{249}Cf \rightarrow _{104}^{257}Unq + 4X$$

(1) $_{7}^{14}H$ (2) $_{0}^{1}n$ (3) $_{2}^{4}He$ (4) $_{-1}^{0}e$

19 The diagram below shows a nuclear reaction in which a neutron is captured by a heavy nucleus.

Which type of reaction is illustrated by the diagram?
(1) an endothermic fission reaction
(2) an exothermic fission reaction
(3) an endothermic fusion reaction
(4) an exothermic fusion reaction

20 In which list can all particles be accelerated by an electric field?
(1) alpha particles, beta particles, and neutrons
(2) alpha particles, beta particles, and protons
(3) alpha particles, protons, and neutrons
(4) beta particles, protons, and neutrons

21 In which process is mass converted to energy by the process of fission?
(1) $_{7}^{14}N + _{0}^{1}n \rightarrow _{6}^{14}C + _{1}^{1}H$
(2) $_{92}^{235}U + _{0}^{1}n \rightarrow _{35}^{87}Br + _{57}^{146}La + 3_{0}^{1}n$
(3) $_{88}^{226}Ra \rightarrow _{86}^{222}Rn + _{2}^{4}He$
(4) $_{1}^{2}H + _{1}^{2}H \rightarrow _{2}^{4}He$

22 Which list of nuclear emissions is arranged in order from the greatest penetrating power to the least penetrating power?
(1) alpha particle, beta particle, gamma ray
(2) alpha particle, gamma ray, beta particle
(3) gamma ray, beta particle, alpha particle

23 Atoms of I-131 spontaneously decay when the
(1) stable nuclei emit alpha particles.
(2) stable nuclei emit beta particles.
(3) unstable nuclei emit alpha particles.
(4) unstable nuclei emit beta particles.

Neutron → Heavy nucleus → Neutron captured in nucleus → Nuclear deformation → + Products

Parts B–2 and C

Base your answers to questions 24 through 26 on the information below.

When a uranium-235 nucleus absorbs a slow moving neutron, different nuclear reactions may occur. One of these possible reactions is represented by the complete, balanced equation below.

Eq. 1: $^{235}_{92}U + ^{1}_{0}n \rightarrow ^{92}_{36}Kr + ^{142}_{56}Ba + 2^{1}_{0}n + energy$

For this reaction, the sum of the masses of the products is slightly less than the sum of the masses of the reactants. Another possible reaction of U-235 is represented by the incomplete, balanced equation below.

Eq. 2: $^{235}_{92}U + ^{1}_{0}n \rightarrow ^{92}_{38}Sr + \underline{\hspace{1cm}} + 2^{1}_{0}n + energy$

24 Identify the type of nuclear reaction represented by equation 1.

25 Write a notation for the missing product in equation 2.

26 The half-life of Kr-92 is known to be 1.84 sec. If 6.0 milligrams remain after 7.36 seconds, what was the original mass of a sample of this isotope?

Base your answers to questions 27 through 29 on the graph below which depicts the zone of stability for elements 6–24.

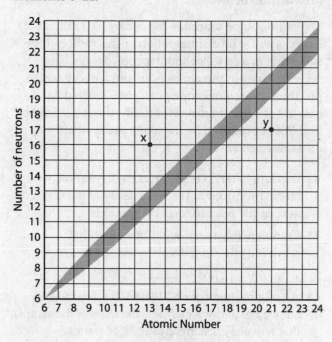

27 Identify the nuclide located at position "x" on the graph. Include the mass and nuclear charge values.

28 Plot the point representing the product formed from the beta decay of particle "x".

29 Write a positron decay equation for the particle located at position "y". Include masses and nuclear charge values for all particles.

Base your answers to questions 30 and 31 on the information below.

In 1955 a team of scientists at the University of California produced a new element by bombarding an Es-253 target with accelerated alpha particles using a cyclotron. The collision of the einsteinium-253 isotope with the alpha particles caused an artificial transmutation in which the new element was produced along with a neutron.

30 Write a nuclear equation that accurately describes the transmutation that took place. Be sure to include the identity of the new element as well as mass and charge values for each particle.

31 The newly discovered element was found to decay at a rate such that a 1.00 milligram sample was reduced to 0.125 milligrams in a period of 3.81 hours. Determine the half-life of the new element.

Base your answers to questions 32 through 35 on the following.

Given the nuclear equation:

$$^{235}_{92}U + ^{1}_{0}n \rightarrow ^{142}_{56}Ba + ^{91}_{36}Kr + 3^{1}_{0}n$$

32 State the type of nuclear reaction represented by the equation.

33 The sum of the masses of the products is slightly less than the sum of the masses of the reactants. Explain this loss of mass.

34 This process releases greater energy than an ordinary chemical reaction does. Name another type of nuclear reaction that releases greater energy than an ordinary chemical reaction.

35 Explain how exposure to the products of this reaction can be harmful to humans.

Base your answers to questions 36 and 37 on the information below.

In living organisms, the ratio of the naturally occurring isotopes of carbon, C-12 to C-13 to C-14 is fairly consistent. When an organism such as a woolly mammoth died, it stopped taking in carbon, and the amount of C-14 present in the mammoth began to decrease. For example, one fossil of a woolly mammoth is found to have 1/32 of the amount of C-14 found in living organisms.

36 Identify the type of nuclear reaction that caused the amount of C-14 in the woolly mammoth to decrease after the organism died.

37 Determine the total time that has elapsed since this woolly mammoth died.

Base your answers to questions 38 and 39 on the information below.

A U-238 atom decays to a Pb-206 atom through a series of steps. Each point on the graph below represents a nuclide and each arrow represents a nuclear decay mode.

Uranium Disintegration Series

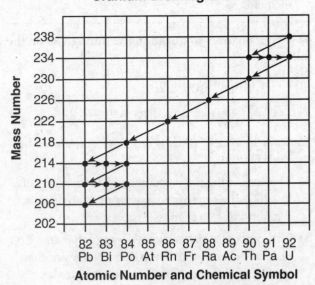

Atomic Number and Chemical Symbol

38 Based on the graph, what particle is emitted during the decay of a Po-218 particle?

39 Explain why the U-238 disintegration series ends with Pb-206.

Base your answers to questions 40 and 41 on the information below.

Some radioisotopes used as tracers make it possible for doctors to see the images of internal body parts and observe their functions. The table below lists information about three radioisotopes and the body part each radioisotope is used to study.

Medical Uses of Some Radioisotopes			
Radioisotopes	Half-Life	Decay Mode	Body Part
Na-24	15 hours	Beta	Circulatory system
Fe-59	44.5 days	Beta	Red blood cells
I-131	8.1 days	Beta	thyroid

40 Write the equation for the nuclear decay of the radioisotope used to study red blood cells.

41 It could take up to 60. hours for a radioisotope to be delivered to a hospital from the laboratory where it was produced. What fraction of an original sample of Na-24 remains unchanged after 60. hours?

Base your answers to questions 42 through 44 on the information below.

The radioisotope uranium-238 occurs naturally in Earth's crust. The disintegration of this radioisotope is the first in a series of spontaneous decays. The seventh decay in this series is an alpha decay which produces the radioisotope polonium-218 that has a half-life of 3.04 minutes. Eventually, the stable isotope lead-206 is produced by the alpha decay of an unstable nuclide.

42 Explain, in terms of electron configuration, why atoms produced in the sixth decay of the series do not readily react to form compounds.

43 Complete the decay equation below that represents the final decay in the series

$$^{210}_{84}\text{Po} \rightarrow \underline{\hspace{1cm}} + ^{206}_{82}\text{Pb}$$

44 An original mass of Po-218 of 8.00 milligrams is allowed to decay. Determine the mass of the sample that remains unchanged after 12.16 minutes.

Appendix 1:
Reference Tables for Physical Setting/Chemistry

Using the Reference Tables

You should become thoroughly familiar with all details of these tables.

Look for the (R) on the topic pages to see where the content is enhanced by the reference tables.

Some of the ways these reference tables are used in Regents Examination questions include:

- Finding a specific fact, such as the value of the heat of vaporization of water.

- Using an equation to determine the concentration of an unknown solution in a titration.

- Determining the solubility of various compounds in water.

- Assessing the relative activity of representative metals and halogens.

- Interpreting the symbols of radioisotopes to determine mode of decay and length of half-life.

- Using the Periodic Table to determine the properties of elements.

- Interpreting the color changes of indicators to determine acidity or alkalinity.

Reference Tables for Physical Setting/CHEMISTRY
2011 Edition

Table A
Standard Temperature and Pressure

Name	Value	Unit
Standard Pressure	101.3 kPa 1 atm	kilopascal atmosphere
Standard Temperature	273 K 0°C	kelvin degree Celsius

Table B
Physical Constants for Water

Heat of Fusion	334 J/g
Heat of Vaporization	2260 J/g
Specific Heat Capacity of $H_2O(\ell)$	4.18 J/g•K

Table C
Selected Prefixes

Factor	Prefix	Symbol
10^3	kilo-	k
10^{-1}	deci-	d
10^{-2}	centi-	c
10^{-3}	milli-	m
10^{-6}	micro-	μ
10^{-9}	nano-	n
10^{-12}	pico-	p

Table D
Selected Units

Symbol	Name	Quantity
m	meter	length
g	gram	mass
Pa	pascal	pressure
K	kelvin	temperature
mol	mole	amount of substance
J	joule	energy, work, quantity of heat
s	second	time
min	minute	time
h	hour	time
d	day	time
y	year	time
L	liter	volume
ppm	parts per million	concentration
M	molarity	solution concentration
u	atomic mass unit	atomic mass

Table E
Selected Polyatomic Ions

Formula	Name	Formula	Name
H_3O^+	hydronium	CrO_4^{2-}	chromate
Hg_2^{2+}	mercury(I)	$Cr_2O_7^{2-}$	dichromate
NH_4^+	ammonium	MnO_4^-	permanganate
$C_2H_3O_2^-$ CH_3COO^- } acetate	acetate	NO_2^-	nitrite
		NO_3^-	nitrate
CN^-	cyanide	O_2^{2-}	peroxide
CO_3^{2-}	carbonate	OH^-	hydroxide
HCO_3^-	hydrogen carbonate	PO_4^{3-}	phosphate
$C_2O_4^{2-}$	oxalate	SCN^-	thiocyanate
ClO^-	hypochlorite	SO_3^{2-}	sulfite
ClO_2^-	chlorite	SO_4^{2-}	sulfate
ClO_3^-	chlorate	HSO_4^-	hydrogen sulfate
ClO_4^-	perchlorate	$S_2O_3^{2-}$	thiosulfate

Table F
Solubility Guidelines for Aqueous Solutions

Ions That Form *Soluble* Compounds	Exceptions	Ions That Form *Insoluble* Compounds*	Exceptions
Group 1 ions (Li^+, Na^+, etc.)		carbonate (CO_3^{2-})	when combined with Group 1 ions or ammonium (NH_4^+)
ammonium (NH_4^+)		chromate (CrO_4^{2-})	when combined with Group 1 ions, Ca^{2+}, Mg^{2+}, or ammonium (NH_4^+)
nitrate (NO_3^-)			
acetate ($C_2H_3O_2^-$ or CH_3COO^-)		phosphate (PO_4^{3-})	when combined with Group 1 ions or ammonium (NH_4^+)
hydrogen carbonate (HCO_3^-)		sulfide (S^{2-})	when combined with Group 1 ions or ammonium (NH_4^+)
chlorate (ClO_3^-)			
halides (Cl^-, Br^-, I^-)	when combined with Ag^+, Pb^{2+}, or Hg_2^{2+}	hydroxide (OH^-)	when combined with Group 1 ions, Ca^{2+}, Ba^{2+}, Sr^{2+}, or ammonium (NH_4^+)
sulfates (SO_4^{2-})	when combined with Ag^+, Ca^{2+}, Sr^{2+}, Ba^{2+}, or Pb^{2+}		

*compounds having very low solubility in H_2O

Table G
Solubility Curves at Standard Pressure

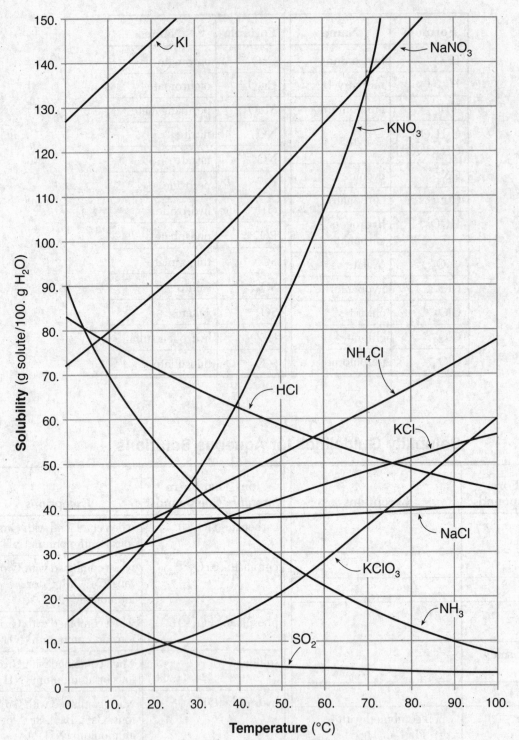

Table H
Vapor Pressure of Four Liquids

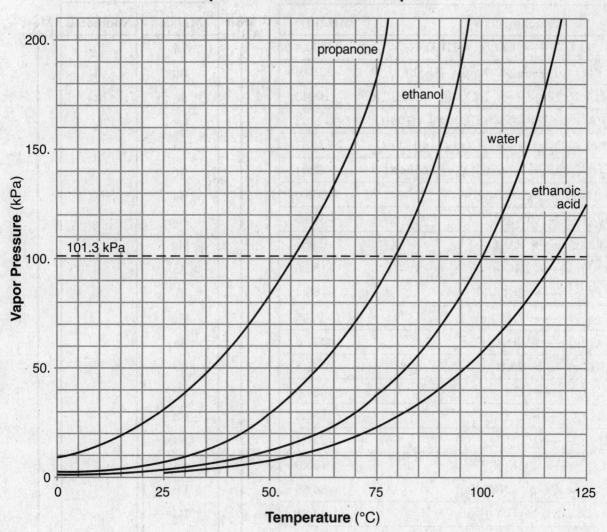

Table I
Heats of Reaction at 101.3 kPa and 298 K

Reaction	ΔH (kJ)*
$CH_4(g) + 2O_2(g) \longrightarrow CO_2(g) + 2H_2O(\ell)$	-890.4
$C_3H_8(g) + 5O_2(g) \longrightarrow 3CO_2(g) + 4H_2O(\ell)$	-2219.2
$2C_8H_{18}(\ell) + 25O_2(g) \longrightarrow 16CO_2(g) + 18H_2O(\ell)$	-10943
$2CH_3OH(\ell) + 3O_2(g) \longrightarrow 2CO_2(g) + 4H_2O(\ell)$	-1452
$C_2H_5OH(\ell) + 3O_2(g) \longrightarrow 2CO_2(g) + 3H_2O(\ell)$	-1367
$C_6H_{12}O_6(s) + 6O_2(g) \longrightarrow 6CO_2(g) + 6H_2O(\ell)$	-2804
$2CO(g) + O_2(g) \longrightarrow 2CO_2(g)$	-566.0
$C(s) + O_2(g) \longrightarrow CO_2(g)$	-393.5
$4Al(s) + 3O_2(g) \longrightarrow 2Al_2O_3(s)$	-3351
$N_2(g) + O_2(g) \longrightarrow 2NO(g)$	$+182.6$
$N_2(g) + 2O_2(g) \longrightarrow 2NO_2(g)$	$+66.4$
$2H_2(g) + O_2(g) \longrightarrow 2H_2O(g)$	-483.6
$2H_2(g) + O_2(g) \longrightarrow 2H_2O(\ell)$	-571.6
$N_2(g) + 3H_2(g) \longrightarrow 2NH_3(g)$	-91.8
$2C(s) + 3H_2(g) \longrightarrow C_2H_6(g)$	-84.0
$2C(s) + 2H_2(g) \longrightarrow C_2H_4(g)$	$+52.4$
$2C(s) + H_2(g) \longrightarrow C_2H_2(g)$	$+227.4$
$H_2(g) + I_2(g) \longrightarrow 2HI(g)$	$+53.0$
$KNO_3(s) \xrightarrow{H_2O} K^+(aq) + NO_3^-(aq)$	$+34.89$
$NaOH(s) \xrightarrow{H_2O} Na^+(aq) + OH^-(aq)$	-44.51
$NH_4Cl(s) \xrightarrow{H_2O} NH_4^+(aq) + Cl^-(aq)$	$+14.78$
$NH_4NO_3(s) \xrightarrow{H_2O} NH_4^+(aq) + NO_3^-(aq)$	$+25.69$
$NaCl(s) \xrightarrow{H_2O} Na^+(aq) + Cl^-(aq)$	$+3.88$
$LiBr(s) \xrightarrow{H_2O} Li^+(aq) + Br^-(aq)$	-48.83
$H^+(aq) + OH^-(aq) \longrightarrow H_2O(\ell)$	-55.8

*The ΔH values are based on molar quantities represented in the equations. A minus sign indicates an exothermic reaction.

Table J
Activity Series**

Most Active → Least Active (Metals)	Most Active → Least Active (Nonmetals)
Li	F_2
Rb	Cl_2
K	Br_2
Cs	I_2
Ba	
Sr	
Ca	
Na	
Mg	
Al	
Ti	
Mn	
Zn	
Cr	
Fe	
Co	
Ni	
Sn	
Pb	
H_2	
Cu	
Ag	
Au	

**Activity Series is based on the hydrogen standard. H_2 is *not* a metal.

Table K
Common Acids

Formula	Name
$HCl(aq)$	hydrochloric acid
$HNO_2(aq)$	nitrous acid
$HNO_3(aq)$	nitric acid
$H_2SO_3(aq)$	sulfurous acid
$H_2SO_4(aq)$	sulfuric acid
$H_3PO_4(aq)$	phosphoric acid
$H_2CO_3(aq)$ or $CO_2(aq)$	carbonic acid
$CH_3COOH(aq)$ or $HC_2H_3O_2(aq)$	ethanoic acid (acetic acid)

Table L
Common Bases

Formula	Name
$NaOH(aq)$	sodium hydroxide
$KOH(aq)$	potassium hydroxide
$Ca(OH)_2(aq)$	calcium hydroxide
$NH_3(aq)$	aqueous ammonia

Table M
Common Acid–Base Indicators

Indicator	Approximate pH Range for Color Change	Color Change
methyl orange	3.1–4.4	red to yellow
bromthymol blue	6.0–7.6	yellow to blue
phenolphthalein	8–9	colorless to pink
litmus	4.5–8.3	red to blue
bromcresol green	3.8–5.4	yellow to blue
thymol blue	8.0–9.6	yellow to blue

Source: *The Merck Index*, 14th ed., 2006, Merck Publishing Group

Table N
Selected Radioisotopes

Nuclide	Half-Life	Decay Mode	Nuclide Name
^{198}Au	2.695 d	β^-	gold-198
^{14}C	5715 y	β^-	carbon-14
^{37}Ca	182 ms	β^+	calcium-37
^{60}Co	5.271 y	β^-	cobalt-60
^{137}Cs	30.2 y	β^-	cesium-137
^{53}Fe	8.51 min	β^+	iron-53
^{220}Fr	27.4 s	α	francium-220
^{3}H	12.31 y	β^-	hydrogen-3
^{131}I	8.021 d	β^-	iodine-131
^{37}K	1.23 s	β^+	potassium-37
^{42}K	12.36 h	β^-	potassium-42
^{85}Kr	10.73 y	β^-	krypton-85
^{16}N	7.13 s	β^-	nitrogen-16
^{19}Ne	17.22 s	β^+	neon-19
^{32}P	14.28 d	β^-	phosphorus-32
^{239}Pu	2.410×10^4 y	α	plutonium-239
^{226}Ra	1599 y	α	radium-226
^{222}Rn	3.823 d	α	radon-222
^{90}Sr	29.1 y	β^-	strontium-90
^{99}Tc	2.13×10^5 y	β^-	technetium-99
^{232}Th	1.40×10^{10} y	α	thorium-232
^{233}U	1.592×10^5 y	α	uranium-233
^{235}U	7.04×10^8 y	α	uranium-235
^{238}U	4.47×10^9 y	α	uranium-238

Source: *CRC Handbook of Chemistry and Physics*, 91st ed., 2010–2011, CRC Press

Table O
Symbols Used in Nuclear Chemistry

Name	Notation	Symbol
alpha particle	$_2^4\text{He}$ or $_2^4\alpha$	α
beta particle	$_{-1}^0\text{e}$ or $_{-1}^0\beta$	β^-
gamma radiation	$_0^0\gamma$	γ
neutron	$_0^1\text{n}$	n
proton	$_1^1\text{H}$ or $_1^1\text{p}$	p
positron	$_{+1}^0\text{e}$ or $_{+1}^0\beta$	β^+

Table P
Organic Prefixes

Prefix	Number of Carbon Atoms
meth-	1
eth-	2
prop-	3
but-	4
pent-	5
hex-	6
hept-	7
oct-	8
non-	9
dec-	10

Table Q
Homologous Series of Hydrocarbons

Name	General Formula	Examples	
		Name	Structural Formula
alkanes	C_nH_{2n+2}	ethane	H H H—C—C—H H H
alkenes	C_nH_{2n}	ethene	H H C=C H H
alkynes	C_nH_{2n-2}	ethyne	H—C≡C—H

Note: n = number of carbon atoms

Table R
Organic Functional Groups

Class of Compound	Functional Group	General Formula	Example
halide (halocarbon)	—F (fluoro-) —Cl (chloro-) —Br (bromo-) —I (iodo-)	$R-X$ (X represents any halogen)	$CH_3CHClCH_3$ 2-chloropropane
alcohol	—OH	$R-OH$	$CH_3CH_2CH_2OH$ 1-propanol
ether	—O—	$R-O-R'$	$CH_3OCH_2CH_3$ methyl ethyl ether
aldehyde	$\overset{\displaystyle O}{\overset{\|}{-C}}-H$	$R-\overset{\displaystyle O}{\overset{\|}{C}}-H$	$CH_3CH_2\overset{\displaystyle O}{\overset{\|}{C}}-H$ propanal
ketone	$-\overset{\displaystyle O}{\overset{\|}{C}}-$	$R-\overset{\displaystyle O}{\overset{\|}{C}}-R'$	$CH_3\overset{\displaystyle O}{\overset{\|}{C}}CH_2CH_2CH_3$ 2-pentanone
organic acid	$-\overset{\displaystyle O}{\overset{\|}{C}}-OH$	$R-\overset{\displaystyle O}{\overset{\|}{C}}-OH$	$CH_3CH_2\overset{\displaystyle O}{\overset{\|}{C}}-OH$ propanoic acid
ester	$-\overset{\displaystyle O}{\overset{\|}{C}}-O-$	$R-\overset{\displaystyle O}{\overset{\|}{C}}-O-R'$	$CH_3CH_2COCH_3$ methyl propanoate
amine	$-\overset{\|}{N}-$	$R-\overset{\displaystyle R'}{\overset{\|}{N}}-R''$	$CH_3CH_2CH_2NH_2$ 1-propanamine
amide	$-\overset{\displaystyle O}{\overset{\|}{C}}-\overset{\|}{N}H$	$R-\overset{\displaystyle O}{\overset{\|}{C}}-\overset{\displaystyle R'}{\overset{\|}{N}}H$	$CH_3CH_2\overset{\displaystyle O}{\overset{\|}{C}}-NH_2$ propanamide

Note: R represents a bonded atom or group of atoms.

Periodic Table of the Elements

KEY

Selected Oxidation States → -4, +2, +4

Atomic Mass → 12.011

Symbol → C

Atomic Number → 6

Electron Configuration → 2-4

Note: Numbers in parentheses are mass numbers of the most stable or common isotope.

Relative atomic masses are based on $^{12}C = 12$ (exact).

Period 1

Group 1		Group 18
+1, -1 1.00794 **H** 1, 1-1		0 4.00260 **He** 2, 2

Groups / Periods

Group 1
- Period 2: +1 6.941 **Li** 3, 2-1
- Period 3: +1 22.98977 **Na** 11, 2-8-1
- Period 4: +1 39.0983 **K** 19, 2-8-8-1
- Period 5: +1 85.4678 **Rb** 37, 2-8-18-8-1
- Period 6: +1 132.905 **Cs** 55, 2-8-18-18-8-1
- Period 7: (223) **Fr** 87, -18-32-18-8-1

Group 2
- Period 2: +2 9.01218 **Be** 4, 2-2
- Period 3: +2 24.305 **Mg** 12, 2-8-2
- Period 4: +2 40.08 **Ca** 20, 2-8-8-2
- Period 5: +2 87.62 **Sr** 38, 2-8-18-8-2
- Period 6: +2 137.33 **Ba** 56, 2-8-18-18-8-2
- Period 7: +2 (226) **Ra** 88, -18-32-18-8-2

Group 3
- +3 44.9559 **Sc** 21, 2-8-9-2
- +3 88.9059 **Y** 39, 2-8-18-9-2
- +3 138.9055 **La** 57, 2-8-18-18-9-2
- +3 (227) **Ac** 89, -18-32-18-9-2

Group 4
- +2, +3, +4 47.867 **Ti** 22, 2-8-10-2
- +4 91.224 **Zr** 40, 2-8-18-10-2
- +4 178.49 **Hf** 72, *18-32-10-2
- +4 (261) **Rf** 104

Group 5
- +2, +3, +4, +5 50.9415 **V** 23, 2-8-11-2
- +5 92.9064 **Nb** 41, 2-8-18-12-1
- +5 180.948 **Ta** 73, -18-32-11-2
- (262) **Db** 105

Group 6
- +2, +3, +6 51.996 **Cr** 24, 2-8-13-1
- +6 95.94 **Mo** 42, 2-8-18-13-1
- +6 183.84 **W** 74, -18-32-12-2
- (266) **Sg** 106

Group 7
- +2, +4, +7 54.9380 **Mn** 25, 2-8-13-2
- +4, +6, +7 (98) **Tc** 43, 2-8-18-13-2
- +4, +6, +7 186.207 **Re** 75, -18-32-13-2
- (272) **Bh** 107

Group 8
- +2, +3 55.845 **Fe** 26, 2-8-14-2
- +3, +4 101.07 **Ru** 44, 2-8-18-15-1
- +3, +4 190.23 **Os** 76, -18-32-14-2
- (277) **Hs** 108

Group 9
- +2, +3 58.9332 **Co** 27, 2-8-15-2
- +3 102.906 **Rh** 45, 2-8-18-16-1
- +3, +4 192.217 **Ir** 77, -18-32-15-2
- (276) **Mt** 109

Group 10
- +2, +3 58.693 **Ni** 28, 2-8-16-2
- +2, +4 106.42 **Pd** 46, 2-8-18-18
- +2, +4 195.08 **Pt** 78, -18-32-17-1
- (281) **Ds** 110

Group 11
- +1, +2 63.546 **Cu** 29, 2-8-18-1
- +1 107.868 **Ag** 47, 2-8-18-18-1
- +1, +3 196.967 **Au** 79, -18-32-18-1
- (280) **Rg** 111

Group 12
- +2 65.409 **Zn** 30, 2-8-18-2
- +2 112.41 **Cd** 48, 2-8-18-18-2
- +1, +2 200.59 **Hg** 80, -18-32-18-2
- (285) **Cn** 112

Group 13
- +3 10.81 **B** 5, 2-3
- +3 26.98154 **Al** 13, 2-8-3
- +3 69.723 **Ga** 31, 2-8-18-3
- +3 114.818 **In** 49, 2-8-18-18-3
- +1, +3 204.383 **Tl** 81, -18-32-18-3
- (284) **Uut** 113**

Group 14
- -4, +2, +4 12.011 **C** 6, 2-4
- -4 28.0855 **Si** 14, 2-8-4
- -4, +2, +4 72.64 **Ge** 32, 2-8-18-4
- +2, +4 118.71 **Sn** 50, 2-8-18-18-4
- +2, +4 207.2 **Pb** 82, -18-32-18-4
- (289) **Uuq** 114

Group 15
- -3, +1, +2, +3, +4, +5 14.0067 **N** 7, 2-5
- -3, +3, +5 30.97376 **P** 15, 2-8-5
- -3, +3, +5 74.9216 **As** 33, 2-8-18-5
- -3, +3, +5 121.760 **Sb** 51, 2-8-18-18-5
- +3, +5 208.980 **Bi** 83, -18-32-18-5
- (288) **Uup** 115

Group 16
- -2 15.9994 **O** 8, 2-6
- -2, +4, +6 32.065 **S** 16, 2-8-6
- -2, +4, +6 78.96 **Se** 34, 2-8-18-6
- -2, +4, +6 127.60 **Te** 52, 2-8-18-18-6
- +2, +4 (209) **Po** 84, -18-32-18-6
- (292) **Uuh** 116

Group 17
- -1, +1, +5, +7 18.9984 **F** 9, 2-7
- -1, +1, +5, +7 35.453 **Cl** 17, 2-8-7
- -1, +1, +5 79.904 **Br** 35, 2-8-18-7
- -1, +1, +5, +7 126.904 **I** 53, 2-8-18-18-7
- (210) **At** 85, -18-32-18-7
- (?) **Uus** 117

Group 18
- 0 20.180 **Ne** 10, 2-8
- 0 39.948 **Ar** 18, 2-8-8
- 0, +2 83.798 **Kr** 36, 2-8-18-8
- 0, +2, +4, +6 131.29 **Xe** 54, 2-8-18-18-8
- (222) **Rn** 86, -18-32-18-8
- (294) **Uuo** 118

Lanthanides (Period 6)

+3 140.116 **Ce** 58	+3, +4 140.908 **Pr** 59	+3 144.24 **Nd** 60
(145) **Pm** 61	+2, +3 150.36 **Sm** 62	+2, +3 151.964 **Eu** 63
+3 157.25 **Gd** 64	+3 158.925 **Tb** 65	+3 162.500 **Dy** 66
+3 164.930 **Ho** 67	+3 167.259 **Er** 68	+3 168.934 **Tm** 69
+2, +3 173.04 **Yb** 70	+3 174.9668 **Lu** 71	

Actinides (Period 7)

+3, +4 232.038 **Th** 90	+4, +5 231.036 **Pa** 91	+3, +4, +5, +6 238.029 **U** 92
+3, +4, +5, +6 (237) **Np** 93	+3, +4, +5, +6 (244) **Pu** 94	+3, +4, +5, +6 (243) **Am** 95
+3, +4 (247) **Cm** 96	+3, +4 (247) **Bk** 97	+3 (251) **Cf** 98
+3 (252) **Es** 99	+3 (257) **Fm** 100	+2, +3 (258) **Md** 101
+2, +3 (259) **No** 102	+3 (262) **Lr** 103	

*denotes the presence of (2-8-) for elements 72 and above

**The systematic names and symbols for elements of atomic numbers 113 and above will be used until the approval of trivial names by IUPAC.

Source: *CRC Handbook of Chemistry and Physics*, 91st ed., 2010–2011, CRC Press

Table S
Properties of Selected Elements

Atomic Number	Symbol	Name	First Ionization Energy (kJ/mol)	Electro-negativity	Melting Point (K)	Boiling* Point (K)	Density** (g/cm³)	Atomic Radius (pm)
1	H	hydrogen	1312	2.2	14	20.	0.000082	32
2	He	helium	2372	—	—	4	0.000164	37
3	Li	lithium	520.	1.0	454	1615	0.534	130.
4	Be	beryllium	900.	1.6	1560.	2744	1.85	99
5	B	boron	801	2.0	2348	4273	2.34	84
6	C	carbon	1086	2.6	—	—	—	75
7	N	nitrogen	1402	3.0	63	77	0.001145	71
8	O	oxygen	1314	3.4	54	90.	0.001308	64
9	F	fluorine	1681	4.0	53	85	0.001553	60.
10	Ne	neon	2081	—	24	27	0.000825	62
11	Na	sodium	496	0.9	371	1156	0.97	160.
12	Mg	magnesium	738	1.3	923	1363	1.74	140.
13	Al	aluminum	578	1.6	933	2792	2.70	124
14	Si	silicon	787	1.9	1687	3538	2.3296	114
15	P	phosphorus (white)	1012	2.2	317	554	1.823	109
16	S	sulfur (monoclinic)	1000.	2.6	388	718	2.00	104
17	Cl	chlorine	1251	3.2	172	239	0.002898	100.
18	Ar	argon	1521	—	84	87	0.001633	101
19	K	potassium	419	0.8	337	1032	0.89	200.
20	Ca	calcium	590.	1.0	1115	1757	1.54	174
21	Sc	scandium	633	1.4	1814	3109	2.99	159
22	Ti	titanium	659	1.5	1941	3560.	4.506	148
23	V	vanadium	651	1.6	2183	3680.	6.0	144
24	Cr	chromium	653	1.7	2180.	2944	7.15	130.
25	Mn	manganese	717	1.6	1519	2334	7.3	129
26	Fe	iron	762	1.8	1811	3134	7.87	124
27	Co	cobalt	760.	1.9	1768	3200.	8.86	118
28	Ni	nickel	737	1.9	1728	3186	8.90	117
29	Cu	copper	745	1.9	1358	2835	8.96	122
30	Zn	zinc	906	1.7	693	1180.	7.134	120.
31	Ga	gallium	579	1.8	303	2477	5.91	123
32	Ge	germanium	762	2.0	1211	3106	5.3234	120.
33	As	arsenic (gray)	944	2.2	1090.	—	5.75	120.
34	Se	selenium (gray)	941	2.6	494	958	4.809	118
35	Br	bromine	1140.	3.0	266	332	3.1028	117
36	Kr	krypton	1351	—	116	120.	0.003425	116
37	Rb	rubidium	403	0.8	312	961	1.53	215
38	Sr	strontium	549	1.0	1050.	1655	2.64	190.
39	Y	yttrium	600.	1.2	1795	3618	4.47	176
40	Zr	zirconium	640.	1.3	2128	4682	6.52	164

Atomic Number	Symbol	Name	First Ionization Energy (kJ/mol)	Electro-negativity	Melting Point (K)	Boiling* Point (K)	Density** (g/cm³)	Atomic Radius (pm)
41	Nb	niobium	652	1.6	2750.	5017	8.57	156
42	Mo	molybdenum	684	2.2	2896	4912	10.2	146
43	Tc	technetium	702	2.1	2430.	4538	11	138
44	Ru	ruthenium	710.	2.2	2606	4423	12.1	136
45	Rh	rhodium	720.	2.3	2237	3968	12.4	134
46	Pd	palladium	804	2.2	1828	3236	12.0	130.
47	Ag	silver	731	1.9	1235	2435	10.5	136
48	Cd	cadmium	868	1.7	594	1040.	8.69	140.
49	In	indium	558	1.8	430.	2345	7.31	142
50	Sn	tin (white)	709	2.0	505	2875	7.287	140.
51	Sb	antimony (gray)	831	2.1	904	1860.	6.68	140.
52	Te	tellurium	869	2.1	723	1261	6.232	137
53	I	iodine	1008	2.7	387	457	4.933	136
54	Xe	xenon	1170.	2.6	161	165	0.005366	136
55	Cs	cesium	376	0.8	302	944	1.873	238
56	Ba	barium	503	0.9	1000.	2170.	3.62	206
57	La	lanthanum	538	1.1	1193	3737	6.15	194

Elements 58–71 have been omitted.

Atomic Number	Symbol	Name	First Ionization Energy (kJ/mol)	Electro-negativity	Melting Point (K)	Boiling* Point (K)	Density** (g/cm³)	Atomic Radius (pm)
72	Hf	hafnium	659	1.3	2506	4876	13.3	164
73	Ta	tantalum	728	1.5	3290.	5731	16.4	158
74	W	tungsten	759	1.7	3695	5828	19.3	150.
75	Re	rhenium	756	1.9	3458	5869	20.8	141
76	Os	osmium	814	2.2	3306	5285	22.587	136
77	Ir	iridium	865	2.2	2719	4701	22.562	132
78	Pt	platinum	864	2.2	2041	4098	21.5	130.
79	Au	gold	890.	2.4	1337	3129	19.3	130.
80	Hg	mercury	1007	1.9	234	630.	13.5336	132
81	Tl	thallium	589	1.8	577	1746	11.8	144
82	Pb	lead	716	1.8	600.	2022	11.3	145
83	Bi	bismuth	703	1.9	544	1837	9.79	150.
84	Po	polonium	812	2.0	527	1235	9.20	142
85	At	astatine	—	2.2	575	—	—	148
86	Rn	radon	1037	—	202	211	0.009074	146
87	Fr	francium	393	0.7	300.	—	—	242
88	Ra	radium	509	0.9	969	—	5	211
89	Ac	actinium	499	1.1	1323	3471	10.	201

Elements 90 and above have been omitted.

*boiling point at standard pressure
**density of solids and liquids at room temperature and density of gases at 298 K and 101.3 kPa
— no data available

Source: *CRC Handbook for Chemistry and Physics*, 91st ed., 2010–2011, CRC Press

Table T
Important Formulas and Equations

Density	$d = \dfrac{m}{V}$	d = density m = mass V = volume
Mole Calculations	number of moles = $\dfrac{\text{given mass}}{\text{gram-formula mass}}$	
Percent Error	% error = $\dfrac{\text{measured value} - \text{accepted value}}{\text{accepted value}} \times 100$	
Percent Composition	% composition by mass = $\dfrac{\text{mass of part}}{\text{mass of whole}} \times 100$	
Concentration	parts per million = $\dfrac{\text{mass of solute}}{\text{mass of solution}} \times 1\,000\,000$	
	molarity = $\dfrac{\text{moles of solute}}{\text{liter of solution}}$	
Combined Gas Law	$\dfrac{P_1 V_1}{T_1} = \dfrac{P_2 V_2}{T_2}$	P = pressure V = volume T = temperature
Titration	$M_A V_A = M_B V_B$	M_A = molarity of H^+ M_B = molarity of OH^- V_A = volume of acid V_B = volume of base
Heat	$q = mC\Delta T$ $q = mH_f$ $q = mH_v$	q = heat H_f = heat of fusion m = mass H_v = heat of vaporization C = specific heat capacity ΔT = change in temperature
Temperature	$K = °C + 273$	K = kelvin $°C$ = degree Celsius

Appendix 2:
Graphing and Math Skills

This appendix provides a review of basic graphing skills that will be helpful in answering various types of questions on the Regents Examination for Physical Setting/Chemistry.

Graphing

A graph of data collected during an experiment provides a single cohesive picture of many separate pieces of data. Graphs often allow you to see patterns and relationships in the data that are not otherwise obvious.

Variables Each of a graph's axes represents a variable. In a typical science experiment, the scientist changes one variable in order to see how a second variable changes in response. The variable that the scientist controls and changes is called the *independent variable*. Normally the independent variable is plotted on the horizontal or *x*-axis. The variable that responds to changes in the independent variable is called the *dependent variable*. The dependent variable is usually plotted on the vertical or *y*-axis.

Data Tables As data is collected during an experiment it is often organized and displayed in the form of a data table. The data table should have a title that briefly describes the experiment or data. This data table title may be the same title used for the graph of the data. Data tables typically have at least two columns, one for the dependent variable and one for the independent variable. The independent variable is placed in the first column, and the dependent variable is placed in the second column. Label each column with the name of the variable being measured.

Preparing a Graph In order to prepare the graph, first look at the data table. Take note of the range of values of each of the variables in the data table. Determine if the origin of the graph will have a value of zero. Although origins with zero values are common, they are not mandatory.

Considering the range of data values, divide each axis into convenient units based on the graph paper's grid. If you are drawing your own axes on blank paper, choose divisions that are convenient for clearly displaying the data.

Be sure that each box represents the same increment. Axis scales should be chosen to spread the data over as much space as possible. Label each axis with the name of the variable being plotted and the units being used.

Now that the blank graph is prepared, the *x-y* data point pairs are plotted. Once the points have been plotted, a best-fit line is drawn to show the trend indicated by the data. The best-fit line does not have to pass through every point. In fact, the chance of that happening is quite small. When a best-fit line is properly drawn, there are often as many points above the line as there are below the line. Remember that the data represents measurements, and that all measurements have some amount of uncertainty. You may want to think of the line as an average relationship between the variables.

SAMPLE PROBLEM

During a lab period each team was assigned to determine the relationship between the volume and mass of an unknown liquid. Each team was assigned two volumes. They carefully filled graduated cylinders to the assigned volumes and then massed the cylinders and their contents. Knowing the masses of the empty graduated cylinders, they calculated the mass of the liquid. The following data were collected and posted on the blackboard. Prepare a data table to display the data in an organized way, and then graph the data.

Team A
volume 10 mL	mass 9.5 g
volume 15 mL	mass 13.0 g

Team D
volume 40 mL	mass 34.4 g
volume 45 mL	mass 37.8 g

Team B
volume 20 mL	mass 17.0 g
volume 25 mL	mass 21.5 g

Team C
volume 30 mL	mass 25.5 g
volume 35 mL	mass 30.1 g

Independent and Dependent Variables:

In this case, each team was assigned two specific volumes. Thus, volume is the variable being changed during the experiment; volume is the independent variable. The teams observed how mass changed in response to the change in volume. Thus, mass is the dependent variable.

1. Preparing the Data Table:

Prepare the data table by placing the volume data in the first column and the mass data in the second column. Order the volume data from the lowest value to highest value. Give the table a title that reflects the type of data it contains.

Relationship Between Volume and Mass of an Unknown Liquid

Volume (mL)	Mass (g)
10.0	9.5
15.0	13.0
20.0	17.0
25.0	21.5
30.0	25.5
35.0	30.1
40.0	34.4
45.0	37.8

Note that with the data organized as shown in the data table, there is a clear relationship between the variables. As the volume of the liquid increases, the mass of the liquid also increases.

2. Preparing the Graph:

Because the volume is the independent variable, it is plotted on the x-axis. The x-label is Volume (mL). Because the x-axis data ranges from 10.0 mL to 45.0 mL, a range of 0.0 mL to 50.0 mL is chosen for the x-axis. Each box along the axis has a value of 2.0 mL.

Mass is the dependent variable and is plotted on the y-axis. The y-axis label is Mass (g). Because the y-axis data ranges from 9.5 g to 37.8 g, a range of 0.0 g to 40.0 g is chosen for the y-axis. Each box along the axis has a value of 2.0 g.

3. Plotting the Data:

Now that the blank graph is prepared, the x-y data point pairs are plotted. For this example, the points are plotted as a solid dot. See Figure A.

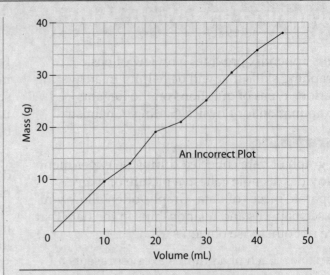

Figure A. Graph of volume versus mass for an unknown liquid

The graph above shows the plotted data and the data points connected by straight lines. The line on the graph indicates that the relationship between the volume of liquid and the mass of the liquid is not uniform. This is unlikely. Figure B shows why the use of a best-fit line is appropriate in this case. The best-fit straight line can be described by the equation $y = mx + b$. In this case, b (the y-intercept) occurs at the origin, so b has a value of zero. This is logical, for if there is no volume, the mass must be zero.

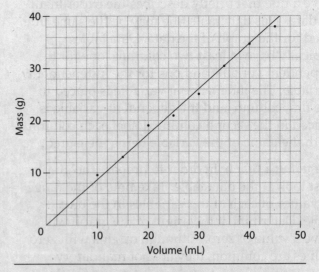

Figure B. Best-fit line drawn of the graph of volume versus mass for an unknown liquid

The slope of the line can be calculated by dividing the rise by the run. The rise over run is equal to $\Delta y/\Delta x$. (Note that the Δ symbol means "change in.") The units of $\Delta y/\Delta x$ are g/mL, which are the units commonly used for the density of a liquid. Thus the slope of the best-fit line represents the density of the unknown liquid. The density of a liquid should be a constant value.

If students had used their own data points to calculate the slope, there would be four different density calculations. Substituting each team's data in the equation

$$\text{density} = \frac{\text{mass}}{\text{volume}} = \frac{\Delta y}{\Delta x}$$

yields the following results:

Team A
$$\text{density} = \frac{(13.0\ g - 9.5\ g)}{(15.0\ mL - 10.0\ mL)} = \frac{0.70\ g}{mL}$$

Team B
$$\text{density} = \frac{(21.5\ g - 17.0\ g)}{(25.0\ mL - 20.0\ mL)} = \frac{0.90\ g}{mL}$$

Team C
$$\text{density} = \frac{(30.1\ g - 25.5\ g)}{(35.0\ mL - 30.0\ mL)} = \frac{0.92\ g}{mL}$$

Team D
$$\text{density} = \frac{(37.8\ g - 34.4\ g)}{(45.0\ mL - 40.0\ mL)} = \frac{0.68\ g}{mL}$$

Constructing the slope using the best-fit line simply involves picking two convenient points on the line and making a calculation using these values. Figure C shows the density to be 0.88 g/mL.

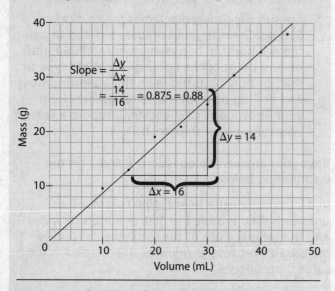

Figure C. Calculation of slope using data points from the best-fit line

Interpolation and Extrapolation A graph is also useful because it allows you to estimate values that are not part of the data table. When a value is read from the graph's curve that falls within the data table's values, the process in called *interpolation*. Interpolating from the graph in Figure B shows that a volume of 37 mL of the unknown liquid has a mass of approximately 32 g.

When the curve or line on a graph is extended beyond the known plotted values and used to make predictions, the process is called extrapolation. Extrapolating from the graph in Figure B shows that a volume of 8.0 mL of the unknown liquid should have a mass of approximately 7 g.

Graph Shapes and Relationships Figure D shows several typical graph shapes. If one variable increases as the other variable increases, the relationship is said to be direct. If one variable increases as the other decreases, the relationship is said to be indirect or inverse.

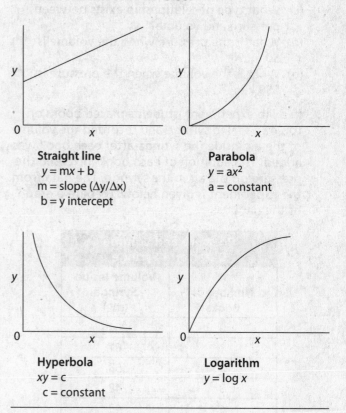

Figure D. Typical graph shapes

Practice Problems

1. In a laboratory experiment, the pressure on a confined gas was increased and the resulting changes in volume were recorded. The temperature of the gas was kept constant during the experiment.

Pressure and Volume Data for a Confined Gas	
Pressure (kPa)	Volume (mL)
100	93.0
200	46.5
300	31.0
400	23.2
500	18.6
600	15.5

(a) What are the independent and dependent variables?

(b) Plot a graph of the data starting with a pressure of 0 kPa.

(c) What type of relationship exists between pressure and volume?

(d) What is the pressure when the volume is 50 mL?

(e) What is the volume when the pressure is 550 kPa?

2. In a lab experiment, students placed books on top of a sealed syringe and recorded the volume of the air inside the syringe after each book was added. The addition of each book increased the pressure on the air in the syringe. The data from the experiment is given below. Prepare a graph of the data.

Pressure and Volume Data for a Syringe	
Number of Books	Volume Inside Syringe (mL)
0	64
1	61
2	53
3	48
4	43
5	39
6	36
7	32

3. In a laboratory exercise, the volume of a gas is measured at various temperatures while the pressure is held constant. Data from the experiment is given in the data table below.

Trial	Temperature (°C)	Volume (cm³)
A	0	100
B	50	120
C	100	135
D	150	155
E	200	173

(a) Graph the data. In preparing the graph, extend the temperature axis out to 300°C. Based on the trend in the behavior of the gas, extend the volume axis so you can extrapolate the volume at a temperature of 300°C. When preparing your graph decide if the axis used for the volume of the gas should begin at 0 cm^3 or 100 cm^3.

(b) What type of relationship exists between temperature and volume?

(c) Identify the independent and dependent variables.

(d) Extrapolate to determine the volume at 300°C.

4. Consult the *Reference Tables for Physical Setting/Chemistry* and prepare a graph to show the relationship between atomic radii and atomic number for the elements in periods 2 and 3. After you have prepared the graph decide if atomic radius is a periodic function. Write a sentence supporting your opinion.

5. Consult the *Reference Tables for Physical Setting/Chemistry* and prepare a graph showing the relationship between atomic number and boiling point of the noble gases. What type of relationship exists between the atomic number and boiling point of the noble gases? Using your knowledge of chemistry, propose a reason why this relationship exists.

Base your answers to questions 6 and 7 on the information below.

In a laboratory experiment, 10.00 grams of an unknown solid is added to 100. milliliters of water and the temperature of the resulting solution is measured over several minutes, as recorded in the table that follows.

Data Table	
Time (minutes)	Temperature (°C)
0	24.0
0.5	28.5
1.0	31.0
1.5	34.5
2.0	41.0
2.5	45.5
3.0	46.5

Base your answers to questions 8 through 10 on the information below.

A substance is a solid at 15°C. A student heated a sample of the solid substance and recorded the temperature at one-minute intervals in the data table below.

Time (min)	0	1	2	3	4	5	6	7	8	9	10	11	12
Temp (°C)	15	32	46	53	53	53	53	53	53	53	53	60	65

Change in Temperature During the Dissolving of a Solid

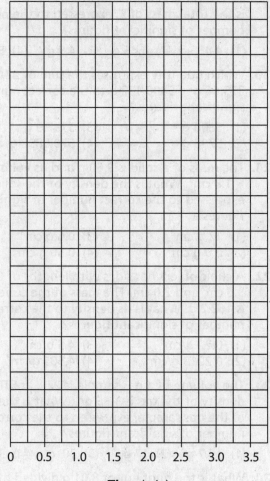

Temperature (°C)

0   0.5   1.0   1.5   2.0   2.5   3.0   3.5

Time (min)

Heating Curve

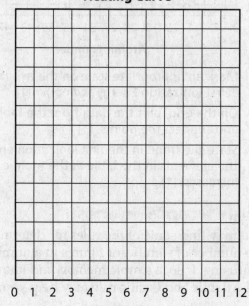

Temperature (°C)

0 1 2 3 4 5 6 7 8 9 10 11 12

Time (min)

8. On the grid mark an appropriate scale on the axis labeled "Temperature (°C). [1]

9. Plot the data from the table. Circle and connect the points. [1]

10. Based on the data table, what is the melting point of this substance? [1]

6. On the grid mark an appropriate scale on the axis labeled "Temperature °C."

7. Plot the data from the data table. Circle and connect the points.

Base your answers to questions 11 through 13 on the information below.

First Ionization Energy of Selected Elements		
Element	Atomic Number	First Ionization Energy (kJ/mol)
Lithium	3	520
Sodium	11	496
Potassium	19	419
Rubidium	37	403
Cesium	55	376

First Ionization Energy Versus Atomic Number of Selected Elements

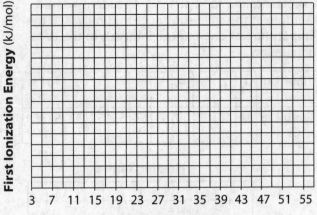

First Ionization Energy (kJ/mol)

Atomic Number

3 7 11 15 19 23 27 31 35 39 43 47 51 55

11. Mark an appropriate scale on the axis labeled "First Ionization Energy (kJ/mol)." [1]

12. On the grid, plot the data from the table. Circle and connect the points. [1]

13. State the trend in the first ionization energy for the elements in the table as the atomic number increases. [1]

Significant Figures

You may find some of the rules for determining the number of significant figures in a number a bit confusing. If so, a simple memory aid known as the Atlantic and Pacific rule may help you.

The Atlantic and Pacific Rule Imagine a map of the United States, with the Pacific Ocean on the left and the Atlantic Ocean on the right.

• When a decimal is **P**resent in a measurement, start on the **P**acific side (left side of the number) with the first nonzero digit. All the following digits are significant.

• When a decimal is **A**bsent in a measurement, start on the **A**tlantic side (right side of the number) with the first nonzero digit. All the preceding digits are significant.

Practice Problems

14. Which milligram quantity contains a total of four significant figures?

(1) 0.30310 mg   (3) 3100. mg
(2) 3010 mg   (4) 30,001 mg

15. Which measurement contains three significant figures?

(1) 0.05 g   (3) 0.056 g
(2) 0.050 g   (4) 0.0563 g

16. Which measurement has the greatest number of significant figures?

(1) 6.060 mg   (3) 606 mg
(2) 60.6 mg   (4) 60,600 mg

17. Which mass measurement contains a total of three significant figures?

(1) 22.0 g   (2) 22.00 g   (3) 220 g   (4) 2200 g

18. Which quantity expresses the sum (2.1 g + 33.566 g + 12.22 g) to the proper degree of precision?

(1) 47.886 g   (3) 47.9 g
(2) 47.89 g   (4) 48.0 g

19. When 1.255 g of X reacts completely with 3.2 g of Y, Z is the only product of the reaction. What is the total mass of Z, expressed to the proper number of significant figures?

(1) 4.455 g   (2) 4.46 g   (3) 4.5 g   (4) 5 g

20. Which quantity expresses the sum of 22.1 g + 375.66 g + 5400.132 g to the correct number of significant figures?

(1) 5800 g   (3) 5797.9 g
(2) 5798 g   (4) 5797.892 g

21. The mass of a solid is 3.60 g and its volume is 1.8 cm^3. What is the density of the solid, expressed to the correct number of significant figures?

(1) 12 g/cm^3 (3) 0.5 g/cm^3
(2) 2.0 g/cm^3 (4) 0.50 g/cm^3

22. A cubic object has sides with lengths of 6.0 cm, 3.0 cm, and 2.0 cm. The mass of the cube is 162.2 g. What is its density to the correct number of significant figures?

(1) 0.22 g/cm^3 (3) 4.5 g/cm^3
(2) 0.2219 g/cm^3 (4) 4.505 g/cm^3

23. The volume of a gas sample is 22 L at STP. The density of the gas is 1.35 g/L. What is the mass of the gas sample, expressed to the correct number of significant figures?

(1) 16.7 g   (2) 17 g   (3) 30. g   (4) 30.0 g

24. What is the quotient of 8.01 g divided by 3.127 g, expressed to the correct number of significant figures?

(1) 2.6   (2) 2.56   (3) 2.5562   (4) 2.5616

25. What is the product of 2.324 cm × 1.11 cm expressed to the correct number of significant figures?

(1) 2.58 cm^2 (3) 2.5796 cm^2
(2) 2.5780 cm^2 (4) 2.57964 cm^2

26. A solution contains 12.55 grams of a solid dissolved in 50.0 milliliters of water. What is the number of grams of solid dissolved per milliliter of water, rounded to the correct number of significant figures?

   (1) 0.25 g/mL   (3) 0.3 g/mL

   (2) 0.251 g/mL   (4) 0.2510 g/mL

27. Add the following using the rules for significant figures.

   (a) 35.7 g + 432.33 g + 5142.312 g

   (b) 0.027 g + 0.0023 g

28. For each of the following, express the answer to the correct number of significant figures.

   (a) Determine the density of a substance that has a mass of 21.6 g and a volume of 8.00 cm^3.

   (b) Determine the mass of an object that has a density of 4.0 g/mL and a volume of 2.55 mL.

29. A student calculates the density of an unknown solid. The mass is 10.04 grams, and the volume is 8.21 cubic centimeters. How many significant figures should appear in the final answer?

   (1) 1   (2) 2   (3) 3   (4) 4

Base your answer to question 30 on the information given below and on the data table.

In each of two trials, a 0.500 M NaOH(aq) solution is added to a flask containing a volume of HCl(aq) solution of unknown concentration.

Volumes of Base and Acid Used in Titration Trials			
		Trial 1	Trial 2
Solution (aq)	Molarity (M)	Volume Used	Volume Used
NaOH	0.500	17.03	16.87
HCl	?	10.22	10.12

30. Based on the information given in the table, how many significant figures should be shown in the calculated molarity of the HCl(aq) used in trial 2?

Base your answer to question 31 on the data showing the calculation of a sample of copper sulfate in a crucible.

Mass of $CuSO_4 \cdot 5H_2O$ and crucible: 21.37 g

Mass of crucible: 19.24 g

Mass of $CuSO_4 \cdot 5H_2O$:   2.13 g

31. What is the total number of significant figures that should be recorded in the calculated mass of $CuSO_4 \cdot 5H_2O$?

Base your answer to question 32 on the information provided in the data table below.

	Standard 0.100 M HCl	Unknown KOH
Initial reading	9.08 mL	0.55 mL
Final reading	19.09 mL	5.56 mL

32. When calculating the molarity of the KOH, how many significant figures can be reported?

33. A student titrates 60.0 mL of HNO$_3$(aq) with 0.30 M NaOH(aq). Phenolphthalein is used as an indicator. After adding 42.2 mL of NaOH(aq), a color change remains for 25 seconds, and the student stops the titration.

How many significant figures should be present in the calculated molarity of the HNO$_3$(aq)?

Base your answer to question 34 on the following information.

In a titration, a few drops of an indicator are added to a flask containing 35.0 milliliters of HNO$_3$(aq) of unknown concentration. After 30.0 milliliters of 0.15 M NaOH(aq) solution is slowly added to the flask, the indicator changes color, showing the acid is neutralized.

34. The volume of the NaOH(aq) is expressed to what number of significant figures?

As you study the Reference Tables for Physical Setting/Chemistry, use this appendix as a guide. An explanation of each table is presented here for review, along with questions for practice.

Table A: Standard Temperature and Pressure

There are questions in which you need to know these values. They are often included as information for part of a question rather than an isolated fact to be answered.

1. When an airbag is inflated the nitrogen gas has a pressure of 1.30 atmospheres, a temperature of 301 K, and a volume of 40.0 liters. Calculate the volume of the nitrogen at STP.

Table B: Physical Constants for Water

This table provides you with the values needed to calculate the heat lost and gained during a phase change (heats of fusion and vaporization, and the specific heat capacity needed to calculate energy exchanged when there is a temperature change.

2. How much heat energy must be absorbed to completely melt 35.0 grams of $H_2O(s)$ at 0°C?
   (1) 9.54 J   (3) 11700 J
   (2) 146 J   (4) 79100 J

3. What is the total number of joules released when a 5.00-gram sample of water changes from liquid to a solid as 0.0°C?
   (1) 334 J   (3) 2260 J
   (2) 1670 J   (4) 11300 J

4. What amount of heat is required to completely melt a 29.95 gram sample of $H_2O(s)$ at 0°C?
   (1) 334 J   (3) 1.00×10^3 J
   (2) 2260 J   (4) 1.00×10^4 J

Table C: Selected Prefixes

A useful reminder between the prefix and the factor of ten that it represents. For example, a kilogram is 10^3 or a thousand times as much mass as a gram, while a milligram is 10^{-3} or a thousandth of a gram.

Table D: Selected Units

The relationships shown may help you to determine which equation to use from Table T to solve a problem.

5. What pressure in atmospheres, is equal to 45.6 kPa?

Table E: Selected Polyatomic Ions

A very useful table showing the formula, charge, and name of common polyatomic ions.

6. What is the name of the polyatomic ion in the compound Na_2O_2?
   (1) hydroxide   (3) oxide
   (2) oxalate   (4) peroxide

7. Which polyatomic ion contains the greatest number of oxygen atoms?
   (1) acetate   (3) hydroxide
   (2) carbonate   (4) peroxide

Table F: Solubility Guidelines

The left table lists soluble combinations. For example, all ammonium (NH_4^+) compounds are soluble. Take note of the exceptions. Sulfates are generally soluble (Na_2SO_4), but there are exceptions ($CaSO_4$).

The same comments apply to the table on the right. The left column list insoluble combinations, the right shows combinations that are soluble.

Soluble compounds contain ionic bonding and are good conductors of electricity (electrolytes). Insoluble compounds also have ionic bonding but the ions are not in solution and are not good conductors.

8. Which of the following compounds is least soluble in water?
   (1) copper (II) chloride
   (2) aluminum acetate
   (3) iron (III) hydroxide
   (4) potassium sulfate

9. Based on Reference Table F, which of these salts is the best electrolyte?

   (1) sodium nitrate
   (2) silver chloride
   (3) magnesium carbonate
   (4) barium sulfate

10. Based on Table F, which of these saturated solutions has the lowest concentration of dissolved ions?

   (1) NaCl(aq)   (3) NiCl$_2$(aq)
   (2) MgCl$_2$(aq)   (4) AgCl(aq)

11. Which ion, when combined with chloride ions, Cl$^-$, forms an insoluble substance with water?

   (1) Fe^{2+} (3) Pb^{2+}
   (2) Mg^{2+} (4) Zn^{2+}

12. Which compound is insoluble in water?

   (1) MgSO$_4$ (3) KClO$_3$
   (2) SrCrO$_4$ (4) Na$_2$S

Table G: Solubility curves

When a quantity of a solute and the temperature is given you can plot its position relative to the line. If the point lies above the line for a given substance the solution is supersaturated, on the line shows a saturated solution, and below the line indicates an unsaturated solution.

Be sure to note that the graph shows conditions in 100. grams of water. If the quantity of water is not 100. grams, the amount of solid is proportional to the amount of water. For example if 40. grams of NH$_4$Cl can be dissolved in 100. grams of water at 25°C, then 80. grams of NH$_4$Cl can be dissolved in 200. grams of water at the same temperature.

Note that all except three of the curves show increasing solubility as the temperature rises, while three show decreases. The three substances, (HCl, NH$_3$, and SO$_2$) are gases at temperatures within the range shown. All gases decrease in solubility as the temperature rises.

13. A solution contains 35 grams of KNO$_3$ dissolved in 100 grams of water at 40°C. How much more KNO$_3$ would have to be added to make it a saturated solution?

   (1) 29 g   (3) 12 g
   (2) 24 g   (4) 4 g

14. A saturated solution of NaNO$_3$ is prepared at 60°C. As this solution is cooled to 10°C, NaNO$_3$ precipitates (settles) out of solution. The resulting solution is saturated. Approximately how many grams of NaNO$_3$ settled out of the original solution?

   (1) 46 g   (3) 85 g
   (2) 61 g   (4) 126 g

15. An unsaturated solution is formed when 80.0 grams of a salt is dissolved in 100. grams of water at 40°C. This salt could be

   (1) KCl   (3) NaCl
   (2) KNO$_3$ (4) NaNO$_3$

16. A student prepares four aqueous solutions in 100 g of H$_2$O at 20°C:

   A: 120 g of KI   C: 25 g of KCl
   B: 88 g of NaNO$_3$ D: 5 g of KClO$_3$

   Which solution is saturated?

   (1) A   (2) B   (3) C   (4) D

17. According to Reference Table G, which substance forms an unsaturated solution when 80 grams of the substance is dissolved in 100 grams of H$_2$O at 10°C?

   (1) KI   (3) NaNO$_3$
   (2) KNO$_3$ (4) NaCl

18. A student prepares a saturated solution by dissolving potassium chloride in 200 grams of water at 60°C.

   a) How many grams of potassium chloride were dissolved?
   b) The solution was cooled to 10°C and excess potassium chloride precipitated resulting in another saturated solution. How many grams of solid potassium chloride settled to the bottom?

19. How many grams of KClO$_3$ must be dissolved in 100 grams of water at 10°C to produce a saturated solution?

Table H: Vapor Pressures of Four Liquids

The boiling point of a substance varies as a combination of the temperature and vapor pressure. When the vapor pressure of propanone is 60 kPa, and the temperature is 45°C, the propanone will boil. It will also boil at 56°C when the pressure is 101.3 kPa (standard pressure).

At any given pressure, the substance to the right has the highest boiling point due to the fact that the intermolecular forces holding the molecules together are greater than those holding the other molecules.

20. As the temperature of a liquid increases, its vapor pressure
    (1) decreases
    (2) increases
    (3) remains the same

21. As the pressure on the surface of a liquid decreases, the temperature at which the liquid will boil
    (1) decreases
    (2) increases
    (3) remains the same

22. Using your knowledge of chemistry and the information in Reference Table H, which statement concerning propanone and water at 50°C is true?
    (1) Propanone has a higher vapor pressure and stronger intermolecular forces than water
    (2) Propanone has a higher vapor pressure and weaker intermolecular forces than water
    (3) Propanone has a lower vapor pressure and stronger intermolecular forces than water
    (4) Propanone has a lower vapor pressure and weaker intermolecular forces than water

23. According to Reference Table H, what is the boiling point of ethanoic acid at 80 kPa?
    (1) 28°C   (3) 111°C
    (2) 100°C   (4) 125°C

24. Which substance has the lowest vapor pressure at 75°C?
    (1) water   (3) ethanol
    (2) propanone   (4) ethanoic acid

25. What is the boiling point of propanone if the pressure on its surface is 48 kilopascals?
    (1) 25°C   (3) 35°C
    (2) 30°C   (4) 40°C

26. Which liquid has the highest vapor pressure at 75°C?
    (1) ethanoic acid (3) propanone
    (2) ethanol   (4) water

27. According to Reference Table H, what is the vapor pressure of propanone at 45°C?
    (1) 22 kPa   (3) 70 kPa
    (2) 33 kPa   (4) 98 kPa

28. At which temperature is the vapor pressure of ethanol equal to the vapor pressure of propanone at 35°C?
    (1) 35°C   (3) 82°C
    (2) 60°C   (4) 95°C

Table I: Heat of Reaction at 101.3 kPa and 298 K

This chart shows the amount of heat gained or lost during the reaction indicated by the equation. In the first example, 890.4 kJ are released when a mole of methane is burned in oxygen. A negative sign for ΔH indicates an exothermic reaction.

If only ½ of a mole of methane had been burned, only one mole of liquid water would have been produced releasing 445.2 kJ.

29. According to table I, which salt releases energy as it dissolves?
    (1) KNO_3 (3) NH_4NO_3
    (2) LiBr   (4) NaCl

Table J: Activity Series

A substance will react with the ion of any element beneath it on the table. Thus Zn will react with Ag^+ ions, which are below Zn, but not with Al^{3+} ions, which are above.

Remember that the H_2 forms H^+ ions and is the "acid line". Any element above H_2 will react with acids, such as HCl, but the elements below will not.

30. Which metal reacts spontaneously with a solution containing zinc ions?
    (1) magnesium   (3) copper
    (2) nickel   (4) silver

31. According to Reference Table J, which of these metals will react most readily with 1.0 M HCl to produce $H_2(g)$
    (1) Ca   (3) Mg
    (2) K   (4) Zn

Tables K and L list some common acids and bases.

32. Which compound is an Arrhenius acid?

    (1) H_2SO_4 (3) NaOH
    (2) KCl   (4) NH_3

33. Which substance is an Arrhenius base?

    (1) KCl   (3) KOH
    (2) CH_3Cl (4) CH_3OH

Table M: Common Acid-Base Indicators

The color change that occurs as each indicator undergoes pH changes is given on the table. Methyl Orange is red when the pH is 3.2 or less and yellow when the pH is 4.4 or greater. In between the two values the color is a mix of red and yellow, that is, orange.

34. According to Table M, what is the color of the indicator methyl orange in a solution that has a pH of 2?

    (1) blue   (3) orange
    (2) yellow   (4) red

35. In which solution is thymol blue indicator blue?

    (1) 0.1M CH_3COOH (3) 0.1 M HCl
    (2) 0.1M KOH   (4) 0.1 M H_2SO_4

36. Which indicator is yellow in a solution with a pH of 9.8?

    (1) methyl orange   (3) bromcresol green
    (2) bromthymol blue   (4) thymol blue

37. A compound whose water solution conducts electricity and turn phenolphthalein pink is

    (1) HCl   (3) NaOH
    (2) $HC_2H_3O_2$ (4) CH_3OH

38. A student was given four unknown solutions. Each solution was checked for conductivity and tested with phenolphthalein. The results are shown in the data table.

Solution	Conductivity	Color with phenolphthalein
A	Good	colorless
B	Poor	colorless
C	Good	pink
D	Poor	pink

Based on the data table, which unknown solution could be 0.1 M NaOH?

    (1) A   (2) B   (3) C   (4) D

39. A student titrates a solution of nitric acid containing phenolphthalein with sodium hydroxide until a color change occurs. What color change took place?

40. A student was studying pH differences in samples from two Adirondack streams. The student measured a pH of 4 in stream A and a pH of 6 in stream B. What is the color of bromthymol blue in the sample from stream A?

Base your answer to question 41 on the following information:

The table below shows the color of the indicators methyl orange and litmus in two samples of the same solution.

Results of Acid-Base Indicator Tests	
Indicator	Color result of test
Methyl orange	yellow
litmus	red

41. Which pH value is consistent with the indicator results?

    (1) 1   (2) 5   (3) 3   (4) 10

42. Which indicator, when added to a solution, changes color from yellow to blue and the pH of the solution is changed from 5.5 to 8.0?

    (1) bromcresol green
    (2) bromthymol blue
    (3) litmus
    (4) methyl orange

Table N: Selected Radioisotopes

This table lists the half-life, decay mode, and names of some radioisotopes.

43. Which radioisotope undergoes beta decay and has a half-life of less than one minute?

    (1) Fr-220   (3) N-16
    (2) K-42   (4) P-32

44. What is the half-life and decay mode of Rn-222?

    (1) 1.91 days and alpha decay
    (2) 1.91 days and beta decay
    (3) 3.82 days and beta decay
    (4) 3.82 days and alpha decay

45. According to Table N, which radioactive isotope is best for determining the actual age of the earth?

    (1) ^{238}U (3) ^{60}Co
    (2) ^{90}Sr (4) ^{14}C

46. Positrons are spontaneously emitted from the nuclei of

    (1) potassium-37   (3) nitrogen-16
    (2) radium-226   (4) thorium-232

47. According to Reference Table N, which pair of isotopes spontaneously decays?

    (1) C-12 and N-14   (3) C-14 and N-14
    (2) C-12 and N-16   (4) C-14 and N-16

48. What is the decay mode of ^{37}K?

    (1) B^- (3) gamma
    (2) B^+ (4) alpha

49. Alpha particles are emitted during the radioactive decay of

    (1) carbon-14   (3) calcium-37
    (2) neon-19   (4) radon-222

50. Which isotope will spontaneously decay and emit particles with a charge of +2?

    (1) Fe-53   (3) Au-198
    (2) Cs-137   (4) Fr-220

51. How many years must pass before an original pure 1.0 gram of radium-226 decays so that only 0.50 gram of radium-226 remains

Table O: Symbols Used in Nuclear Chemistry

This table can be used to find the name, charge, symbol, and mass of some radioactive particles.

52. Which of these particles has the greatest mass?

    (1) alpha   (3) neutron
    (2) beta   (4) positron

53. Which subatomic particle has a negative charge?

    (1) proton   (3) neutron
    (2) electron   (4) positron

54. What is the mass number of an alpha particle?

    (1) 1   (2) 2   (3) 0   (4) 4

55. Which subatomic particle has no charge?

    (1) alpha particle   (3) neutron
    (2) beta particle   (4) electron

56. Which group of nuclear emissions is listed in order of increasing charge?

    (1) alpha particle, beta particle, gamma radiation
    (2) gamma radiation, alpha particle, beta particle
    (3) positron, alpha particle, neutron
    (4) neutron, positron, alpha particle

57. Which two particles each have a mass approximately equal to one atomic mass unit?

    (1) electron and neutron
    (2) proton and electron
    (3) electron and positron
    (4) proton and neutron

Periodic Table of the Elements

An entire topic, Topic 5, was presented explaining the arrangement and significance of the Periodic Table. The following questions can be answered by referencing it.

58. What is the total number of protons in the nucleus of an atom of potassium-42?

    (1) 15   (2) 19   (3) 39   (4) 42

59. The elements of the periodic table are arranged in order of increasing

    (1) atomic number   (3) mass number
    (2) atomic mass   (4) neutron number

60. The element in Period 4 and Group 1 of the Periodic Table would be classified as a

    (1) metal   (3) metalloid
    (2) nonmetal   (4) noble gas

61. Which pair of symbols represents a metalloid and a noble gas?

    (1) Si and Bi   (3) Ge and Te
    (2) As and Ar   (4) Ne and Xe

62. In comparison to an atom of F-19, an atom of C-12 in the ground state has

    (1) three fewer neutrons
    (2) three more neutrons
    (3) three fewer valence electrons
    (4) three more valence electrons

63. Which set of symbols represents atoms with valence electrons in the same electron shell?

    (1) Ba, Br, Bi   (3) O, S, Te
    (2) Sr, Sn, I   (4) Mn, Hg, Cu

64. Which group of the periodic table contains atoms with a stable outer electron configuration?

    (1) 1   (2) 8   (3) 16   (4) 18

65. Which list of elements contains a metal, a metalloid, and a nonmetal?

    (1) Zn, Ga, Ge   (3) Cd, Sb, I
    (2) Si, Ge, Sn   (4) F, Cl, Br

66. Lithium and potassium have similar chemical properties because the atoms of both elements have the same

    (1) number of valence electrons
    (2) number of electron shells
    (3) atomic number
    (4) mass number

67. Which group on the Periodic Table of the Elements contains elements that react with oxygen to form compounds with the general formula X_2O?

    (1) Group 1   (3) Group 14
    (2) Group 2   (4) Group 18

Table R: Organic Functional Groups

This table can be useful in identifying the type of organic compound represented by a formula. In the General Formula column, the functional group is shown with R and R′ used to show the remainder of the compound.

68. The functional group –COOH is found in

    (1) esters   (3) alcohols
    (2) aldehydes   (4) organic acids

69. The organic compound represented by the condensed structural formula $CH_3CH_2CH_2CHO$ is classified as an

    (1) alcohol   (3) ester
    (2) aldehyde   (4) ether

Table S: Properties of Selected Elements

There are values for various properties of the elements. Some questions can be answered by reading the table and applying your knowledge of chemistry.

Many of the questions are linked to both the Periodic Table and Table S.

70. Which of the following elements has the highest electronegativity?

    (1) H   (2) K   (3) Al   (4) Ca

71. Which element is a solid at STP?

    (1) H_2 (2) I_2 (3) N_2 (4) O_2

72. Which of these elements has the least attraction for electrons in a chemical bond?

    (1) oxygen   (3) nitrogen
    (2) fluorine   (4) chlorine

73. From which of these atoms in the ground state can a valence electron be removed using the least amount of energy?

    (1) nitrogen   (3) oxygen
    (2) carbon   (4) chlorine

74. Which of these formulas contains the most polar bond?

    (1) H-Br   (3) H-F
    (2) H-Cl   (4) H-I

75. Which list of elements is arranged in order on increasing atomic radii?

    (1) Li, Be, B, C   (3) Sc, Ti, V, Cr
    (2) Sr, Ca, Mg, Be   (4) F, Cl, Br, I

76. Based on Reference Table S, the atoms of which of these elements have the strongest attraction for electrons in a chemical bond?

    (1) N   (2) Na   (3) P   (4) Pt

77. Compared to the nonmetals in Period 2, the metals in Period 2 generally have larger

    (1) ionization energies
    (2) electronegativities
    (3) atomic radii
    (4) atomic numbers

78. Which of the following Group 2 elements has the lowest first ionization energy?

    (1) Be   (2) Mg   (3) Ca   (4) Ba

79. Which element is a liquid at STP?

    (1) H_2 (2) Br_2 (3) Cl_2 (4) O_2

80. Based on electronegativity values, which type of elements tends to have the greatest attraction for electrons?

    (1) metals   (3) nonmetals
    (2) metalloids   (4) noble gases

81. Which of these elements has the lowest melting point?

    (1) Li   (2) Na   (3) K   (4) Rb

82. A 10.0 gram sample of which element has the smallest volume at STP?

    (1) aluminum   (3) titanium
    (2) magnesium   (4) zinc

83. At standard pressure, which element has a melting point higher than standard temperature?

(1) F_2 (2) Br_2 (3) Fe   (4) Hg

Table T: Important Formulas and Equations

Each of the first six formulas is a form of the simple algebra relationship that you learned in math class.

$$a = b/c$$

Can you solve for b in terms of a and c?

Can you solve for c in terms of a and b?

If so, simply substitute and solve in the following relationships. (Density, % error, % comp, concentration)

Density

84. A student determines the mass of an object to be 10.23 g. When placed into a graduated cylinder containing 20.0 mL of water, the level rises to 21.5 mL. Calculate the density of the object. (2-62a)

85. The volume of 1.00 mole of hydrogen bromide at STP is 22.4 liters. The gram-formula mass of hydrogen bromide is 80.9 grams per mole. What is the density of hydrogen bromide at STP?

Mole Calculations

86. The molar mass of $Ba(OH)_2$ is

(1) 154.3 g   (3) 171.3 g
(2) 155.3 g   (4) 308.6 g

87. What is the gram-formula mass of $(NH_4)_2CO_3$?

Percent Error

88. A student determines the density of an object to be 6.82 g/mL. The accepted value is 6.93 g/mL. Calculate the student's percent error.

89. A student determines the density of zinc to be 7.56 g/mL. If the accepted value is 7.14 g/mL, what is the percent error?

Percent Composition

90. What is the percent by mass of oxygen in propanal, CH_3CH_2CHO?

(1) 10.0%   (3) 38.1%
(2) 27.6%   (4) 62.1%

91. What is the percent composition by mass of aluminum in $Al_2(SO_4)_3$

(1) 7.89%   (3) 20.8%
(2) 15.8 %   (4) 36.0%

92. What is the percent composition by mass of nitrogen in NH_4NO_3 (gram-formula mass = 80.0 grams/mole)?

(1) 17.5%   (3) 53.5%
(2) 35.0%   (4) 60.0%

93. In which compound is the percent composition by mass of chlorine equal to 42%

(1) HClO (gram formula mass = 52 g/mol)
(2) $HClO_2$ (gram formula mass = 68 g/mol)
(3) $HClO_3$ (gram formula mass = 84 g/mol)
(4) $HClO_4$ (gram formula mass = 100 g/mol)

94. The percent composition by mass of magnesium in $MgBr_2$ (gram formula mass = 184 grams/mole) is equal to

(1) $24/184 \times 100$
(2) $160/184 \times 100$
(3) $184/24 \times 100$
(4) $184/160 \times 100$

Concentration

95. Which unit can be used to express solution concentration?

(1) J/mol   (3) mol/L
(2) L/mol   (4) mol/s

96. A 3.0 M HCl(aq) solution contains a total of

(1) 3.0 grams of HCl per liter of water
(2) 3.0 grams of HCl per mole of solution
(3) 3.0 moles of HCl per liter of solution
(4) 3.0 moles of HCl per mole of water

97. How many moles of solute are contained in 200 milliliters of a 1 M solution?

(1) 1   (3) 0.8
(2) 0.2   (4) 200

98. What is the total number of grams of NaI(s) needed to make 1.0 liter of a 0.01 M solution?

(1) 0.015   (3) 1.5
(2) 0.15   (4) 15

99. What is the molarity of a solution containing 20 grams of NaOH in 500 milliliters of solution?

(1) 1 M   (3) 0.05 M
(2) 2 M   (4) 0.5 M

100. What is the molarity of a solution of NaOH if 2 liters of the solution contains 4 moles of NaOH?

(1) 0.5 M   (2) 2 M   (3) 8 M   (4) 80 M

101. What is the concentration of a solution, in parts per million is 0.02 gram of Na_3PO_4 is dissolved in 1000 grams of water?

(1) 20 ppm   (3) 0.2 ppm
(2) 2 ppm   (4) 0.02 ppm

102. If 0.025 gram of $Pb(NO_3)_2$ is dissolved in 100. grams of H_2O, what is the concentration of the resulting solution in parts per million?

(1) 2.5×10^{-4} ppm   (3) 250 ppm
(2) 2.5 ppm   (4) 4.0×10^3 ppm

103. A sample of water is analyzed and it is determined that a 175-gram sample of the water contains 0.000250 gram of fluoride ions. How many parts per million of fluoride ion are contained in the sample?

104. What is the concentration of $O_2(g)$ in parts per million, in a solution that contains 0.008 gram of $O_2(g)$ dissolved in 1000. grams of $H_2O(l)$?

(1) 0.8 ppm   (3) 80 ppm
(2) 8 ppm   (4) 800 ppm

105. How many liters of a 1.2 M solution can be prepared with 0.50 mole of $C_6H_{12}O_6$?

106. An aqueous solution contains 300. parts per million of KOH. Determine the number of grams of KOH present in 1000. g of this solution.

107. What is the molarity of a solution of NaOH containing 0.500 mole of NaOH dissolved in distilled water to make 400. mL of solution?

Combined Gas Law

108. A gas occupies a volume of 444 mL at 273 K and 79.0 kPa. What is the final Kelvin temperature when the volume of the gas is changed to 1880 mL and the pressure is changed to 38.7 kPa?

(1) 31.5 K   (3) 566 K
(2) 292 K   (4) 2360 K

109. A sample of helium gas has a volume of 900. mLs and a pressure of 2.50 atm at 298 K. What is the new pressure when the temperature is changed to 336 K and the volume is decreased to 450 mLs?

(1) 0.177 atm   (3) 5.64 atm
(2) 4.43 atm   (4) 14.1 atm

110. A weather balloon has a volume of 52.5 liters at 295K, and a pressure of 100.8 kPa. At a higher altitude the temperature was 252 K and the pressure was 45.6 kPa. What is the new volume of the balloon?

Titration

111. When 50. milliliters of an HNO_3 solution is exactly neutralized by 150 millliters of a 0.50 M solution of KOH, what is the concentration of HNO_3?

(1) 1.0 M   (3) 3.0 M
(2) 1.5 M   (4) 0.5 M

112. A student neutralized 16.4 milliliters of HCl by adding 12.7 milliliters of 0.620 M KOH. What was the molarity of the HCl acid?

(1) 0.168 M   (3) 0.620 M
(2) 0.480 M   (4) 0.801 M

113. How many milliliters of 0.100 M NaOH (aq) are needed to completely neutralize 50.0 milliliters of 0.300 M HCl?

(1) 16.7 mL   (3) 150 mL
(2) 50.0 mL   (4) 300 mL

114. What volume of 0.500M HNO_3 (aq) must completely react to neutralize 100.0 milliliters of 0.100 M KOH?

(1) 10.0 mL   (3) 50.0 mL
(2) 20.0 mL   (4) 500 mL

Heat

115. How much heat is released when 25.0 g of water at $O°C$ freezes to ice at the same temperature?

Temperature

116. Which Kelvin temperature is equivalent to $-24°C$?

(1) 226 K   (3) 273 K
(2) 249 K   (4) 297 K

117. Which Kelvin temperature is equal to $56°C$?

(1) -327 K   (3) 217 K
(2) -217 K   (4) 329 K

118. At which Celsius temperature does lead change from a solid to a liquid?

(1) 874°C   (2) 601°C   (3) 328°C   (4) 0°C

119. What Celsius temperature is equal to 252K?

120. Convert the melting temperature of iron to degrees Celsius.

Radioactive Decay

These calculations are often used in conjunction with information found on Table N. The following questions are being included even though the equation has been eliminated from the reference tables. You are still responsible for solving the principles involved.

121. Based on Reference Table N, what fraction of a sample of gold-198 remains radioactive after 2.69 days?

    (1) 1/4   (2) 1/2   (3) 3/4   (4) 7/8

122. How many days are required for 200 grams of radon-222 to decay to 50.0 grams?

    (1) 1.91 days   (3) 7.64 days
    (2) 3.82 days   (4) 11.5 days

123. If 1/8 of an original sample of krypton-74 remains unchanged after 34.5 minutes, what is the half-life of krypton-74?

    (1) 11.5 min   (3) 34.5 min
    (2) 23.0 min   (4) 46.0 min

124. What is the half-life of sodium-25 if 1.00 gram of a 16.00 gram sample remains unchanged after 237 seconds?

    (1) 47.4 s   (3) 79.0 s
    (2) 59.3 s   (4) 118 sec

125. Based on Reference Table N, what fraction of a sample of I-131 remains radioactive after 16.14 days?

    (1) 1/2   (2) 1/4   (3) 1/8   (4) 1/16

126. How many years are required for 160. grams of C-14 to decay to a mass of 20.0 grams?

    (1) 5730 years   (3) 17,190 years
    (2) 11,460 years   (4) 22,920 years

127. Based on Reference Table N, what fraction of a radioactive Sr-90 would remain unchanged after 56.2 years?

    (1) 1/2   (2) 1/4   (3) 1/8   (4) 1/16

128. How much time must elapse before only 1/32 of a sample of cesium-137 remains unchanged?

Authored by Alfred Snider and Patrick Kavanah
Keyed to *Chemistry: The Physical Setting*

These are concepts that you need to review before your final exam. As you read each item, decide whether or not you have a good command of the idea. If you do, place a check mark in the box preceding the item. If the concept is not fresh in your mind, a page reference is given so that you can quickly review the idea.

I. Atomic Structure

☐ In the modern model of the atom there is mostly space with a dense positively charged area called the nucleus. (pp. 4–5)

☐ The model of the atom has progressed from the cannonball to the wave-mechanical model (electron cloud). (p. 5)

☐ Atoms contain three subatomic particles: the positively charged proton and the neutral neutron which are found in the nucleus, and the negatively charged electron found in regions outside the nucleus of the atom called orbitals. (pp. 3–4)

☐ The proton and neutron have a mass of one atomic mass unit, while the electron has little mass. (p. 6)

☐ The number of protons is called the atomic number and identifies the element. (p. 6)

☐ The sum of the protons and neutrons of an atom is the mass number of the atom. (p. 7)

☐ Atoms with the same atomic number, but different numbers of neutrons, are called isotopes. (p. 7)

☐ The atomic mass of an element is the weighted average of the isotopes of that element. (pp. 7–8)

☐ The most energetic electrons are the outermost electrons and are called valence electrons. The number of valence electrons affects the chemical properties of the element. (p. 12)

☐ When electrons occupy the lowest available energy level, the atom is in the ground state. If the atom gains energy, one or more electrons may move to a higher energy level and the atom is in an excited state. When electrons return to lower energy levels they emit line spectra that can be used to identify an element. (pp. 8–9)

II. Formulas and Equations

☐ A chemical compound is a pure substance made of two or more elements combined in a fixed proportion by mass. (p. 18)

☐ Chemical compounds can be broken down by chemical means to form two or more pure substances with properties that differ from the original compound. (pp. 18–19)

☐ The particle (atomic) structure of a compound can be represented by: (p. 28)

○ Empirical formulas showing the simplest whole-number ratio of atoms

○ Molecular formulas showing the actual ratio of atoms

○ Structural formulas showing all atoms with dashes representing bonds

☐ The Stock System is used to name compounds and uses Roman Numerals to show the oxidation number of metals capable of multiple oxidation states in ionic compounds. (pp. 31–32)

☐ The prefix system is used to name molecular binary compounds in which both elements are nonmetals. (p. 32)

☐ Chemical reactions are represented using balanced chemical equations in which the total numbers and types of atoms found in the reactant particles is equal to the total numbers and types of atoms present in the products. This accounts for the conservation of mass. (pp. 34–35)

☐ The five most common types of chemical reactions include: (pp. 37–40)

○ Synthesis ($2H_2 + O_2 \rightarrow 2H_2O$)

- ○ Decomposition ($H_2O \rightarrow 2H_2 + O_2$)
- ○ Single Replacement ($Zn + 2HCl \rightarrow ZnCl_2 + H_2$)
- ○ Double Replacement ($AgNO_3 + NaCl \rightarrow AgCl + NaNO_3$)
- ○ Combustion ($CH_4 + 2O_2 \rightarrow CO_2 + 2H_2O$)
- ☐ Coefficients are used to balance chemical equations and to identify mole ratios among the reactants and products. (p. 29, p. 35)
- ☐ In addition to the conservation of mass, energy and charge are also conserved during a chemical reaction. (p. 34, p. 163)

III. The Mathematics of Formulas and Equations

- ☐ The sum of the atomic masses of all the atoms in a formula is called the formula mass. (pp. 46–47)
- ☐ Formula mass is used to convert between moles (6.02×10^{23} atoms) and grams of a substance. (p. 49)
- ☐ The percent composition of a substance is calculated by dividing the atomic mass of the desired element by the formula mass of the compound, then multiplying by 100. (p. 47)
- ☐ Empirical formulas represent the simplest whole number ratio of atoms in a particle. Molecular formulas are determined as a multiple of a simplified empirical formula. (p. 51)
- ☐ The unknown quantity of a reactant or product (expressed in moles, grams, number of particles, or liters of gas) can be predicted using simple proportions that employ the coefficients of a balanced equation. (p. 52)

IV. Physical Behavior of Matter

- ☐ Matter can be classified as a pure substance (element or compound) or as a mixture. (p. 18)
- ☐ Pure substances have a definite and constant composition, while the proportions of a mixture can vary. (pp. 18–19)
- ☐ Compounds (H_2O, NH_3) can be decomposed by chemical means while elements (H_2, Ag) cannot. (p. 19)

- ☐ Elements, compounds, and solutions are homogeneous, while mixtures can be heterogeneous. (p. 19)
- ☐ When particles are simply rearranged, the change is physical ($H_2O(l) \rightarrow H_2O(g)$). When they are rearranged and form new substances ($2H_2O \rightarrow 2H_2 + O_2$), the change is chemical. (p. 33)
- ☐ Temperature is a measure of the average kinetic energy of a substance regardless of the size of the sample. Temperature is not a form of energy. Energy may be mechanical, chemical, electrical, electromagnetic, thermal, or nuclear. (p. 60)
- ☐ Heat (thermal energy) is transferred from a body at high temperature to a body at a lower temperature. (p. 62)
- ☐ Phase changes involve a change in potential energy, while the kinetic energy (temperature) remains the same. (p. 59)
- ☐ A heating or cooling curve can be constructed to illustrate the phase changes of a substance as energy is added or removed at a constant rate. (pp. 59–60)
- ☐ An ideal gas is a model used to explain the behavior of gases. Gases are most like ideal when the temperature is high and the pressure is low. Hydrogen and helium gases approach ideal behavior. (pp. 68–69)
- ☐ The kinetic molecular theory states that gas particles: (pp. 66–67)
    1. are in random straight-line motion.
    2. have collisions with other gas molecules resulting in a transfer of energy, but there is no loss of energy to the system.
    3. do not occupy volume.
    4. do not have attractive forces between them.
- ☐ Assumptions #3 & 4 are not true and cause real gases to behave slightly differently than predicted by the gas laws. This is especially true under conditions of low temperature and high pressure. (pp. 68–69)
- ☐ Avogadro's hypothesis states that equal volumes of gases contain equal numbers of molecules when measured at the same temperature and pressure. (p. 69)
- ☐ One mole (6.02×10^{23} particles) of any gas at STP has a mass equal to the formula mass. (p. 69)

□ There are several methods available for separating mixtures. They include filtration, distillation, and chromatography. Each separation method relies on the physical properties of the mixture. (pp. 71–73)

V. Periodic Table

□ Although the original Periodic Table (proposed by Mendeleev) arranged the elements in order of increasing atomic mass, the elements on the Modern Periodic Table are arranged in increasing atomic number. (p. 78)

□ Elements can be classified as metals (on the left), metalloids (on the "staircase"), nonmetals (in the upper right corner), and noble gases (members of column 18). (p. 80)

□ Metals have 1, 2, or 3 valence electrons, have luster, are solids (except for mercury) and are good conductors of heat and electricity. (p. 81)

□ Nonmetals have 5, 6, or 7 valence electrons, are brittle, and are poor conductors of heat and electricity. (p. 82)

□ The horizontal rows of the Periodic Table are called periods, while the vertical columns are groups or families. (pp. 80–81)

□ Members of Groups 1, 2, and 13–18 have the same number of valence electrons as other members of the same group, and therefore have similar chemical properties. (p. 81)

□ Special names are assigned to members of certain groups: Group 1 elements are the alkali metals; Group 2 are the alkaline earth metals; Group 17 are the halogens; Group 18 are the noble gases. (pp. 87–90)

□ Atomic radius decreases across a period and increases from top to bottom in a family or column of elements. (p. 85)

□ Generally, ionization energy increases across a period and decreases from top to bottom of a family. (p. 85)

□ Electronegativity increases across a period and decreases from top to bottom of a group. (pp. 86, 87)

□ Metallic characteristics tend to decrease from left to right across a period and increase from top to bottom within a group. (pp. 80–81)

□ Comparisons of properties may be found by consulting Reference Table S.

□ Some elements exist in two or more forms in the same phase. These forms are called allotropes. Oxygen $O_2(g)$ and ozone $O_3(g)$ are examples of allotropes. (p. 83)

VI. Chemical Bonding

□ Chemical bonds are attractions between atoms. When bonds are broken, energy is absorbed (endothermic). When bonds are formed, energy is released (exothermic). (p. 98)

□ Atoms tend to react by losing or gaining electrons to achieve the electron configuration of a noble gas. (p. 103)

□ There are three types of bonds between atoms: (pp. 102–110)

○ When electrons are transferred, the bond is ionic (NaCl). These bonds exhibit high melting points, are nonconductors as solids, but are conductors as liquids or in aqueous solutions.

○ When electrons are shared, the bond is covalent (CH_4). Compounds with covalent bonding generally have low melting points and are nonconductors.

○ When electrons are mobile among many atoms, the bond is metallic (Cu *(s)*). Metals are generally solids and are good conductors.

□ Bond types and properties can be identified based on electronegativity values. (p. 109)

□ A covalent bond is the sharing of one pair of electrons between atoms. Double and triple covalent bonds are the sharing of two and three pairs of electrons. (p. 101)

□ Metals tend to lose electrons to become positive ions with smaller radii, and form ionic bonds with nonmetals that gain electrons to become negative ions with larger radii. (p. 108)

□ A compound containing only covalent bonds is a molecule and the bonds are described as: (pp. 105–107)

○ nonpolar when the electrons are shared evenly between the atoms (H_2).

○ polar when the electrons are shared unequally between the atoms (H_2O).

□ Compounds containing polyatomic ions exhibit both covalent and ionic bonds ($NaNO_3$). (p. 110)

☐ The degree of bond polarity can be determined by comparing the electronegativity values of the two atoms. The greater the electronegativity difference, the greater the polarity. (pp. 109–110)

☐ Hydrogen bonding occurs between molecules when hydrogen of one molecule is attracted to the nonmetal part of another molecule and results in an abnormally high boiling point. (p. 111)

☐ If molecules contain polar bonds and are asymmetrical, the molecule is polar (NH_3, H_2O, HCl). If the molecule contains polar bonds, but is symmetrical, the molecule is nonpolar (CO_2, CH_4). (pp. 106–107)

☐ Electron–dot diagrams (Lewis structures) can be drawn to illustrate bonding and help determine the symmetry of molecules. (pp. 99–102)

☐ H_2, F_2, Cl_2, Br_2 and I_2 each contain a single covalent bond. O_2 contains a double covalent bond, and N_2 contains a triple covalent bond. (p. 104)

☐ Molecules are attracted to each other by dipole-dipole attraction, hydrogen bonding, or London dispersion forces. These forces are collectively known as intermolecular forces. (pp. 111–112)

VII. Solutions

☐ Solutions are homogeneous mixtures which contain one or more solutes dissolved in a solvent. The amount of dissolved solute depends on the temperature, pressure and the chemical nature of the solute and solvent. The phrase "Likes dissolve likes" helps predict whether substances will dissolve to form a solution. (pp. 118–120)

☐ Solubility tables and graphs (Reference Tables **F** and **G**) can be used to predict the solubility of substances and determine the concentrations of unsaturated, saturated and supersaturated solutions. (pp. 121–122)

☐ Solution concentration can be expressed in several ways including molarity, percent by mass, percent by volume, and parts per million. (pp. 124–126)

☐ Preparation of a solution is a process in which the desired amount of solute is added to enough solvent to obtain the desired volume of solution completes the solution. (p. 128)

☐ The addition of a solute to a solvent causes the boiling point of the solvent to increase and the freezing point to decrease. The increase or decrease is accentuated by increasing the number of dissolved particles. (p. 129)

☐ The boiling point of a substance is the temperature at which the vapor pressure of the substance is equal to the atmospheric pressure. (p. 130)

VIII. Kinetics and Equilibrium

☐ For any chemical reaction to take place there must be effective collisions between the reacting particles. To be an "effective" collision, the particles must collide with proper energy and orientation to initiate change to the particles. (p. 136)

☐ The rate of a chemical reaction is influenced by the temperature, presence of a catalyst, and pressure (when a gas is present). (pp. 136–137)

☐ The energy dynamics of a reaction can be represented using a potential energy diagram. The diagram plots potential energy in the reaction system for the reaction and can be utilized to evaluate the heat of reaction (ΔH), potential energy of reactants, potential energy of products, activation energy, and the potential energy of activated complex. (pp. 138–139)

☐ The heat of reaction (ΔH) is equal to the potential energy of the products minus the potential energy of the reactants. A negative ΔH indicates an exothermic reaction, while a positive ΔH indicates an endothermic reaction. (pp. 139–140)

☐ A catalyst speeds up the rate of a reaction by providing an alternate pathway with lower activation energy. The potential energies of the reactants and products remain the same, as does the net change in potential energy (ΔH). (p. 137, p. 147)

☐ Many chemical and physical reactions are reversible. If kept in a closed system, the rate of the forward reaction may become equal to the rate of the reverse reaction. When this takes place, the reaction system is said to be in a state of dynamic equilibrium. In this state, the measureable quantities of reactant and product remain constant (but are not necessarily equal). (p. 142)

- [ ] Equilibrium systems can involve phase changes, saturated solutions, and chemical reactions. (pp. 142–144)

- [ ] If a system at equilibrium is exposed to some type of stress (such as a change in concentration of any reactant or product, a temperature change, or a change in pressure), the system may respond by shifting the equilibrium in order to counteract the change. LeChatelier's Principle can be used to predict the response of an equilibrium system to such a stress. (pp. 144–146)

- [ ] Reaction spontaneity (ability for a reaction to take place) can be predicted by knowing the heat of reaction (enthalpy) and degree of randomness or disorder (entropy) of a chemical system. (pp. 148–149)

- [ ] In nature, reactions tend to undergo changes that release energy (exothermic) while moving towards a state of increased randomness (higher entropy). (pp. 148–149)

IX. Oxidation and Reduction

- [ ] Oxidation numbers can be assigned to atoms. (p. 158)

- [ ] Oxidation is the loss of electrons (and increase in oxidation number) and reduction is the gain of electrons (lowering of the oxidation number). (LEO says GER). (pp. 157–158)

- [ ] In a redox reaction, the oxidation number of one or more elements will change. (p. 161)

- [ ] Oxidation and reduction can be represented by half reactions, which show the exchange of electrons. The number of electrons lost must equal the number of electrons gained. (p. 163)

- [ ] In a voltaic (electrochemical) cell, chemical energy is converted to electrical energy. In these cells, oxidation occurs at the negative anode (an Ox) and reduction at the positive cathode (red Cat). (p. 165)

- [ ] The features of an electrochemical cell include cathode, anode, and salt bridge. Electrons flow from the anode to the cathode. (p. 165)

- [ ] The salt bridge provides a path for the flow of ions between the anode and the cathode. (p. 165)

- [ ] An electrolytic cell requires electricity to produce a change. The electrolytic cell draws electrical energy from an external source in order to drive a nonspontaneous reaction and the cathode is labeled as the negative electrode. (p. 167)

- [ ] The Activity Series (Table J) is used to determine if a reaction is spontaneous or not. (p. 166)

X. Acids, Bases, and Salts

- [ ] Arrhenius acids yield H^+ (hydrogen) ions in solution; bases yield OH^- (hydroxide) ions. (pp. 175–176)

- [ ] The H^+ ion may also be written as H_3O^+ (hydronium ion). (p. 176)

- [ ] Strong acids and bases are highly ionized and are good electrolytes. Weak acids and bases are only slightly ionized and are weak electrolytes. (p. 177)

- [ ] Salts are compounds that do not directly produce H^+ or OH^- ions when dissolved in solution. (p. 180)

- [ ] Acid solutions react with some metals (those listed above reference H_2 on Table J) to produce hydrogen gas and salt. (pp. 178–179)

- [ ] Neutralization is the reaction between an acid and a base to form salt and water. (pp. 179–180)

- [ ] Titration is the process of using a solution of known concentration to determine the strength of an unknown. (pp. 182–183)

- [ ] The pH scale shows the acidity (pH < 7) or alkalinity (pH = or > 7) of a solution. One pH unit change shows a tenfold change in the hydronium ion concentration of the solution. (p. 186)

- [ ] Indicators (listed on Table M) will change color with varying pH values (pp. 185–186)

- [ ] Brönsted acids are proton donors, bases are proton acceptors. (p. 188)

- [ ] Conjugate acid base pairs are formulas that differ by a hydrogen ion. The one with greater hydrogen content is an acid, the other a base. (p. 188)

XI. Organic Chemistry

☐ Organic compounds contain carbon atoms, which bond covalently to other atoms. The carbon atoms may bond to each other forming chains, rings, and networks in a variety of shapes. (pp. 194–195)

☐ The physical and chemical properties of each organic molecule are largely dependent upon shape (as described in the boding section). (pp. 106–107)

☐ The names for organic molecules are derived using the IUPAC system as described in Tables **P**, **Q** and **R**. (pp. 199–200)

☐ Hydrocarbons are a class of organic compound in which there are no elements other than carbon and hydrogen. Saturated hydrocarbons contain only single carbon-carbon bonds. Unsaturated hydrocarbons contain at least one multiple carbon-carbon bond (double or triple bond). Tables **P** and **Q** are used to identify and properly name these structures. (pp. 195–199)

☐ Various "functional groups" are frequently imbedded in organic molecules and provide their distinctive molecules with unique properties. Primary functional groups are listed in detail on Table **R**. (pp. 201–204)

☐ Due to the flexible bonding abilities of carbon, most of the organic compounds can be rearranged into alternate structures with the same molecular formula but with different properties. These variations are called isomers. (pp. 198–199)

☐ There are a number of chemical reactions that are associated with organic compounds. They include: addition, substitution, polymerization, esterification, fermentation, saponification, and combustion. (pp. 206–208)

XII. Nuclear Chemistry

☐ Some nuclei are unstable due to their neutron/proton ratios. All nuclei with atomic number greater than 82 are unstable. (p. 216)

☐ Radioactive decay emissions have different masses, charges, and penetrating power. Gamma rays are the most penetrating, followed by beta particles and the least penetrating alpha particles. (pp. 217–218)

☐ When nuclei decay they emit alpha, beta, positron and/or gamma radiation at a specific rate called half-life. (pp. 223–225)

☐ Unstable nuclei decay by alpha, beta or positron decay until they reach stable neutron/proton ratios. (pp. 217–218)

☐ The change of an atom from one element to another is called transmutation. Transmutations may be natural or artificial. (p. 219)

☐ Equations can be written to show transmutations. In all nuclear equations there will be changes in the atomic numbers of the reactants and products. (pp. 218–219)

☐ Fission and fusion are artificial transmutations that emit large amounts of energy caused by the conversion of matter into energy. The energy released during these processes is much greater than that released in ordinary chemical changes. (p. 221)

☐ Both fission and fusion have benefits and risks. (pp. 226–227)

☐ Radioisotopes have many uses. (pp. 226–227)

Graphing and Math Skills

The Regents exam consists, not only of knowledge level questions, but also tests your ability to apply these concepts. Be sure to review the concepts of selecting appropriate scales, plotting and interpreting data all of which are covered in Appendix 2.

There may be a question to test your knowledge about significant figures (pp. A-21-A-22), especially the number of significant figures to be represented in a multiplication or division. You do not need to solve problems to the correct number of significant figures unless specifically told to do so.

You will also be tested on your ability to apply math skills to solve problems relating to many of the concepts that you have learned. Appendix 3 presents specific values related to many of these concepts, while Table T presents the math relations for many of these relationships. Review this table to remind yourself of these relationships and the variables involved.

Glossary

acidity a measure of the hydrogen (hydronium) ion concentration of a solution

activated complex the temporary, intermediate product in a chemical reaction

activation energy the amount of energy needed to form an activated complex from reactants

addition polymerization joining of monomers of unsaturated compounds

addition reaction an organic reaction in which a substance such as hydrogen or a halogen is added to the site of a double or triple bond

alcohol an organic compound containing the hydroxyl group (−OH) as the functional group

aldehyde an organic compound in which the carbonyl group (−C=O) is at the end of a carbon chain

alkali metal an element of Group 1

alkaline earth metal an element of Group 2

alkalinity a measure of the hydroxide ion concentration of a solution

alkane one of a homologous series of saturated hydrocarbons

alkene one of a homologous series of hydrocarbons that contain one double covalent bond

alkyl group a group that contains one less hydrogen atom than an alkane with the same number of carbon atoms

alkyne one of a homologous series of hydrocarbons that contain one triple covalent bond

allotrope one of two or more different forms of an element in the same phase

alloy a homogeneous mixture of a metal with another element, usually another metal

alpha particle a helium nucleus

amide the product obtained from the reaction of an organic acid with an amine

amine an ammonia derivative in which one or more of the hydrogen atoms are replaced by an alkyl group

amino acid an organic compound containing both the amine group (−NH$_2$) and the carboxylic group (−COOH)

analysis a chemical reaction in which a compound is broken down (decomposed) into simpler substances

anode the site in an electrochemical cell where oxidation occurs

Arrhenius acid a substance that produces hydronium ions (H$_3$O$^+$) as the only positive ions when dissolved in water

Arrhenius base a substance that produces hydroxide ions (OH$^-$) as the only negative ions when dissolved in water

artificial transmutation a transmutation caused by bombarding a nucleus with a high-energy particle, such as a neutron or an alpha particle

asymmetrical molecule a molecule that lacks identical atomic structure on each side of an axis

atom the smallest particle of an element that can enter into a chemical reaction

atomic mass the average mass of all the isotopes in a sample of an element

atomic mass unit one-twelfth the mass of a carbon-12 atom

atomic number the number of protons in the nucleus of an atom

atomic radius half the distance between two adjacent atoms in a crystal or half the distance between nuclei of identical atoms bonded together

Avogadro's number the number of representative particles contained in one mole of a substance; equal to 6.02×10^{23} particles

beta particles high-energy electrons whose source is an atomic nucleus

boiling point the temperature at which the vapor pressure of a liquid is equal to the atmospheric pressure

catalyst a substance that alters the speed of a chemical reaction without being permanently changed

cathode the site in an electrochemical cell where reduction occurs

chemical change a reaction in which the composition of a substance is changed

chemistry the study of the composition of matter and changes that occur in it

coefficient the number placed before a formula indicating the number of units of that substance

collision theory for a chemical reaction to occur, reactant particles must collide

combustion an exothermic reaction with oxygen, releasing heat

compound a substance composed of two or more elements that are chemically combined in definite proportions by mass

condensation an exothermic process in which a vapor or a gas changes into the liquid phase; the potential energy of the substance decreases during this constant temperature process; the reverse of the vaporization process

condensation polymerization the bonding of monomers by removing water from hydroxyl groups and joining the monomers by an ether or ester linkage

conductivity a measure of the ability of an electric current to flow through a substance

conjugate acid–base pair a pair of chemical formulas that differ only by the presence of a hydrogen ion

covalent bond a bond formed by the sharing of electrons between two nuclei

decomposition a chemical reaction in which a compound is broken down into simpler substances

deposition the process in which a gas changes directly into a solid; the reverse of sublimation

diatomic molecule a molecule containing two identical atoms

dipole-dipole forces a force of attraction between adjacent polar molecules

double covalent bond the sharing of two pairs of electrons between two nuclei

double replacement a chemical reaction in which ions exchange places

ductility property of a metal that enables it to be drawn into a wire

electrochemical cell a system in which there is an electric current flowing while a chemical reaction occurs

electrode the site at which oxidation or reduction occurs; an anode or a cathode

electrolysis a process in which an electric current forces a nonspontaneous redox reaction to occur

electrolyte a substance whose water solution conducts an electric current

electrolytic cell a cell that requires electricity to cause a nonspontaneous chemical reaction to occur

electron a fundamental particle of matter having a negative charge

electron configuration the distribution of the electrons in an atom

electronegativity a measure of the attraction of a nucleus for a bonded electron

element substances that cannot be broken down or decomposed into simpler substances by chemical means

empirical formula the simplest integer ratio in which atoms combine to form a compound

endothermic a chemical reaction that absorbs heat, producing products with more potential energy than the reactants

entropy a measure of the disorder or randomness of a system

equilibrium a condition in which the rates of opposing reactions are equal

equilibrium expression a mathematical expression that shows the relationship of reactants and products of a system at equilibrium

ester the organic product of an esterification reaction containing $-COOC-$ as the functional group

esterification a chemical reaction between an alcohol and an acid to produce an ester and water

ether an organic compound in which oxygen is bonded to two carbon atoms (R_1-O-R_2)

evaporation the process by which molecules in the liquid phase escape into the gaseous phase

excited state the condition that exists when the electrons of an atom occupy higher energy levels while lower energy levels are vacant

exothermic a chemical reaction that releases heat, producing products with less potential energy than the reactants

family a vertical column on the periodic table

fermentation an organic reaction in which ethanol and carbon dioxide are produced from a carbohydrate

fission splitting of large nuclei into middle-weight nuclei and neutrons

formula mass the sum of the atomic masses of all atoms present

formula symbols and subscripts used to represent the composition of a substance

freezing point the temperature at which both the solid and liquid phases of a substance exist in equilibrium; the same temperature as the substance's melting point

freezing the constant temperature process in which particles in the liquid phase lose energy and change into the solid phase; also known as solidification; the reverse of the melting process

functional group the atom or atoms that replace a hydrogen atom in a hydrocarbon and give a class of organic compounds characteristic properties

fusion the constant temperature process in which particles in the solid phase gain enough energy to break away into the liquid phase; also known as melting; the reverse of the freezing process; (in nuclear chemistry) the combining of light nuclei into a heavier nucleus

gamma ray high-energy ray similar to an X ray

gaseous phase a phase of matter without definite shape or volume

gram formula mass the formula mass expressed in grams instead of atomic mass units

ground state the condition of an atom or ion in which the electrons occupy the lowest available energy levels

group a vertical column on the periodic table

half-life the length of time for half of a given sample of a radioisotope to decay

half-reaction a reaction that shows either the oxidation or reduction portion of a redox reaction

halide a salt that includes a halogen

halogen an element of Group 17

heat energy transferred from one substance to another; measured in units of calories or joules

heat of fusion the amount of heat needed to convert a unit mass of a substance from a solid to a liquid at its melting point

heat of vaporization the amount of heat needed to convert a unit mass of a substance from a liquid to a vapor at its boiling point

heterogeneous a mixture in which the substances are not uniformly mixed

homogeneous a substance in which the particles are uniformly mixed

homologous series a group of related compounds in which each member differs from the one before it by the same additional unit

hydrate the crystalline form of an ionic substance that contains a definite number of water molecules

hydrocarbon organic compound containing only hydrogen and carbon atoms

hydrogen bond the attraction of a hydrogen atom in one molecule for an oxygen, nitrogen, or fluorine atom in another molecule

hydrogen ion a hydrogen atom without its electron (consisting solely of a proton)

hydronium ion H_3O^+, formed by the combination of water with a hydrogen ion

hydroxide ion the polyatomic anion produced by the ionization of a water molecule

hydroxyl group the group comprised of an oxygen atom and a hydrogen atom ($-OH$) responsible for the properties of alcohols

indicator a substance that undergoes a color change that can be used to determine when a reaction is complete

inert gas group former name of the Group 18 noble gases

insoluble material with a low solubility

ion-dipole forces a force of attraction between ions and adjacent polar molecules

ionic bond a bond formed by the transfer of electrons from one atom to another

ionic radius the distance from the nucleus to the outer energy level of the ion

ionization energy the amount of energy needed to remove the most loosely bound electron from a neutral gaseous atom

isomers compounds with the same molecular formula but different structural arrangement

isotope atom of an element that has a specific number of protons and neutrons

ketone an organic compound in which the carbonyl group ($-C=O$) is joined to two other carbon atoms

kinetic molecular theory a theory used to explain the behavior of gases in terms of the motion of their particles

law of conservation of mass matter is neither created nor destroyed in chemical reactions

law of definite proportions types of atoms in a compound exist in a fixed ratio

Le Châtelier's principle a system at equilibrium will react to reduce a stress

Lewis dot diagram a diagram that depicts valence electrons as dots around the atomic symbol (representing the nucleus and nonvalence electrons) of the element

liquid phase a phase of matter having definite volume but no definite shape (takes the shape of its container)

London dispersion forces a force of attraction between adjacent nonpolar molecules due to uneven distribution of electrons in otherwise symmetrical molecules

malleability the property of metals that allows them to be hammered into shapes

mass number the total number of protons and neutrons in the nucleus of an atom

matter anything that has mass and volume

melting point the temperature at which both the solid and liquid phases exist in equilibrium; the same temperature as the substance's freezing point

metal element whose atoms lose electrons in chemical reactions to become positive ions

metallic bond the attraction of valence electrons for the positive kernels of metallic atoms

metalloid an element that has both metallic and nonmetallic properties

molarity the concentration of a substance in moles per liter of solution

mole the number of atoms of carbon present in 12.000 g of carbon-12

molecular formula the actual ratio of the atoms in a molecule

molecule the smallest unit of a covalently bonded substance that has the properties of that substance

monomer each individual unit of a polymer

multiple covalent bond a double or triple covalent bond

neutralization the reaction between an acid and a base to produce water and a salt

neutron the uncharged particle in the nucleus of an atom

noble gas a nonreactive element that is in group 18 on the periodic table

nonmetal element whose atoms will gain or share electrons in chemical reactions

nonpolar covalent bond a bond formed by the equal sharing of a pair of electrons between two nuclei

nucleus the dense, positively charged central core of an atom

octet of electrons the stable valence electron configuration of eight electrons

orbital a region in an atom in which an electron of a particular amount of energy is most likely to be located

organic acid an organic compound containing one or more carboxyl groups ($-COOH$)

organic halide an organic compound in which one or more hydrogen atoms have been replaced by an atom of a halogen; also known as a halocarbon

oxidation number (state) number assigned to keep track of electron gain or loss in redox reactions

oxidation the loss of electrons and an increase in oxidation state

oxidizing agent the substance reduced in a redox reaction

parts per million the ratio between the parts of solute per million parts of solution

percent by volume the concentration of a solution expressed as the ratio between the volume of the solute and total volume of the solution, expressed as a percent

percent mass the concentration of a solution expressed as the ratio between the mass of the solute and the total mass of the solution, expressed as a percent

percentage composition the composition of a compound as a percentage of each element compared with the total mass of the compound

period a horizontal row of the periodic table

periodic law the properties of elements are periodic functions of their atomic numbers

pH scale a logarithmic scale that measures the acidity or alkalinity of a solution on a scale of 1 to 14

pH the negative logarithm of a solution's hydrogen ion concentration

physical change a change that does not alter the chemical properties of a substance

polar covalent bond a bond formed by the unequal sharing of electrons between two nuclei

polyatomic ion a covalently bonded group of atoms that have a net electric charge

polymer organic compound made up of chains of smaller units bonded together

polymerization an organic reaction in which many small units are joined together to form a long chain

positron particle identical to an electron except that it has a positive charge

potential energy diagram a diagram showing the changes in potential energy as a reaction proceeds

primary alcohol an alcohol with a hydroxyl group attached to a carbon atom at the end of a chain

product a substance formed in a chemical reaction, shown to the right of the arrow in an equation

proton the positively charged particle in the nucleus of an atom

pure substance a compound or an element; a material in which the composition is the same throughout

qualitative information that cannot be counted or measured

quantitative information that can be either counted or measured

quantum number one of a set of four numbers that describes a property of an electron in an atom

quantum theory a concept that relates the chemical behavior of atoms to energy being transferred in discrete units called quanta

radioisotope an unstable nucleus that is radioactive

reactant a starting substance in a reaction, shown to the left of the arrow in an equation

redox an oxidation-reduction reaction

reducing agent the substance oxidized in a redox reaction

reduction the gain of electrons and the loss of oxidation number

salt the product (other than water) of a neutralization reaction; an ionic substance consisting of a metallic cation and anion other than the hydroxide ion

salt bridge a part of a voltaic cell that connects two containers and allows the flow of ions

saponification the reaction of an alkali and a fat to produce glycerol and a soap

saturated (in regard to a solution) a solution containing the maximum amount of solute that will dissolve at a given temperature; (in regard to organic chemistry) organic compounds containing only single covalent bonds

secondary alcohol an alcohol with a hydroxyl group attached to a carbon atom that is attached to two other carbon atoms

single covalent bond only one pair of electrons is shared between two atoms

single replacement a reaction in which an element replaces a less reactive element in a compound

solid phase a phase of matter having a definite shape and volume; particles in this phase have a definite crystalline arrangement

solubility a measure of how much solute will dissolve in a certain amount of solvent at a specific temperature

soluble material with a high solubility

solute the substance being dissolved

solution a homogeneous mixture of substances in the same physical state

solvent the substance that dissolves the solute

stress any change in concentration, pressure, or temperature on an equilibrium system

sublimation the process in which a solid changes directly into a gas; the reverse of deposition

subscript the number written after a chemical symbol in a formula indicating the number of atoms present

substitution reaction one or more hydrogen atoms is removed from a saturated hydrocarbon and replaced by another atom

supersaturated a solution that contains more solute than would dissolve in a saturated solution at a given temperature

symbol a one-, two- or three-letter designation of an element

symmetrical molecule a molecule with identical atomic structure on each side of an axis

synthesis a reaction in which two or more substances combine to form one product

temperature the measure of the average kinetic energy of a substance's particles

tertiary alcohol an alcohol with a hydroxyl group attached to a carbon atom that is attached to three other carbon atoms

titration the process of determining the concentration of an unknown solution by a reaction with a solution of known concentration

tracer a radioisotope used to track a chemical reaction

transmutation the changing of a nucleus of one element into that of a different element

triple bond the sharing of three pairs of electrons between two nuclei

unsaturated (in regard to a solution) a solution in which more solute can be dissolved at a given temperature; (in regard to organic chemistry) an organic compound containing one or more double or triple covalent bond

valence electrons the electrons in the outer energy level of an atom

vapor the gaseous state of a substance that is normally a liquid at room temperature

vapor pressure the pressure that a vapor exerts

vaporization the constant temperature process in which particles in the liquid phase gain enough energy to break away into the gaseous phase; also known as boiling; the reverse of the condensation process

voltaic cell an electrochemical cell in which a spontaneous chemical reaction causes a flow of electrons

wave-mechanical model the current model of the atom that deals with the wave-particle duality of nature

Index

acid-base indicators 175, 186, A-6

acidity 185–186

acids 173–188, A-6
  Arrhenius 175–176
  Brønsted-Lowry 188
  monoprotic, diprotic, and triprotic 176, 183
  naming 177
  neutralization reactions 179–180
  properties 174–175
  reactions with bases 174, 179
  reactions with metals 178–179
  strong 173–174, 177, 180, 186
  weak 173–174, 177, 180, 186

activated complexes 138

activation energy 135, 139

addition reactions 206–207

alcohols 201–202
  classification of 202
  compared to bases 176–177

aldehydes 202–203

alkali metals 87–88

alkaline earth metals 87–88

alkalinity 185–186

alkanes 196, 199–200
  and amines 203

alkenes 196–197

alkyl groups 203
  and naming alkanes 199–200

alkynes 197

allotropes 83

alloys 118

alpha decay 217

alpha particles 216–217

amides 204

amines 176, 203

amino acids 203

ammonia 176

ammonium ion 29, 32

analysis reaction 37

anodes 165–166
  and electrolysis 167

aqueous solutions 118–119

Arrhenius theory 175–177, 179
  and Brønsted-Lowry acids and bases 188

atomic mass 7–8, 46–47
  and the periodic table 78–79

atomic mass units 6–7, 46

atomic number 6
  and isotopes 7
  and the periodic table 78–79

atomic radii 85, A-10 to A-11
  and the periodic table 85–86

atoms 2–15
  charge of 29
  early theories 2–3
  emission spectra 9–10
  excited states 9
  ground states 9
  models of 3–5
  modern theories about 4–5
  stability and electron configuration 14–15
  theories about 2–5

Avogadro's hypothesis 69

Avogadro's number 49

bases 174–188, A-6
  alkalinity 185–186
  Arrhenius 176–177
  Brønsted-Lowry 188
  naming 177
  neutralization reactions 179–180
  properties 175
  reactions with acids 174–175
  strong 175, 177, 180, 186
  weak 175, 180, 186

batteries 157, 167

beta decay 217–218

beta particles 216–218

Bohr, Neils 4–5

boiling 59, 64–65, 129–131, A-4

bonding 97–112
  of carbon atoms 194–195
  covalent 104–105
  distinguishing bond types 110–111
  hydrogen 111–112
  ionic 108–110
  metallic 102–103

Boyle, Robert 2

Brønsted-Lowry acids and bases 188

buckminsterfullerene 195

butane 198–199

calcium chloride
  effects on solutions 129

calorimeter 64

carbon
  allotropes 83
  bonding of 194–195
  carbon-14 226–227
  chains 195
  compounds 194
  and organic chemistry 194
  and standard mass 6

carbon-14 226–227

carbon dioxide 206–207

carbon monoxide 206

carbonyl groups 202–203

carboxyl groups 203
  and acids 176

catalysts 136–137, 146
  effect on activation energy 139–140

cathodes 165
  and electrolysis 167

Celsius scale 62

charge
  and atomic particles 3–4, 6
  and atoms 29
  and compounds 29
  conservation of 163, 218
  and quarks 6
  on salts in neutralization reactions 180

chemical bonds 98–112

chemical changes 33

chemical equations 34–36
  balancing 35–36, 41, 180
  mole ratios in 52–53

chemical formulas 27–30
  coefficients 29–30
  empirical formulas 28
  molecular formulas 28–29

chemical reactions
  with acids and bases 178–184
  and catalysts 136–137, 139–140, 146
  between elements of different groups 90
  forward and reverse 139, 142, 144, 146
  kinetics 136–137
  Le Châtelier's principle 144–146, 185–186
  neutralization 174, 179–180, 182–183, 186

and the octet rule 103–104
organic 206–208
potential energy diagrams
138–140
rates of 136–137
redox 158–159, 161
types of 37–40, 179, 206–208
writing 34
chemical symbols 25–27
and the periodic table 79–80
chemistry
definition 2
Chernobyl, Ukraine 228
chromatography 73
cobalt-60 227
coefficients 29–30, 52
in balancing equations 35
colligative properties
of solutions 129–131
collision theory 136
combined gas law 67
combustion 206
compounds 18
charge of 29, 31
and chemical formulas 27–28
distinguishing from mixtures
19
and entropy 149
formation of 29
and mass 46–47
naming 31–32
and oxidation numbers 159
percentage composition 47
concentration, solutions
122–128
and equilibrium expressions
150–151
and Le Châtelier's principle
144–146
molarity 124, A-12
parts per million 126–127
percent by mass 125–126
percent by volume 125–126
and rate of chemical reaction
136, 144
condensation 60, 65
conductivity
and bond types 110–111
conjugate acid-base pairs 188
conversions
between Celsius and Kelvin
scales 62

between grams and moles 49
cooling curves 60
covalent bonds 104–105, 194–195
and carbon atoms 194–195
double 195
and molecules 106–107
and polyatomic ions 110
single 195
triple 195
covalent compounds
naming 31–32
and rate of chemical reaction
136
cyclotrons 220

Dalton, John 2–3
decomposition reactions 37
deposition 60
diamonds 195
diatomic molecules 27, 104
dipole-dipole forces 112, 130
dipoles 112
distillation 72, 119
of crude oil 72
double covalent bonds 104

electricity
and acids 174
and bases 175
electrochemical cells 157,
165–168
electrodes 165
electrolysis 167
electrolytes 174, 177
strong 177
weak 177
electrolytic cells 165, 167–168
electron-cloud atomic model 4
electron dot diagrams 99–102
of carbon atoms 195
electronegativity 32, 86–87, A-10
to A-11
and bonding 104–105, 109
electrons
in the atom 3–6, 8–9, 12–15
configurations 13–15, 79–80
discovery of 3
levels 8, 14–15
mass 6
models of 3–5
octet rule 103–104, 108–109,
158

orbitals 12–14
spin 12
valence 12
element 118 79
elements 78–90
and atomic number 6
early ideas about 2
electron configurations 13–15
and emission spectra 10
and entropy 149
oxidation numbers 31
properties of 85–87
as pure substances 18
in replacement reactions
38–40
symbols for 26–27
types of 80–83
emission spectra 9–10
of ions of transition
elements 82
empirical formulas 28, 51
endothermic processes 34
and chemical bonds 97–98
and energy of reaction
products 140
and heating curves 59
and Le Châtelier's
principle 145
energy
activation 139
in chemical equations 34
enthalpy and entropy 148–149
during heating and cooling
58–60
as particles and waves 4–5
potential energy diagrams
138–140
energy levels
of electrons 12–14
enthalpy 148
entropy 148–149
equilibrium 136, 142–146
chemical equilibrium 143–144
expressions 150–151
Le Châtelier's principle
144–146
phase 142
physical equilibrium 142–143
solution 143
equilibrium constants 150–151
equilibrium expressions
150–151

Acknowledgments

Staff Credits:
The people who make up the *Chemistry Science Brief Review team*—representing design, editorial, marketing, and production services—are listed below. Bold type denotes the core team members.

Lynn Baldridge, **Jane Breen, Glen Dixon, Becky Napoleon,** Linda Johnson, Rachel Youdelman

Additional Credits:
The Quarasan Group, Inc.: Chicago, IL

Lapiz Digital Services: Chennai, India
Lapiz, Inc.: Boston, MA

Independent Reviewer: Alfred E. Snider

Photographs
Photo locators denoted as follows: Top (T), Center (C), Bottom (B), Left (L), Right (R), Background (Bkgd)

Cover Kesu/Shutterstock; **i** Kesu/Shutterstock; **1, 57, 77, 135, 215** DK Images.

Reference Tables
A-6 Republished with permission of Taylor & Francis Group, from CRC Handbook of Chemistry and Physics, 91st Ed, 2010; permission conveyed through Copyright Clearance Center, Inc.; **A-7** The Merck Index, 14th ed., 2006, Merck Publishing Group.; **A-10, A-11** Republished with permission of Taylor & Francis Group, from CRC Handbook of Chemistry and Physics, 91st Ed, 2010; permission conveyed through Copyright Clearance Center, Inc.

Consultant:
Alfred E. Snider

New York Regents Examinations

The New York Regents Examinations that follow are provided so that you can practice taking actual Chemistry Regents Examinations. All of the tests included in this book cover the key concepts of the Physical Setting: Chemistry Core Curriculum. You will find that the content of this book provides specifically what you need to review for the Physical Setting: Chemistry Regents Examination.

Using the Regents Examinations

The best way to use these examinations is to take the entire test after you have reviewed the course content. Use the tests to determine if you have reviewed enough to do well on the Regents Examination and to determine where further review will be most helpful.

Do not look up any information or answers while you take the examinations. Answer each question just as you would during a real test. As you take the examination, use the margin of the paper to note any question where you are just guessing. Leave the more difficult questions for last, but be sure to answer each question. Every point counts so do not skip over a long question

that is only worth a point or two. A long question could be easier than it looks and may make the difference between an A or a B or between passing or failing.

When you finish, have your teacher score your Examination and help you determine the areas where you need the most work. Also review the "guesses" you noted in the margin to find out what you need to study to ensure that you will be able to answer similar questions on the next test. Once you have determined your weaknesses, you can focus your review on those topics in this book.

Reviewing the areas where you know the least will give you the best chance of improving your final score. Spending time on areas where you are doing quite well will not produce much improvement in your total score, but it is still important if time permits.

Answer Key All answers to these Regents Examinations are included in the Answer Key, which also includes Diagnostic Tests to help you assess what you know before starting to study a topic.

Part A

Answer all questions in this part.

Directions (1–30): For *each* statement or question, record on your separate answer sheet the *number* of the word or expression that, of those given, best completes the statement or answers the question. Some questions may require the use of the *2011 Edition Reference Tables for Physical Setting/Chemistry*.

1 Which statement describes a concept included in the wave-mechanical model of the atom?

(1) Protons, neutrons, and electrons are located in the nucleus.
(2) Electrons orbit the nucleus in shells at fixed distances.
(3) Atoms are hard, indivisible spheres.
(4) Electrons are located in regions called orbitals.

2 As an electron in an atom moves from a higher energy state to a lower energy state, the atom

(1) becomes a negative ion
(2) becomes a positive ion
(3) releases energy
(4) absorbs energy

3 Two atoms that are different isotopes of the same element have

(1) the same number of protons and the same number of neutrons
(2) the same number of protons but a different number of neutrons
(3) a different number of protons but the same number of neutrons
(4) a different number of protons and a different number of neutrons

4 The element in Group 14, Period 3, of the Periodic Table is classified as a

(1) metal   (3) metalloid
(2) noble gas   (4) nonmetal

5 Which element has chemical properties that are most similar to potassium?

(1) calcium   (3) nitrogen
(2) cesium   (4) sulfur

6 Which element requires the *least* amount of energy to remove the most loosely held electron from a gaseous atom in the ground state?

(1) Na   (3) P
(2) Ar   (4) Cl

7 Which terms identify two different categories of compounds?

(1) covalent and molecular
(2) covalent and empirical
(3) ionic and molecular
(4) ionic and empirical

8 Which statement describes the energy and bonding changes as two atoms of fluorine become a molecule of fluorine?

(1) Energy is absorbed as a bond is broken.
(2) Energy is absorbed as a bond is formed.
(3) Energy is released as a bond is broken.
(4) Energy is released as a bond is formed.

9 Which part of a calcium atom in the ground state is represented by the dots in its Lewis electron-dot diagram?

(1) the electrons in the first shell
(2) the electrons in the fourth shell
(3) the protons in the nucleus
(4) the neutrons in the nucleus

10 Based on Table S, an atom of which element has the strongest attraction for electrons in a chemical bond?

(1) aluminum   (3) magnesium
(2) chlorine   (4) sulfur

11 Which substance can *not* be broken down by chemical means?

(1) aluminum
(2) ammonia
(3) aluminum oxide
(4) ammonium chloride

12 Which statement describes the particles of an ideal gas, based on the kinetic molecular theory?

(1) There are attractive forces between the particles.
(2) The particles move in circular paths.
(3) The collisions between the particles reduce the total energy of the gas.
(4) The volume of the gas particles is negligible compared with the total volume of the gas.

13 What is the amount of heat released by 1.00 gram of liquid water at 0°C when it changes to 1.00 gram of ice at 0°C?

(1) 4.18 J
(2) 273 J
(3) 334 J
(4) 2260 J

14 Which term identifies a type of intermolecular force?

(1) covalent bonding
(2) hydrogen bonding
(3) ionic bonding
(4) metallic bonding

15 Which statement describes a reaction at equilibrium?

(1) The mass of the products must equal the mass of the reactants.
(2) The entropy of the reactants must equal the entropy of the products.
(3) The rate of formation of the products must equal the rate of formation of the reactants.
(4) The number of moles of the reactants must equal the number of moles of the products.

16 Entropy is a measure of

(1) accuracy
(2) precision
(3) the disorder of a system
(4) the attraction of a nucleus for an electron

17 Systems in nature tend to undergo changes toward

(1) lower energy and less randomness
(2) higher energy and less randomness
(3) lower energy and greater randomness
(4) higher energy and greater randomness

18 Which organic prefix is matched with the number of carbon atoms that it represents?

(1) hept-, 7
(2) non-, 8
(3) pent-, 3
(4) prop-, 4

19 Which terms represent two types of organic reactions?

(1) sublimation and deposition
(2) sublimation and fermentation
(3) saponification and deposition
(4) saponification and fermentation

20 Given the organic functional group:

Which class of organic compounds has molecules with this functional group?

(1) aldehydes
(2) esters
(3) ketones
(4) organic acids

21 Which particles are transferred during a redox reaction?

(1) atoms
(2) electrons
(3) neutrons
(4) positrons

22 Which process can be represented by a half-reaction equation?

(1) distillation
(2) oxidation
(3) sublimation
(4) vaporization

23 Which form of energy is converted to electrical energy in a voltaic cell?

(1) chemical
(2) mechanical
(3) nuclear
(4) thermal

24 Which compound is an Arrhenius base?

(1) HCl
(2) H_3PO_4
(3) $Ca(OH)_2$
(4) CH_3COOH

25 In a neutralization reaction, an aqueous solution of an Arrhenius acid reacts with an aqueous solution of an Arrhenius base to produce

(1) an ether and water
(2) an ether and an alcohol
(3) a salt and water
(4) a salt and an alcohol

26 According to one acid-base theory, a base is an

(1) H_2 acceptor
(2) H_2 donor
(3) H^+ acceptor
(4) H^+ donor

27 Based on Table N, uranium-238 and uranium-235 have different

(1) decay modes
(2) half-lives
(3) numbers of protons
(4) numbers of electrons

28 A change in the nucleus of an atom that converts the atom from one element to another element is called

(1) oxidation-reduction
(2) single replacement
(3) substitution
(4) transmutation

29 Which radioactive emission has the greatest penetrating power, but the *least* ionizing power?

(1) alpha particle
(2) beta particle
(3) gamma ray
(4) positron

30 Which statement describes a benefit of using fission reactions?

(1) Radioactive waste must be stored for long periods of time.
(2) Nuclear fuel consists of stable isotopes.
(3) Gamma radiation is produced.
(4) Large amounts of energy are produced per mole of reactant.

Part B–1

Answer all questions in this part.

Directions (31–50): For *each* statement or question, record on your separate answer sheet the *number* of the word or expression that, of those given, best completes the statement or answers the question. Some questions may require the use of the *2011 Edition Reference Tables for Physical Setting/Chemistry*.

31 Given the table representing the subatomic particles in four different atoms:

Atom	Number of Protons	Number of Neutrons	Number of Electrons
A	4	4	4
E	5	7	5
G	6	7	6
J	12	12	12

Which atom has a mass of 12 u?

(1) *A* (3) *G*
(2) *E* (4) *J*

32 Which electron configuration could represent the electrons in a sodium atom in an excited state?

(1) 2-8   (3) 2-7-1
(2) 2-8-1   (4) 2-7-2

33 What is the number of valence electrons in a nitrogen atom in the ground state?

(1) 5   (3) 7
(2) 2   (4) 14

34 Graphite and diamond are both solid forms of the element carbon. Which statement explains the different properties of these two forms of carbon?

(1) Diamond has ionic bonding and graphite has metallic bonding.
(2) Diamond has metallic bonding and graphite has ionic bonding.
(3) Diamond has a different crystal structure from graphite.
(4) Diamond has carbon atoms with more valence electrons than graphite.

35 A measured value for the atomic radius of platinum atoms was determined to be 143 picometers. Based on Table *S*, what is the percent error of this measured value?

(1) 0.10%   (3) 10.%
(2) 9.1%   (4) 13%

36 What is the chemical formula for sodium oxalate?

(1) NaO   (3) NaC_2O_4
(2) Na_2O (4) $Na_2C_2O_4$

37 Given the formula of a compound:

$$\begin{array}{c} H \quad\quad H \quad H \\ \backslash \quad | \quad | \\ C = C - C - H \\ \diagup \quad\quad | \\ H \quad\quad\quad H \end{array}$$

What is the molecular formula for this compound?

(1) CH   (3) CH_3
(2) CH_2 (4) C_3H_6

38 Which equation represents conservation of charge?

(1) $I^- + 2e^- \rightarrow I_2$ (3) $Br_2 \rightarrow 2Br^- + 2e^-$
(2) $2I^- \rightarrow I_2 + 2e^-$ (4) $Br + 2e^- \rightarrow Br^-$

39 Which equation represents a single replacement reaction?

(1) $2Al(s) + 3Cl_2(g) \rightarrow 2AlCl_3(s)$
(2) $2Al(s) + 6HCl(aq) \rightarrow 2AlCl_3(aq) + 3H_2(g)$
(3) $2AlCl_3(s) \rightarrow 2Al(s) + 3Cl_2(g)$
(4) $AlCl_3(aq) + 3KOH(aq) \rightarrow Al(OH)_3(s) + 3KCl(aq)$

40 The bond between which two atoms is most polar?

(1) C–O   (3) H–O
(2) F–F   (4) N–H

41 The table below shows the volume and temperature of four different gas samples at 100. kPa.

Gas Sample	Volume (L)	Temperature (°C)
helium	1	25
neon	2	50.
argon	1	25
krypton	2	25

Which two gas samples contain equal numbers of atoms?

(1) helium and neon
(2) helium and argon
(3) neon and argon
(4) neon and krypton

42 Given the equation representing a solution equilibrium:

$$BaSO_4(s) \xrightleftharpoons{H_2O} Ba^{2+}(aq) + SO_4^{2-}(aq)$$

What occurs when $Na_2SO_4(s)$ is added to this system, increasing the concentration of $SO_4^{2-}(aq)$?

(1) The equilibrium shifts to the left, and the concentration of $Ba^{2+}(aq)$ decreases.
(2) The equilibrium shifts to the left, and the concentration of $Ba^{2+}(aq)$ increases.
(3) The equilibrium shifts to the right, and the concentration of $Ba^{2+}(aq)$ decreases.
(4) The equilibrium shifts to the right, and the concentration of $Ba^{2+}(aq)$ increases.

43 Given the formula for a compound:

H H H O
| | | ||
H−C−C−C−C−N−H
| | | |
H H H H

What is a chemical name for the compound?

(1) 1-butanamine
(2) 1-butanol
(3) butanamide
(4) butanoic acid

44 Given the potential energy diagram representing a reaction:

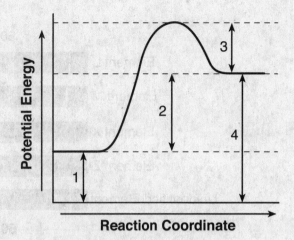

Reaction Coordinate

Which numbered interval represents the heat of reaction?

(1) 1
(2) 2
(3) 3
(4) 4

45 When comparing voltaic cells to electrolytic cells, oxidation occurs at the

(1) anode in both types of cells
(2) cathode in both types of cells
(3) anode in voltaic cells, only
(4) cathode in voltaic cells, only

46 Based on Table *J*, which metal is more active than tin, but *less* active than zinc?

(1) Ag
(2) Cr
(3) Cs
(4) Mn

47 In a titration, 10.0 mL of 0.0750 M HCl(aq) is exactly neutralized by 30.0 mL of KOH(aq) of unknown concentration. What is the concentration of the KOH(aq) solution?

(1) 0.0250 M
(2) 0.0750 M
(3) 0.225 M
(4) 0.333 M

48 Which emission causes the atomic number of a nuclide to decrease by 2 and its mass number to decrease by 4?

(1) an alpha particle
(2) a beta particle
(3) gamma radiation
(4) a positron

49 The diagram below represents the bright-line spectra of four elements and a bright-line spectrum produced by an unidentified element.

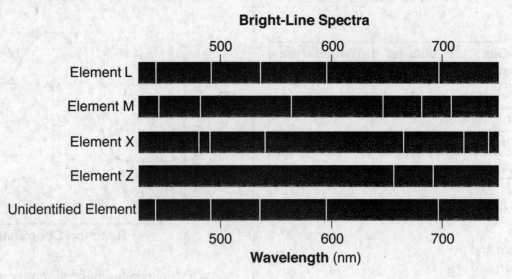

Bright-Line Spectra

What is the unidentified element?

(1) L

(2) M

(3) X

(4) Z

50 Given two equations representing reactions:

$$\text{Equation 1:} \quad {}^{235}_{92}U + {}^{1}_{0}n \rightarrow {}^{141}_{56}Ba + {}^{92}_{36}Kr + 3{}^{1}_{0}n$$

$$\text{Equation 2:} \quad {}^{1}_{1}H + {}^{2}_{1}H \rightarrow {}^{3}_{2}He$$

Which type of reaction is represented by each of these equations?

(1) Both equations represent fission.

(2) Both equations represent fusion.

(3) Equation 1 represents fission and equation 2 represents fusion.

(4) Equation 1 represents fusion and equation 2 represents fission.

January '20 Regents Examination

Part B–2

Answer all questions in this part.

Directions (51-65): Record your answers in the spaces provided in your answer booklet. Some questions may require the use of the *2011 Edition Reference Tables for Physical Setting/Chemistry*.

Base your answers to questions 51 through 53 on the information below and on your knowledge of chemistry.

The four naturally occurring isotopes of sulfur are S-32, S-33, S-34, and S-36. The table below shows the atomic mass and percent natural abundance for these isotopes.

Naturally Occurring Isotopes of Sulfur

Isotope	Atomic Mass (u)	Natural Abundance (%)
S-32	31.972	94.99
S-33	32.971	0.75
S-34	33.968	4.25
S-36	35.967	0.01

51 State *both* the number of protons and the number of neutrons in an S-33 atom. [1]

52 In the space *in your answer booklet*, show a numerical setup for calculating the atomic mass of sulfur. [1]

53 Compare the energy of an electron in the third shell of a sulfur atom to the energy of an electron in the first shell of the same atom. [1]

Base your answers to questions 54 through 57 on the information below and on your knowledge of chemistry.

During a laboratory activity, appropriate safety equipment is used and safety procedures are followed. A student separates a sample of rock salt that has two components; NaCl(s) and small insoluble rock particles. First, the student thoroughly stirs the sample of rock salt into a sample of water in a flask. The mixture in the flask is filtered using the lab apparatus shown below.

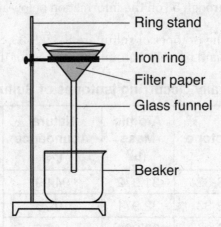

The water is evaporated from the beaker. The filter paper and its contents are dried. The data collected by the student are shown in the table below.

Rock Salt Separation Lab Data

Object or Material	Mass (g)
rock salt sample	16.4
filter paper	1.6
clean empty beaker	224.2
filter paper with dry rock particles	2.2
beaker with dry NaCl(s)	240.0

54 State evidence, other than mass, from the information given that the components of rock salt have different properties. [1]

55 Explain, in terms of particle size, why the rock particles are trapped by the filter paper. [1]

56 State the number of significant figures in the mass of the beaker with dry NaCl(s). [1]

57 Show a numerical setup for calculating the percent by mass of NaCl in the rock salt sample. [1]

Base your answers to questions 58 through 61 on the information below and on your knowledge of chemistry.

Cylinder A and cylinder B are sealed, rigid cylinders with movable pistons. Each cylinder contains 500. milliliters of a gas sample at 101.3 kPa and 298 K. Cylinder A contains $H_2(g)$ and cylinder B contains $N_2(g)$. The diagrams below represent these two cylinders.

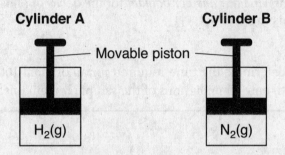

58 Compare the mass of the gas in cylinder A to the mass of the gas in cylinder B. [1]

59 State a change in temperature and a change in pressure that will cause the gas in cylinder A to behave more like an ideal gas. [1]

60 Explain, in terms of collisions between gas molecules and the walls of the container, why pushing the movable piston farther into cylinder B at constant temperature would increase the pressure of the N_2 gas. [1]

61 Show a numerical setup for calculating the volume of the gas in cylinder B at STP. [1]

_____

Base your answers to questions 62 and 63 on the information below and on your knowledge of chemistry.

The electrical conductivity of three aqueous solutions was tested at room temperature. A 0.1 M HCl(aq) solution conducted, but a 6.0 M HCl(aq) solution was a better conductor. A 0.1 M $C_6H_{12}O_6$(aq) solution was also tested. During this laboratory activity, appropriate safety equipment was used and safety procedures were followed.

62 State, in terms of the concentration of ions, why the 6.0 M HCl(aq) is a better conductor of electricity than the 0.1 M HCl(aq). [1]

63 Identify the element in $C_6H_{12}O_6$ that allows it to be classified as an organic compound. [1]

_____

Base your answers to questions 64 and 65 on the information below and on your knowledge of chemistry.

Phosphorus-30 and phosphorus-32 are radioisotopes. Phosphorus-30 decays by positron emission.

64 Complete the equation *in your answer booklet* for the decay of phosphorus-30 by writing a notation for the missing product. [1]

65 Based on Table *N*, determine the time required for an original 100.-milligram sample of P-32 to decay until only 25 milligrams of the sample remain unchanged. [1]

Part C

Answer all questions in this part.

Directions (66-85): Record your answers in the spaces provided in your answer booklet. Some questions may require the use of the *2011 Edition Reference Tables for Physical Setting/Chemistry*.

Base your answers to questions 66 through 69 on the information below and on your knowledge of chemistry.

Sir William Ramsey is one scientist credited with identifying the noble gas argon. Sir Ramsey separated nitrogen gas from the air and reacted it with an excess of magnesium, producing solid magnesium nitride. However, a small sample of an unreactive gas remained with a density different from the density of the nitrogen gas. Sir Ramsey identified the unreactive gas as argon and later went on to discover neon, krypton, and xenon.

66 Compare the chemical reactivities of nitrogen gas and argon gas based on Sir Ramsey's experiment using magnesium. [1]

67 Compare the density of nitrogen gas to the density of argon gas when both gases are at 298 K and 101.3 kPa. [1]

68 State, in terms of valence electrons, why the noble gases that Sir Ramsey discovered have similar chemical properties. [1]

69 State the trend, at standard pressure, of the boiling points of these noble gases, as they are considered in order of increasing atomic number. [1]

Base your answers to questions 70 through 72 on the information below and on your knowledge of chemistry.

A sample of normal rainwater has a pH value of 5.6 due to dissolved carbon dioxide gas from the atmosphere. Acid rain is formed when other gases, such as sulfur dioxide, dissolve in rainwater, which can result in lake water with a pH value of 4.6. The equation below represents the reaction of water with $SO_2(g)$.

$$H_2O(\ell) + SO_2(g) \rightarrow H_2SO_3(aq)$$

70 State how many times greater the hydronium ion concentration in the lake water is than the hydronium concentration in the sample of normal rainwater. [1]

71 State the color of methyl orange in a sample of normal rainwater. [1]

72 Based on Table *G*, describe what happens to the solubility of $SO_2(g)$ as the temperature increases from 10.°C to 30.°C at standard pressure. [1]

January '20   Regents Examination

Base your answers to questions 73 through 77 on the information below and on your knowledge of chemistry.

A metal worker uses a cutting torch that operates by reacting acetylene gas, $C_2H_2(g)$, with oxygen gas, $O_2(g)$, as shown in the unbalanced equation below.

$$C_2H_2(g) + O_2(g) \rightarrow CO_2(g) + H_2O(g) + heat$$

73 Write the empirical formula for acetylene. [1]

74 *In your answer booklet,* use the key to draw a particle model diagram to represent the phase of the $O_2(g)$. Your response must include *at least six* molecules. [1]

75 Balance the equation *in your answer booklet* for the reaction of acetylene and oxygen, using the smallest whole-number coefficients. [1]

76 Determine the mass of 25 moles of acetylene (gram-formula mass = 26 g/mol). [1]

77 Explain, in terms of bonding, why the hydrocarbon gas used in the cutting torch is classified as an alkyne. [1]

Base your answers to questions 78 through 82 on the information below and on your knowledge of chemistry.

Water, H_2O, and hexane, C_6H_{14}, are commonly used as laboratory solvents because they have different physical properties and are able to dissolve different types of solutes. Some physical properties of water and hexane are listed on the table below.

Physical Properties of H_2O and C_6H_{14}

Solvent	Boiling Point (°C)	Melting Point (°C)	Vapor Pressure at 69°C (kPa)
H_2O	100.	0.	?
C_6H_{14}	69	–95	101.3

78 Compare the thermal energy of a 10.-gram sample of water at 25°C to the thermal energy of a 1000.-gram sample of water at 25°C. [1]

79 State what happens to the potential energy of the molecules in a solid sample of hexane at –95°C as heat is added until the hexane is completely melted. [1]

80 Determine the vapor pressure of water at 69°C. [1]

81 Explain, in terms of the molecular polarity, why hexane is nearly insoluble in water. [1]

82 Explain, in terms of molecular formulas and structural formulas, why 2,2-dimethylbutane is an isomer of hexane. [1]

Base your answers to questions 83 through 85 on the information below and on your knowledge of chemistry.

In a laboratory investigation, a student constructs an electrochemical cell to decompose water, as represented in the diagram below. The water in the electrochemical cell contains a small amount of dissolved sodium sulfate, to increase conductivity. The three equations represent the reaction in each test tube and the overall reaction. During this laboratory activity, appropriate safety equipment is used and safety procedures are followed.

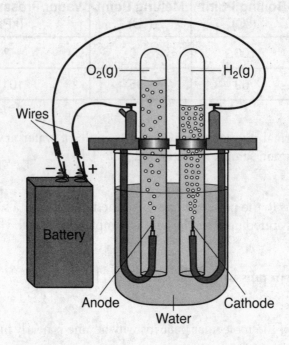

O$_2$ Test Tube: $2H_2O(\ell) \longrightarrow O_2(g) + 4H^+(aq) + 4e^-$

H$_2$ Test Tube: $2H^+(aq) + 2e^- \longrightarrow H_2(g)$

Overall Reaction: $2H_2O(\ell) \longrightarrow O_2(g) + 2H_2(g)$

83 State the change in oxidation number that occurs for oxygen in the overall reaction. [1]

84 Compare the number of electrons lost by oxygen to the number of electrons gained by hydrogen in the overall reaction. [1]

85 Determine the number of moles of hydrogen gas produced when 0.0004 mole of oxygen gas is produced in the cell by the overall reaction. [1]

January '20   Regents Examination

PHYSICAL SETTING
CHEMISTRY

Friday, January 24, 2020 — 9:15 a.m. to 12:15 p.m., only

ANSWER BOOKLET

Student . . . .

Teacher . . . .

School . . . . Grade . . . .

Record your answers for Part B–2 and Part C in this booklet.

Part B–2

51 Protons: _____

   Neutrons: _____

52

53 _____

_____

_____

---

54 _____

_____

_____

55 _____

_____

_____

56 _____

57

P.S./Chem. Answer Booklet–Jan. '20   [2]

January '20   Regents Examination

58 _____

_____

_____

59 Temperature: _____

Pressure: _____

60 _____

_____

_____

61

January '20   Regents Examination

62 _____

_____

_____

63 _____

64 $^{30}_{15}P \rightarrow \,^{0}_{+1}e +$ _____

65 _____ **d**

Part C

66 _____

_____

_____

67 _____

_____

_____

68 _____

_____

_____

69 _____

_____

_____

70 _____

71 _____

72 _____

_____

_____

January '20 Regents Examination

73 _____

74

Key
⬭⬭ = an oxygen molecule

75 _____ $C_2H_2(g)$ + _____ $O_2(g) \rightarrow$ _____ $CO_2(g)$ + _____ $H_2O(g)$ + heat

76 _____ g

77 _____

_____

_____

78 _____

_____

_____

79 _____

_____

_____

80 _____ kPa

81 _____

_____

_____

82 _____

_____

_____

83 From _____ to _____

84 _____

_____

_____

85 _____ mol

Part A

Answer all questions in this part.

Directions (1–30): For *each* statement or question, record on your separate answer sheet the *number* of the word or expression that, of those given, best completes the statement or answers the question. Some questions may require the use of the *2011 Edition Reference Tables for Physical Setting/Chemistry.*

1 Which statement describes the earliest model of the atom?

(1) An atom is an indivisible hard sphere.
(2) An atom has a small, dense nucleus.
(3) Electrons are negative particles in an atom.
(4) Electrons in an atom have wave-like properties.

2 In all atoms of bismuth, the number of electrons must equal the

(1) number of protons
(2) number of neutrons
(3) sum of the number of neutrons and protons
(4) difference between the number of neutrons and protons

3 Which symbol represents a particle that has a mass approximately equal to the mass of a neutron?

(1) α (3) β^-
(2) β^+ (4) p

4 An orbital is a region in an atom where there is a high probability of finding

(1) an alpha particle   (3) a neutron
(2) an electron   (4) a positron

5 Which electron shell in an atom of calcium in the ground state has an electron with the greatest amount of energy?

(1) 1   (3) 3
(2) 2   (4) 4

6 As the elements in Period 2 are considered in order from lithium to fluorine, there is an increase in the

(1) atomic radius
(2) electronegativity
(3) number of electron shells
(4) number of electrons in the first shell

7 Which element is classified as a metalloid?

(1) boron   (3) sulfur
(2) potassium   (4) xenon

8 Strontium and barium have similar chemical properties because atoms of these elements have the same number of

(1) protons   (3) electron shells
(2) neutrons   (4) valence electrons

9 Which term represents the fixed proportion of elements in a compound?

(1) atomic mass   (3) chemical formula
(2) molar mass   (4) density formula

10 Which two terms represent types of chemical formulas?

(1) mechanical and structural
(2) mechanical and thermal
(3) molecular and structural
(4) molecular and thermal

11 Which element has metallic bonds at room temperature?

(1) bromine   (3) krypton
(2) cesium   (4) sulfur

12 What is the number of electrons shared between the atoms in a molecule of nitrogen, N_2?

(1) 8
(3) 3
(2) 2
(4) 6

13 Given the equation representing a reaction:

$$H + H \rightarrow H_2$$

What occurs during this reaction?

(1) A bond is broken and energy is absorbed.
(2) A bond is broken and energy is released.
(3) A bond is formed and energy is absorbed.
(4) A bond is formed and energy is released.

14 An atom of which element has the strongest attraction for electrons in a chemical bond?

(1) chlorine
(3) phosphorus
(2) carbon
(4) sulfur

15 At STP, a 50.-gram sample of $H_2O(\ell)$ and a 100.-gram sample of $H_2O(\ell)$ have

(1) the same chemical properties
(2) the same volume
(3) different temperatures
(4) different empirical formulas

16 Which statement describes a mixture of sand and water at room temperature?

(1) It is heterogeneous, and its components are in the same phase.
(2) It is heterogeneous, and its components are in different phases.
(3) It is homogeneous, and its components are in the same phase.
(4) It is homogeneous, and its components are in different phases.

17 Distillation is a process used to separate a mixture of liquids based on different

(1) boiling points
(3) freezing points
(2) densities
(4) solubilities

18 According to the kinetic molecular theory, which statement describes the particles in a sample of an ideal gas?

(1) The particles are constantly moving in circular paths.
(2) The particles collide, decreasing the total energy of the system.
(3) The particles have attractive forces between them.
(4) The particles are considered to have negligible volume.

19 Which sample of matter has the greatest distance between molecules at STP?

(1) $N_2(g)$
(3) $C_6H_{14}(\ell)$
(2) $NH_3(aq)$
(4) $C_6H_{12}O_6(s)$

20 For a chemical system at equilibrium, the concentrations of both the reactants and the products must

(1) decrease
(3) be constant
(2) increase
(4) be equal

21 In terms of disorder and energy, systems in nature have a tendency to undergo changes toward

(1) less disorder and lower energy
(2) less disorder and higher energy
(3) greater disorder and lower energy
(4) greater disorder and higher energy

22 The only two elements in alkenes and alkynes are

(1) carbon and nitrogen
(2) carbon and hydrogen
(3) oxygen and nitrogen
(4) oxygen and hydrogen

23 Which functional group contains a nitrogen atom and an oxygen atom?

(1) ester
(3) amide
(2) ether
(4) amine

24 When a sample of Mg(s) reacts completely with $O_2(g)$, the Mg(s) loses 5.0 moles of electrons. How many moles of electrons are gained by the $O_2(g)$?

(1) 1.0 mol   (3) 5.0 mol
(2) 2.5 mol   (4) 10.0 mol

25 Which statement describes the reactions in an electrochemical cell?

(1) Oxidation occurs at the anode, and reduction occurs at the cathode.
(2) Oxidation occurs at the cathode, and reduction occurs at the anode.
(3) Oxidation and reduction both occur at the cathode.
(4) Oxidation and reduction both occur at the anode.

26 A 0.050 M aqueous solution of which compound is the best conductor of electric current?

(1) C_3H_7OH (3) $MgSO_4$
(2) $C_6H_{12}O_6$ (4) K_2SO_4

27 What is the color of bromcresol green indicator in a solution with a pH value of 2.0?

(1) blue   (3) red
(2) green   (4) yellow

28 Which formula can represent hydrogen ions in an aqueous solution?

(1) $OH^-(aq)$ (3) $H_3O^+(aq)$
(2) $Hg_2^{2+}(aq)$ (4) $NH_4^+(aq)$

29 In which reaction is an atom of one element converted into an atom of another element?

(1) combustion
(2) fermentation
(3) oxidation-reduction
(4) transmutation

30 In which type of nuclear reaction do nuclei combine to form a nucleus with a greater mass?

(1) alpha decay   (3) fusion
(2) beta decay   (4) fission

Answer all questions in this part.

Directions (31–50): For *each* statement or question, record on your separate answer sheet the *number* of the word or expression that, of those given, best completes the statement or answers the question. Some questions may require the use of the *2011 Edition Reference Tables for Physical Setting/Chemistry*.

31 The bright-line spectra produced by four elements are represented in the diagram below.

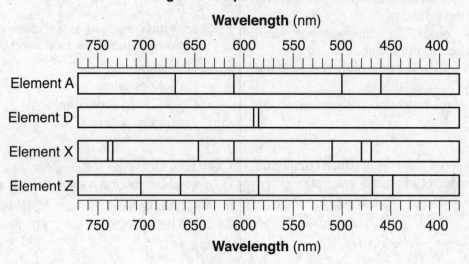

Bright-Line Spectra of Four Elements

Given the bright-line spectrum of a mixture formed from two of these elements:

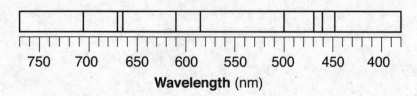

Which elements are present in this mixture?

(1) *A* and *X*   (3) *D* and *X*
(2) *A* and *Z*   (4) *D* and *Z*

32 Which electron configuration represents the electrons in an atom of sulfur in an excited state?

(1) 2 – 8 – 6   (3) 2 – 8 – 7
(2) 2 – 7 – 7   (4) 2 – 7 – 8

33 Which notations represent atoms that have the same number of protons but a different number of neutrons?

(1) H-3 and He-3   (3) Cl-35 and Cl-37
(2) S-32 and S-32   (4) Ga-70 and Ge-73

34 What is the chemical name of the compound NH_4SCN?

(1) ammonium thiocyanate
(2) ammonium cyanide
(3) nitrogen hydrogen cyanide
(4) nitrogen hydrogen sulfate

35 Which equation represents a conservation of atoms?

(1) $2Fe + 2O_2 \rightarrow Fe_2O_3$
(2) $2Fe + 3O_2 \rightarrow Fe_2O_3$
(3) $4Fe + 2O_2 \rightarrow 2Fe_2O_3$
(4) $4Fe + 3O_2 \rightarrow 2Fe_2O_3$

36 Which compound has covalent bonds?

(1) H_2O
(2) Li_2O
(3) Na_2O
(4) K_2O

37 Which particle diagram represents a sample of oxygen gas at STP?

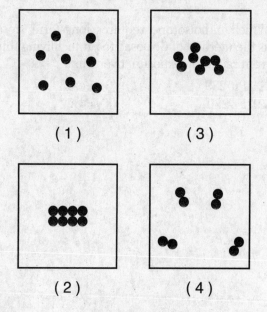

Key
● = one atom of oxygen

(1)   (3)

(2)   (4)

38 At which temperature and pressure will a sample of neon gas behave most like an ideal gas?

(1) 300. K and 2.0 atm   (3) 500. K and 2.0 atm
(2) 300. K and 4.0 atm   (4) 500. K and 4.0 atm

39 What is the molarity of 2.0 liters of an aqueous solution that contains 0.50 mole of potassium iodide, KI?

(1) 1.0 M   (3) 0.25 M
(2) 2.0 M   (4) 0.50 M

40 The volumes of four samples of gaseous compounds at 298 K and 101.3 kPa are shown in the table below.

Sample	Compounds	Volume (L)
1	$NH_3(g)$	44.0
2	$CO_2(g)$	33.0
3	$HF(g)$	44.0
4	$CH_4(g)$	22.0

Which two samples contain the same number of molecules?

(1) 1 and 2   (3) 2 and 3
(2) 1 and 3   (4) 2 and 4

41 Hydrochloric acid reacts faster with powdered zinc than with an equal mass of zinc strips because the greater surface area of the powdered zinc

(1) decreases the frequency of particle collisions
(2) decreases the activation energy of the reaction
(3) increases the frequency of particle collisions
(4) increases the activation energy of the reaction

42 Given the equation representing a system at equilibrium in a sealed, rigid container:

$$2HI(g) \rightleftharpoons H_2(g) + I_2(g) + \text{energy}$$

Increasing the temperature of the system causes the concentration of

(1) HI to increase
(2) H_2 to increase
(3) HI to remain constant
(4) H_2 to remain constant

43 Based on Table *I*, which equation represents a reaction with the greatest difference between the potential energy of the products and the potential energy of the reactants?

(1) $4Al(s) + 3O_2(g) \rightarrow 2Al_2O_3(s)$

(2) $2H_2(g) + O_2(g) \rightarrow 2H_2O(\ell)$

(3) $C_3H_8(g) + 5O_2(g) \rightarrow 3CO_2(g) + 4H_2O(\ell)$

(4) $C_6H_{12}O_6(s) + 6O_2(g) \rightarrow 6CO_2(g) + 6H_2O(\ell)$

44 Which phase change results in an increase in entropy?

(1) $I_2(g) \rightarrow I_2(s)$ (3) $Br_2(\ell) \rightarrow Br_2(g)$
(2) $CH_4(g) \rightarrow CH_4(\ell)$ (4) $H_2O(\ell) \rightarrow H_2O(s)$

45 Given the formula for a compound:

```
    H   H   H   O       H
    |   |   |   ||      |
H — C — C — C — C — O — C — H
    |   |   |           |
    H   H   H           H
```

What is the name of this compound?

(1) methyl butanoate   (3) pentanone
(2) methyl butyl ether   (4) pentanoic acid

46 Given the equation representing a reaction:

$$2Ca(s) + O_2(g) \rightarrow 2CaO(s)$$

During this reaction, each element changes in

(1) atomic number
(2) oxidation number
(3) number of protons per atom
(4) number of neutrons per atom

47 Which equation represents a spontaneous reaction?

(1) $Ca + Ba^{2+} \rightarrow Ca^{2+} + Ba$
(2) $Co + Zn^{2+} \rightarrow Co^{2+} + Zn$
(3) $Fe + Mg^{2+} \rightarrow Fe^{2+} + Mg$
(4) $Mn + Ni^{2+} \rightarrow Mn^{2+} + Ni$

48 Which equation represents a neutralization reaction?

(1) $6HClO \rightarrow 4HCl + 2HClO_3$

(2) $CH_4 + 2O_2 \rightarrow CO_2 + 2H_2O$

(3) $Ca(OH)_2 + H_2SO_4 \rightarrow CaSO_4 + 2H_2O$

(4) $Ba(OH)_2 + Cu(NO_3)_2 \rightarrow Ba(NO_3)_2 + Cu(OH)_2$

49 Which radioisotope requires long-term storage as the method of disposal, to protect living things from radiation exposure over time?

(1) Pu-239   (3) Fe-53
(2) Fr-220   (4) P-32

50 Given the equation representing a reaction:

$$^{235}_{92}U + ^{1}_{0}n \longrightarrow ^{140}_{56}Ba + ^{93}_{36}Kr + 3^{1}_{0}n + energy$$

total mass equals
236.053 u

total mass equals
235.868 u

Which statement explains the energy term in this reaction?

(1) Mass is gained due to the conversion of mass to energy.
(2) Mass is gained due to the conversion of energy to mass.
(3) Mass is lost due to the conversion of mass to energy.
(4) Mass is lost due to the conversion of energy to mass.

Part B–2

Answer all questions in this part.

Directions (51–65): Record your answers in the spaces provided in your answer booklet. Some questions may require the use of the *2011 Edition Reference Tables for Physical Setting/Chemistry*.

Base your answers to questions 51 through 53 on the information below and on your knowledge of chemistry.

The only naturally occurring isotopes of nitrogen are N-14 and N-15.

51 State the number of protons in an atom of N-15. [1]

52 State the number of electrons in each shell of a N-14 atom in the ground state. [1]

53 Based on the atomic mass of the element nitrogen on the Periodic Table, compare the relative abundances of the naturally occurring isotopes of nitrogen. [1]

Base your answers to questions 54 through 56 on the information below and on your knowledge of chemistry.

The melting points and boiling points of five substances at standard pressure are listed on the table below.

Melting Points and Boiling Points of Five Substances

Substance	Melting Point (K)	Boiling Point (K)
HCl	159	188
NO	109	121
F_2	53	85
Br_2	266	332
I_2	387	457

54 Identify the substance in this table that is a liquid at STP. [1]

55 State, in terms of the strength of intermolecular forces, why I_2 has a higher boiling point than F_2. [1]

56 State what happens to the potential energy of a sample of NO(ℓ) at 121 K as it changes to NO(g) at constant temperature and standard pressure. [1]

Base your answers to questions 57 through 59 on the information below and on your knowledge of chemistry.

A 100.-gram sample of liquid water is heated from 20.0°C to 50.0°C. Enough $KClO_3(s)$ is dissolved in the sample of water at 50.0°C to form a saturated solution.

57 Using the information on Table *B*, determine the amount of heat absorbed by the water when the water is heated from 20.0°C to 50.0°C. [1]

58 Based on Table *H*, determine the vapor pressure of the water sample at its final temperature. [1]

59 Based on Table *G*, determine the mass of $KClO_3(s)$ that must dissolve to make a saturated solution in 100. g of H_2O at 50.0°C. [1]

___

Base your answers to questions 60 through 62 on the information below and on your knowledge of chemistry.

The diagram and ionic equation below represent an operating voltaic cell.

Voltaic Cell

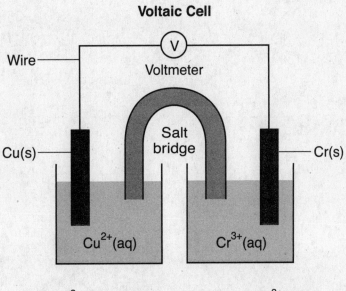

$$3Cu^{2+}(aq) + 2Cr(s) \longrightarrow 3Cu(s) + 2Cr^{3+}(aq)$$

60 Identify the subatomic particles that flow through the wires as the cell operates. [1]

61 State the purpose of the salt bridge in completing the circuit in this cell. [1]

62 Write a balanced equation for the half-reaction that occurs in the copper half-cell when the cell operates. [1]

___

Base your answers to questions 63 through 65 on the information below and on your knowledge of chemistry.

A NaOH(aq) solution with a pH value of 13 is used to determine the molarity of a HCl(aq) solution. A 10.0-mL sample of the HCl(aq) is exactly neutralized by 16.0 mL of 0.100 M NaOH(aq). During this laboratory activity, appropriate safety equipment was used and safety procedures were followed.

63 Determine the molarity of the HCl(aq) sample, using the titration data. [1]

64 Compare the hydronium ion concentration to the hydroxide ion concentration when the HCl(aq) solution is exactly neutralized by the NaOH(aq) solution. [1]

65 Determine the pH value of a solution that has a H^+(aq) ion concentration 10 times greater than the original NaOH(aq) solution. [1]

Part C

Answer all questions in this part.

Directions (66-85): Record your answers in the spaces provided in your answer booklet. Some questions may require the use of the *2011 Edition Reference Tables for Physical Setting/Chemistry*.

Base your answers to questions 66 through 68 on the information below and on your knowledge of chemistry.

A hydrate is a compound that has water molecules within its crystal structure. Magnesium sulfate heptahydrate, $MgSO_4 \cdot 7H_2O$, is a hydrated form of magnesium sulfate. The hydrated compound has 7 moles of H_2O for each mole of $MgSO_4$. When 5.06 grams of $MgSO_4 \cdot 7H_2O$ are heated to at least 300.°C in a crucible by using a laboratory burner, the water molecules are released. The sample was heated repeatedly, until the remaining $MgSO_4$ had a constant mass of 2.47 grams. During this laboratory activity, appropriate safety equipment was used and safety procedures were followed.

66 Explain why the sample in the crucible was heated repeatedly until the sample had a constant mass. [1]

67 Using the lab data, show a numerical setup for calculating the percent composition by mass of water in the hydrated compound. [1]

68 Determine the gram-formula mass of the magnesium sulfate heptahydrate. [1]

Base your answers to questions 69 through 71 on the information below and on your knowledge of chemistry.

Solid sodium chloride, also known as table salt, can be obtained by the solar evaporation of seawater and from underground mining. Liquid sodium chloride can be decomposed by electrolysis to produce liquid sodium and chlorine gas, as represented by the equation below.

$$2NaCl(\ell) \rightarrow 2Na(\ell) + Cl_2(g)$$

69 State, in terms of electrons, why the radius of a Na^+ ion in the table salt is smaller than the radius of a Na atom. [1]

70 Identify the noble gas that has atoms with the same number of electrons as a chloride ion in table salt. [1]

71 In the space *in your answer booklet*, draw a Lewis electron-dot diagram of a Cl_2 molecule. [1]

Base your answers to questions 72 through 75 on the information below and on your knowledge of chemistry.

The enclosed cabin of a submarine has a volume of 2.4×10^5 liters, a temperature of 312 K, and a pressure of 116 kPa. As people in the cabin breathe, carbon dioxide gas, $CO_2(g)$, can build up to unsafe levels. Air in the cabin becomes unsafe to breathe when the mass of $CO_2(g)$ in this cabin exceeds 2156 grams.

72 State what happens to the average kinetic energy of the gas molecules if the cabin temperature *decreases*. [1]

73 Show a numerical setup for calculating the pressure in the submarine cabin if the cabin temperature changes to 293 K. [1]

74 Determine the number of moles of $CO_2(g)$ in the submarine cabin at which the air becomes unsafe to breathe. The gram-formula mass of CO_2 is 44.0 g/mol. [1]

75 Convert the original air pressure in the cabin of the submarine to atmospheres. [1]

_____

Base your answers to questions 76 through 78 on the information below and on your knowledge of chemistry.

Automobile catalytic converters use a platinum catalyst to reduce air pollution by changing emissions such as carbon monoxide, $CO(g)$, into carbon dioxide, $CO_2(g)$. The uncatalyzed reaction is represented by the balanced equation below.

$$2CO(g) + O_2(g) \rightarrow 2CO_2(g) + \text{heat}$$

76 On the labeled axes *in your answer booklet*, draw a potential energy diagram for the reaction represented by this equation. [1]

77 Compare the activation energy of the catalyzed reaction to the activation energy of the uncatalyzed reaction. [1]

78 Determine the number of moles of $O_2(g)$ required to completely react with 28 moles of $CO(g)$ during this reaction. [1]

_____

August '19 Regents Examination

Base your answers to questions 79 through 81 on the information below and on your knowledge of chemistry.

The solvent 2-chloropropane can be made when chemists react propene with hydrogen chloride, as shown in the equation below.

$$\begin{array}{c} \text{H} \quad \text{H} \\ | \quad | \\ \text{H}-\text{C}-\text{C}=\text{C}-\text{H} + \text{HCl} \longrightarrow \\ | \quad | \\ \text{H} \quad \text{H} \end{array} \quad \begin{array}{c} \text{H} \quad \text{H} \quad \text{H} \\ | \quad | \quad | \\ \text{H}-\text{C}-\text{C}-\text{C}-\text{H} \\ | \quad | \quad | \\ \text{H} \quad \text{Cl} \quad \text{H} \end{array}$$

79 Identify the element in propene that is in all organic compounds. [1]

80 Explain, in terms of chemical bonds, why the hydrocarbon reactant is classified as unsaturated. [1]

81 Write the general formula for the homologous series to which propene belongs. [1]

Base your answers to questions 82 through 85 on the information below and on your knowledge of chemistry.

Radioactive emissions can be detected by a Geiger counter. When radioactive emissions enter the Geiger counter probe, which contains a noble gas such as argon or helium, some of the atoms are ionized. The ionized gas allows for a brief electric current. The current causes the speaker to make a clicking sound. To make sure that the Geiger counter is measuring radiation properly, the device is tested using the radioisotope Cs-137.

To detect gamma radiation, an aluminum shield can be placed over the probe window, to keep alpha and beta radiation from entering the probe. A diagram that represents the Geiger counter is shown below.

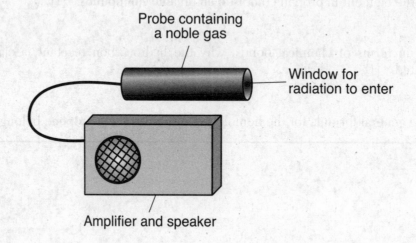

Probe containing
a noble gas

Window for
radiation to enter

Amplifier and speaker

82 Compare the first ionization energy of argon to the first ionization energy of helium. [1]

83 State evidence from the passage that gamma radiation has greater penetrating power than alpha or beta radiation. [1]

84 Determine the time required for a sample of cesium-137 to decay until only $\frac{1}{8}$ of the original sample remains unchanged. [1]

85 Complete the nuclear equation *in your answer booklet* for the decay of Cs-137 by writing a notation for the missing product. [1]

The University of the State of New York

REGENTS HIGH SCHOOL EXAMINATION

PHYSICAL SETTING
CHEMISTRY

Tuesday, August 13, 2019 — 8:30 to 11:30 a.m., only

ANSWER BOOKLET

Student . . . .

Teacher . . . .

School . . . . Grade . . . .

Record your answers for Part B–2 and Part C in this booklet.

Part B–2

51 _____

52 First shell: _____

Second shell: _____

53 _____

_____

_____

54 _____

55 _____

_____

_____

56 _____

_____

_____

57 _____ J

58 _____ kPa

59 _____ g

60 _____

61 _____

_____

_____

62 _____

P.S./Chem. Answer Booklet–Aug. '19   [2]

August '19   Regents Examination

63 _____ M

64 _____

_____

_____

65 _____

August '19   Regents Examination

Part C

66 _____

_____

_____

67

68 _____ g/mol

August '19   Regents Examination

69 _____

_____

_____

70 _____

71

72 _____

_____

_____

73

P.S./Chem. Answer Booklet–Aug. '19   [5]   [OVER]

August '19   Regents Examination

74 _____ mol

75 _____ atm

76

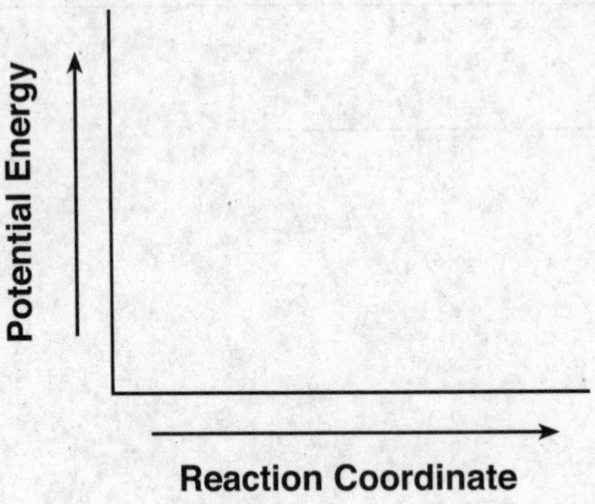

Potential Energy ↑

→ Reaction Coordinate

77 _____

_____

_____

78 _____ mol

79 _____

80 _____

_____

_____

81 _____

August '19   Regents Examination

82 _____

_____

_____

83 _____

_____

_____

84 _____ y

85 $^{137}_{55}Cs \rightarrow \ ^{0}_{-1}e + $ _____

Part A

Answer all questions in this part.

Directions (1–30): For *each* statement or question, record on your separate answer sheet the *number* of the word or expression that, of those given, best completes the statement or answers the question. Some questions may require the use of the *2011 Edition Reference Tables for Physical Setting/Chemistry*.

1 Which particles are found in the nucleus of an argon atom?

(1) protons and electrons
(2) positrons and neutrons
(3) protons and neutrons
(4) positrons and electrons

2 The diagram below represents a particle traveling through an electric field.

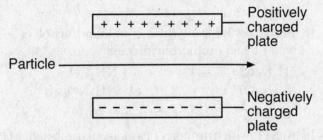

An electric field exists between the two plates.

Which particle remains undeflected when passing through this electric field?

(1) proton   (3) neutron
(2) electron   (4) positron

3 The mass of an electron is

(1) equal to the mass of a proton
(2) equal to the mass of a neutron
(3) greater than the mass of a proton
(4) less than the mass of a neutron

4 Compared to the energy of an electron in the second shell of an atom of sulfur, the energy of an electron in the

(1) first shell is lower
(2) first shell is the same
(3) third shell is lower
(4) third shell is the same

5 In the ground state, an atom of which element has seven valence electrons?

(1) sodium   (3) nitrogen
(2) phosphorus   (4) fluorine

6 Which information is sufficient to differentiate a sample of sodium from a sample of silver?

(1) the mass of each sample
(2) the volume of each sample
(3) the reactivity of each sample with water
(4) the phase of each sample at room temperature

7 Graphite and diamond are two forms of solid carbon at STP. These forms have

(1) different molecular structures and different properties
(2) different molecular structures and the same properties
(3) the same molecular structures and different properties
(4) the same molecular structures and the same properties

8 As the first five elements in Group 14 are considered in order from top to bottom, there are changes in both the

(1) number of valence shell electrons and number of first shell electrons
(2) electronegativity values and number of first shell electrons
(3) number of valence shell electrons and atomic radii
(4) electronegativity values and atomic radii

9 Which statement explains why NaBr is classified as a compound?

(1) Na and Br are chemically combined in a fixed proportion.
(2) Na and Br are both nonmetals.
(3) NaBr is a solid at 298 K and standard pressure.
(4) NaBr dissolves in H_2O at 298 K.

10 Which two terms represent types of chemical formulas?

(1) fission and fusion
(2) oxidation and reduction
(3) empirical and structural
(4) endothermic and exothermic

11 During all chemical reactions, charge, mass and energy are

(1) condensed
(2) conserved
(3) decayed
(4) decomposed

12 The degree of polarity of a covalent bond between two atoms is determined by calculating the difference in their

(1) atomic radii
(2) melting points
(3) electronegativities
(4) ionization energies

13 Which substance can *not* be broken down by a chemical change?

(1) ammonia
(2) magnesium
(3) methane
(4) water

14 Which statement describes the components of a mixture?

(1) Each component gains new properties.
(2) Each component loses its original properties.
(3) The proportions of components can vary.
(4) The proportions of components cannot vary.

15 Table sugar can be separated from a mixture of table sugar and sand at STP by adding

(1) sand, stirring, and distilling at 100.°C
(2) sand, stirring, and filtering
(3) water, stirring, and distilling at 100.°C
(4) water, stirring, and filtering

16 Which statement describes the particles of an ideal gas, based on the kinetic molecular theory?

(1) The volume of the particles is considered negligible.
(2) The force of attraction between the particles is strong.
(3) The particles are closely packed in a regular, repeating pattern.
(4) The particles are separated by small distances, relative to their size.

17 During which two processes does a substance release energy?

(1) freezing and condensation
(2) freezing and melting
(3) evaporation and condensation
(4) evaporation and melting

18 Based on Table *I*, which compound dissolves in water by an exothermic process?

(1) NaCl
(2) NaOH
(3) NH_4Cl
(4) NH_4NO_3

19 At STP, which property of a molecular substance is determined by the arrangement of its molecules?

(1) half-life
(2) molar mass
(3) physical state
(4) percent composition

20 Equilibrium can be reached by

(1) physical changes, only
(2) nuclear changes, only
(3) both physical changes and chemical changes
(4) both nuclear changes and chemical changes

21 Which value is defined as the difference between the potential energy of the products and the potential energy of the reactants during a chemical change?

(1) heat of fusion
(2) heat of reaction
(3) heat of deposition
(4) heat of vaporization

22 The effect of a catalyst on a chemical reaction is to provide a new reaction pathway that results in a different

(1) potential energy of the products
(2) heat of reaction
(3) potential energy of the reactants
(4) activation energy

23 Chemical systems in nature tend to undergo changes toward

(1) lower energy and lower entropy
(2) lower energy and higher entropy
(3) higher energy and lower entropy
(4) higher energy and higher entropy

24 The atoms of which element bond to one another in chains, rings, and networks?

(1) barium   (3) iodine
(2) carbon   (4) mercury

25 What is the general formula for the homologous series that includes ethene?

(1) C_nH_{2n} (3) C_nH_{2n-2}
(2) C_nH_{2n-6} (4) C_nH_{2n+2}

26 When an F atom becomes an F⁻ ion, the F atom

(1) gains a proton   (3) gains an electron
(2) loses a proton   (4) loses an electron

27 Which substance is an Arrhenius base?

(1) HNO_3 (3) $Ca(OH)_2$
(2) H_2SO_3 (4) CH_3COOH

28 In which type of nuclear reaction do two light nuclei combine to produce a heavier nucleus?

(1) positron emission   (3) fission
(2) gamma emission   (4) fusion

29 Using equal masses of reactants, which statement describes the relative amounts of energy released during a chemical reaction and a nuclear reaction?

(1) The chemical and nuclear reactions release equal amounts of energy.
(2) The nuclear reaction releases half the amount of energy of the chemical reaction.
(3) The chemical reaction releases more energy than the nuclear reaction.
(4) The nuclear reaction releases more energy than the chemical reaction.

30 The ratio of the mass of U-238 to the mass of Pb-206 can be used to

(1) diagnose thyroid disorders
(2) diagnose kidney function
(3) date geological formations
(4) date once-living things

Part B–1

Answer all questions in this part.

Directions (31–50): For *each* statement or question, record on your separate answer sheet the *number* of the word or expression that, of those given, best completes the statement or answers the question. Some questions may require the use of the *2011 Edition Reference Tables for Physical Setting/Chemistry*.

31 The bright-line spectra of four elements, *G, J, L,* and *M,* and a mixture of *at least two* of these elements is given below.

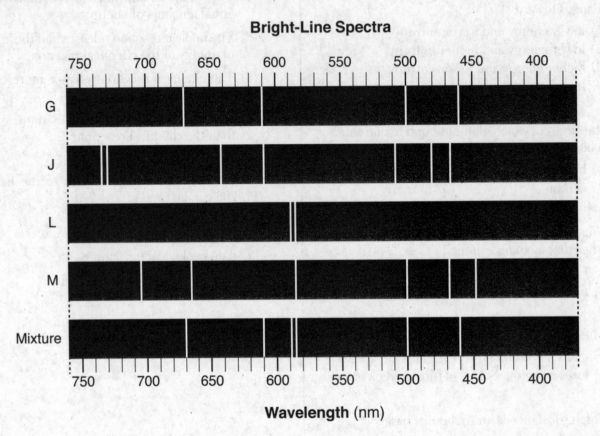

Bright-Line Spectra

Wavelength (nm)

Which elements are present in the mixture?

(1) *G* and *J*

(2) *G* and *L*

(3) *M, J,* and *G*

(4) *M, J,* and *L*

32 Which electron configuration represents an atom of chlorine in an excited state?

(1) 2-8-7-2

(2) 2-8-7

(3) 2-8-8

(4) 2-7-8

33 A student measures the mass and volume of a sample of aluminum at room temperature, and calculates the density of Al to be 2.85 grams per cubic centimeter. Based on Table *S*, what is the percent error for the student's calculated density of Al?

(1) 2.7%

(2) 5.3%

(3) 5.6%

(4) 95%

34 Magnesium and calcium have similar chemical properties because their atoms in the ground state have

(1) equal numbers of protons and electrons
(2) equal numbers of protons and neutrons
(3) two electrons in the first shell
(4) two electrons in the outermost shell

35 As the elements in Period 2 of the Periodic Table are considered in order from left to right, which property generally *decreases*?

(1) atomic radius   (3) ionization energy
(2) electronegativity   (4) nuclear charge

36 Given the balanced equation for the reaction of butane and oxygen:

$$2C_4H_{10} + 13O_2 \rightarrow 8CO_2 + 10H_2O + energy$$

How many moles of carbon dioxide are produced when 5.0 moles of butane react completely?

(1) 5.0 mol   (3) 20. mol
(2) 10. mol   (4) 40. mol

37 What is the percent composition by mass of nitrogen in the compound N_2H_4 (gram-formula mass = 32 g/mol)?

(1) 13%   (3) 88%
(2) 44%   (4) 93%

38 Which ion in the ground state has the same electron configuration as an atom of neon in the ground state?

(1) Ca^{2+} (3) Li^+
(2) Cl^- (4) O^{2-}

39 The molar masses and boiling points at standard pressure for four compounds are given in the table below.

Compound	Molar Mass (g/mol)	Boiling Point (K)
HF	20.01	293
HCl	36.46	188
HBr	80.91	207
HI	127.91	237

Which compound has the strongest intermolecular forces?

(1) HF   (3) HBr
(2) HCl   (4) HI

40 Which particle model diagram represents xenon at STP?

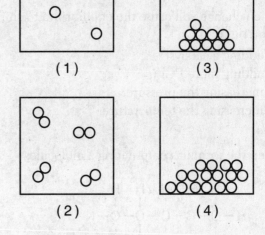

41 What is the amount of heat absorbed when the temperature of 75 grams of water increases from 20.°C to 35°C?

(1) 1100 J   (3) 6300 J
(2) 4700 J   (4) 11 000 J

42 Which sample of HCl(aq) reacts at the fastest rate with a 1.0-gram sample of iron filings?

(1) 10. mL of 1 M HCl(aq) at 10.°C
(2) 10. mL of 1 M HCl(aq) at 25°C
(3) 10. mL of 3 M HCl(aq) at 10.°C
(4) 10. mL of 3 M HCl(aq) at 25°C

43 Given the equation representing a system at equilibrium:

$$N_2O_4(g) \rightleftharpoons 2NO_2(g)$$

Which statement describes the concentration of the two gases in this system?

(1) The concentration of $N_2O_4(g)$ must be less than the concentration of $NO_2(g)$.

(2) The concentration of $N_2O_4(g)$ must be greater than the concentration of $NO_2(g)$.

(3) The concentration of $N_2O_4(g)$ and the concentration of $NO_2(g)$ must be equal.

(4) The concentration of $N_2O_4(g)$ and the concentration of $NO_2(g)$ must be constant.

44 Given the equation representing a system at equilibrium:

$$PCl_5(g) + energy \rightleftharpoons PCl_3(g) + Cl_2(g)$$

Which change will cause the equilibrium to shift to the right?

(1) adding a catalyst
(2) adding more $PCl_3(g)$
(3) increasing the pressure
(4) increasing the temperature

45 Given the formula representing a molecule:

A chemical name for this compound is

(1) pentanone   (3) 1-pentanamine
(2) 1-pentanol   (4) pentanamide

46 Given the formula of a compound:

This compound is classified as an

(1) aldehyde   (3) alkyne
(2) alkene   (4) alcohol

47 Which equation represents fermentation?

(1) $C_2H_4 + H_2O \rightarrow CH_3CH_2OH$
(2) $C_2H_4 + HCl \rightarrow CH_3CH_2Cl$
(3) $C_6H_{12}O_6 \rightarrow 2CH_3CH_2OH + 2CO_2$
(4) $2CH_3CHO \rightarrow C_3H_5CHO + H_2O$

48 Given the equation representing a reaction:

$$3CuCl_2(aq) + 2Al(s) \rightarrow 3Cu(s) + 2AlCl_3(aq)$$

The oxidation number of copper changes from

(1) +1 to 0   (3) +2 to +1
(2) +2 to 0   (4) +6 to +3

49 Given the equation representing a reversible reaction:

$$CH_3COOH(aq) + H_2O(\ell) \rightleftharpoons$$
$$CH_3COO^-(aq) + H_3O^+(aq)$$

According to one acid-base theory, the two H^+ donors in the equation are

(1) CH_3COOH and H_2O
(2) CH_3COOH and H_3O^+
(3) CH_3COO^- and H_2O
(4) CH_3COO^- and H_3O^+

50 Which nuclear equation represents a spontaneous decay?

(1) $^{222}_{86}Rn \rightarrow ^{218}_{84}Po + ^{4}_{2}He$

(2) $^{27}_{13}Al + ^{4}_{2}He \rightarrow ^{30}_{15}P + ^{1}_{0}n$

(3) $^{235}_{92}U + ^{1}_{0}n \rightarrow ^{139}_{56}Ba + ^{94}_{36}Kr + 3^{1}_{0}n$

(4) $^{7}_{3}Li + ^{1}_{1}H \rightarrow ^{4}_{2}He + ^{4}_{2}He$

Answer all questions in this part.

Directions (51-65): Record your answers in the spaces provided in your answer booklet. Some questions may require the use of the *2011 Edition Reference Tables for Physical Setting/Chemistry*.

51 Draw a structural formula for methanal. [1]

Base your answers to questions 52 through 54 on the information below and on your knowledge of chemistry.

The atomic mass and natural abundance of the naturally occuring isotopes of hydrogen are shown in the table below.

Naturally Occuring Isotopes of Hydrogen

Isotope	Common Name of Isotope	Atomic Mass (u)	Natural Abundance (%)
H-1	protium	1.0078	99.9885
H-2	deuterium	2.0141	0.0115
H-3	tritium	3.0160	negligible

The isotope H-2, also called deuterium, is usually represented by the symbol "D." Heavy water forms when deuterium reacts with oxygen, producing molecules of D_2O.

52 Explain, in terms of subatomic particles, why atoms of H-1, H-2, and H-3 are each electrically neutral. [1]

53 Determine the formula mass of heavy water, D_2O. [1]

54 Based on Table *N*, identify the decay mode of tritium. [1]

_____

Base your answers to questions 55 through 57 on the information below and on your knowledge of chemistry.

At 23°C, 85.0 grams of $NaNO_3$(s) are dissolved in 100. grams of H_2O(ℓ).

55 Convert the temperature of the $NaNO_3$(s) to kelvins. [1]

56 Based on Table G, determine the additional mass of $NaNO_3$(s) that must be dissolved to saturate the solution at 23°C. [1]

57 State what happens to the boiling point and freezing point of the solution when the solution is diluted with an additional 100. grams of H_2O(ℓ). [1]

Base your answers to questions 58 through 61 on the information below and on your knowledge of chemistry.

A 200.-milliliter sample of CO_2(g) is placed in a sealed, rigid cylinder with a movable piston at 296 K and 101.3 kPa.

58 State a change in temperature and a change in pressure of the CO_2(g) that would cause it to behave more like an ideal gas. [1]

59 Determine the volume of the sample of CO_2(g) if the temperature and pressure are changed to 336 K and 152.0 kPa. [1]

60 State, in terms of *both* the frequency and force of collisions, what would result from decreasing the temperature of the original sample of CO_2(g), at constant volume. [1]

61 Compare the mass of the original 200.-milliliter sample of CO_2(g) to the mass of the CO_2(g) sample when the cylinder is adjusted to a volume of 100. milliliters. [1]

Base your answers to questions 62 through 65 on the information below and on your knowledge of chemistry.

Cobalt-60 is an artificial isotope of Co-59. The incomplete equation for the decay of cobalt-60, including beta and gamma emissions, is shown below.

$$^{60}_{27}\text{Co} \rightarrow X + ^{0}_{-1}\text{e} + ^{0}_{0}\gamma$$

62 Explain, in terms of *both* protons and neutrons, why Co-59 and Co-60 are isotopes of cobalt. [1]

63 Compare the penetrating power of the beta and gamma emissions. [1]

64 Complete the nuclear equation, *in your answer booklet*, for the decay of cobalt-60 by writing a notation for the missing product. [1]

65 Based on Table *N*, determine the total time required for an 80.00-gram sample of cobalt-60 to decay until only 10.00 grams of the sample remain unchanged. [1]

Part C

Answer all questions in this part.

Directions (66-85): Record your answers in the spaces provided in your answer booklet. Some questions may require the use of the *2011 Edition Reference Tables for Physical Setting/Chemistry*.

Base your answers to questions 66 through 69 on the information below and on your knowledge of chemistry.

During a laboratory activity, appropriate safety equipment was used and safety procedures were followed. A laboratory technician heated a sample of solid $KClO_3$ in a crucible to determine the percent composition by mass of oxygen in the compound. The unbalanced equation and the data for the decomposition of solid $KClO_3$ are shown below.

$$KClO_3(s) \rightarrow KCl(s) + O_2(g)$$

Lab Data and Calculated Results

Object or Material	Mass (g)
empty crucible and cover	22.14
empty crucible, cover, and $KClO_3$	24.21
$KClO_3$	2.07
crucible, cover, and KCl after heating	23.41
KCl	?
O_2	0.80

66 Write a chemical name for the compound that decomposed. [1]

67 Based on the lab data, show a numerical setup to determine the number of moles of O_2 produced. Use 32 g/mol as the gram-formula mass of O_2. [1]

68 Based on the lab data, determine the mass of KCl produced in the reaction. [1]

69 Balance the equation *in your answer booklet* for the decomposition of $KClO_3$, using the smallest whole-number coefficients. [1]

Base your answers to questions 70 through 73 on the information below and on your knowledge of chemistry.

A bottled water label lists the ions dissolved in the water. The table below lists the mass of some ions dissolved in a 500.-gram sample of the bottled water.

Ions in 500. g of Bottled Water

Ion Formula	Mass (g)
Ca^{2+}	0.040
Mg^{2+}	0.013
Na^+	0.0033
SO_4^{2-}	0.0063
HCO_3^-	0.180

70 State the number of significant figures used to express the mass of hydrogen carbonate ions in the table above. [1]

71 Based on Table F, write the formula of the ion in the bottled water table that would form the *least* soluble compound when combined with the sulfate ion. [1]

72 Show a numerical setup for calculating the parts per million of the Na^+ ions in the 500.-gram sample of the bottled water. [1]

73 Compare the radius of a Mg^{2+} ion to the radius of a Mg atom. [1]

_____

Base your answers to questions 74 through 77 on the information below and on your knowledge of chemistry.

Ethyl ethanoate is used as a solvent for varnishes and in the manufacture of artificial leather. The formula below represents a molecule of ethyl ethanoate.

$$\begin{array}{ccccccc} & H & O & & H & H & \\ & | & \| & & | & | & \\ H- & C- & C- & O- & C- & C- & H \\ & | & & & | & | & \\ & H & & & H & H & \end{array}$$

74 Identify the element in ethyl ethanoate that makes it an organic compound. [1]

75 Write the empirical formula for this compound. [1]

76 Write the name of the class of organic compounds to which this compound belongs. [1]

77 Determine the number of electrons shared in the bond between a hydrogen atom and a carbon atom in the molecule. [1]

_____

Base your answers to questions 78 through 80 on the information below and on your knowledge of chemistry.

An operating voltaic cell has magnesium and silver electrodes. The cell and the ionic equation representing the reaction that occurs in the cell are shown below.

Voltaic Cell

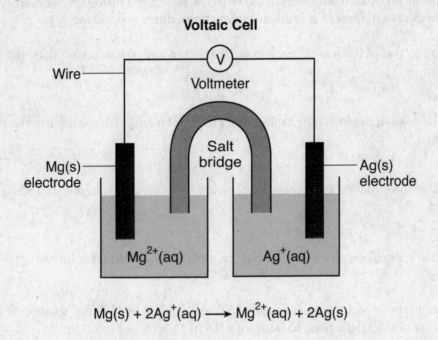

$$Mg(s) + 2Ag^+(aq) \longrightarrow Mg^{2+}(aq) + 2Ag(s)$$

78 State the purpose of the salt bridge in this cell. [1]

79 Write a balanced equation for the half-reaction that occurs at the magnesium electrode in this cell. [1]

80 Explain, in terms of electrical energy, how electrolysis reactions differ from voltaic cell reactions. [1]

Base your answers to questions 81 through 85 on the information below and on your knowledge of chemistry.

In a laboratory investigation, an HCl(aq) solution with a pH value of 2 is used to determine the molarity of a KOH(aq) solution. A 7.5-milliliter sample of the KOH(aq) is exactly neutralized by 15.0 milliliters of the 0.010 M HCl(aq). During this laboratory activity, appropriate safety equipment is used and safety procedures are followed.

81 Determine the pH value of a solution that is ten times *less* acidic than the HCl(aq) solution. [1]

82 State the color of the indicator bromcresol green if it is added to a sample of the KOH(aq) solution. [1]

83 Complete the equation *in your answer booklet* by writing the chemical formula for *each* product. [1]

84 Show a numerical setup for calculating the molarity of the KOH solution. [1]

85 Explain, in terms of aqueous ions, why 15.0 mL of a 1.0 M HCl(aq) solution is a better conductor of electricity than 15.0 mL of a 0.010 M HCl(aq) solution. [1]

PHYSICAL SETTING
CHEMISTRY

Tuesday, June 25, 2019 — 9:15 a.m to 12:15 p.m., only

ANSWER BOOKLET

Student ....

Teacher ....

School .... Grade ....

Record your answers for Part B–2 and Part C in this booklet.

Part B–2

51

52 _____

_____

_____

53 _____ u

54 _____

55 _____ K

56 _____ g

57 Boiling point: _____

Freezing point: _____

58 Temperature: _____

Pressure: _____

59 _____ mL

60 _____

_____

_____

61 _____

_____

_____

62 _____

_____

_____

63 _____

_____

_____

64 $^{60}_{27}\text{Co} \rightarrow$ _____ $+ {}^{0}_{-1}e + {}^{0}_{0}\gamma$

65 _____ **y**

P.S./Chem. Answer Booklet–June '19   [3]   [OVER]

June '19   Regents Examination

66 _____

67

68 _____ g

69 _____ KClO$_3$(s) → _____ KCl(s) + _____ O$_2$(g)

70 _____

71 _____

72

73 _____

_____

_____

June '19 Regents Examination

74 _____

75 _____

76 _____

77 _____

78 _____

_____

_____

79 _____

80 _____

_____

_____

81 _____

82 _____

83 HCl(aq) + KOH(aq) → _____ + _____

P.S./Chem. Answer Booklet–June '19   [5]   [OVER]

June '19   Regents Examination

84

85 _____

_____

_____

P.S./Chem. Answer Booklet–June '19   [6]

June '19   Regents Examination

Part A

Answer all questions in this part.

Directions (1–30): For *each* statement or question, record on your separate answer sheet the *number* of the word or expression that, of those given, best completes the statement or answers the question. Some questions may require the use of the *2011 Edition Reference Tables for Physical Setting/Chemistry*.

1 The results of the gold foil experiment led to the conclusion that an atom is

(1) mostly empty space and has a small, negatively charged nucleus
(2) mostly empty space and has a small, positively charged nucleus
(3) a hard sphere and has a large, negatively charged nucleus
(4) a hard sphere and has a large, positively charged nucleus

2 Atoms are neutral because the number of

(1) protons equals the number of neutrons
(2) protons equals the number of electrons
(3) neutrons is greater than the number of protons
(4) neutrons is greater than the number of electrons

3 In the ground state, valence electrons of a krypton atom are found in

(1) the first shell
(2) the outermost shell
(3) both the nucleus and the first shell
(4) both the first shell and the outermost shell

4 According to the wave-mechanical model of the atom, electrons are located in

(1) orbitals
(2) circular paths
(3) a small, dense nucleus
(4) a hard, indivisible sphere

5 Which electron configuration represents the electrons in an atom of sodium in the ground state at STP?

(1) 2-8-1   (3) 2-8-6
(2) 2-7-2   (4) 2-7-7

6 The elements on the Periodic Table of the Elements are arranged in order of increasing

(1) atomic number
(2) mass number
(3) number of neutrons
(4) number of valence electrons

7 Which element is malleable at STP?

(1) chlorine   (3) helium
(2) copper   (4) sulfur

8 At 298 K and 1 atm, which noble gas has the lowest density?

(1) Ne   (3) Xe
(2) Kr   (4) Rn

9 Which two terms represent types of chemical formulas?

(1) empirical and molecular
(2) polar and nonpolar
(3) synthesis and decomposition
(4) saturated and concentrated

10 Which quantities are conserved in all chemical reactions?

(1) charge, pressure, and energy
(2) charge, mass, and energy
(3) volume, pressure, and energy
(4) volume, mass, and pressure

11 Which term represents the sum of the atomic masses of the atoms in a molecule?

(1) atomic number
(2) mass number
(3) formula mass
(4) percent composition by mass

12 Which equation represents energy being absorbed as a bond is broken?

(1) $H + H \rightarrow H_2$ + energy
(2) $H + H$ + energy $\rightarrow H_2$
(3) $H_2 \rightarrow H + H$ + energy
(4) H_2 + energy $\rightarrow H + H$

13 Which term is used to describe the attraction that an oxygen atom has for the electrons in a chemical bond?

(1) alkalinity
(2) electronegativity
(3) electron configuration
(4) first ionization energy

14 Which substance can *not* be decomposed by chemical means?

(1) C
(2) CO
(3) CO_2
(4) C_3O_2

15 A beaker contains a dilute sodium chloride solution at 1 atmosphere. What happens to the number of solute particles in the solution and the boiling point of the solution, as more sodium chloride is dissolved?

(1) The number of solute particles increases, and the boiling point increases.
(2) The number of solute particles increases, and the boiling point decreases.
(3) The number of solute particles decreases, and the boiling point increases.
(4) The number of solute particles decreases, and the boiling point decreases.

16 Which form of energy is transferred when an ice cube at 0°C is placed in a beaker of water at 50°C?

(1) chemical
(2) electrical
(3) nuclear
(4) thermal

17 The average kinetic energy of the particles in a sample of matter is expressed as

(1) density
(2) volume
(3) pressure
(4) temperature

18 At STP, which gas sample has the same number of molecules as 2.0 liters of $CH_4(g)$ at STP?

(1) 1.0 liter of $C_2H_6(g)$
(2) 2.0 liters of $O_2(g)$
(3) 5.0 liters of $N_2(g)$
(4) 6.0 liters of $CO_2(g)$

19 Given the equation:

$$I_2(s) \rightarrow I_2(g)$$

Which phrase describes this change?

(1) endothermic chemical change
(2) endothermic physical change
(3) exothermic chemical change
(4) exothermic physical change

20 Which term identifies a factor that will shift a chemical equilibrium?

(1) atomic radius
(2) catalyst
(3) decay mode
(4) temperature

21 According to which theory or law is a chemical reaction most likely to occur when two particles with the proper energy and orientation interact with each other?

(1) atomic theory
(2) collision theory
(3) combined gas law
(4) law of conservation of matter

22 Addition of a catalyst can speed up a reaction by providing an alternate reaction pathway that has a

(1) lower activation energy
(2) higher activation energy
(3) lower heat of reaction
(4) higher heat of reaction

23 Which compound is saturated?

(1) butane
(2) ethene
(3) heptene
(4) pentyne

[3]

[OVER]

24 An alcohol and an ether have the same molecular formula, C_2H_6O. These two compounds have

(1) the same functional group and the same physical and chemical properties
(2) the same functional group and different physical and chemical properties
(3) different functional groups and the same physical and chemical properties
(4) different functional groups and different physical and chemical properties

25 Which metal is most easily oxidized?

(1) Ag
(2) Co
(3) Cu
(4) Mg

26 Which substance is an Arrhenius acid?

(1) H_2
(2) HCl
(3) KCl
(4) NH_3

27 Which statement describes an electrolyte?

(1) An electrolyte conducts an electric current as a solid and dissolves in water.
(2) An electrolyte conducts an electric current as a solid and does not dissolve in water.
(3) When an electrolyte dissolves in water, the resulting solution conducts an electric current.
(4) When an electrolyte dissolves in water, the resulting solution does not conduct an electric current.

28 Which type of reaction occurs when an Arrhenius acid reacts with an Arrhenius base to form a salt and water?

(1) combustion
(2) decomposition
(3) neutralization
(4) saponification

29 Compared to the energy released per mole of reactant during chemical reactions, the energy released per mole of reactant during nuclear reactions is

(1) much less
(2) much greater
(3) slightly less
(4) slightly greater

30 Which phrase describes a risk of using the radioisotope Co-60 in treating cancer?

(1) production of acid rain
(2) production of greenhouse gases
(3) increased biological exposure
(4) increased ozone depletion

[4]

Part B–1

Answer all questions in this part.

Directions (31–50): For *each* statement or question, record on your separate answer sheet the *number* of the word or expression that, of those given, best completes the statement or answers the question. Some questions may require the use of the *2011 Edition Reference Tables for Physical Setting/Chemistry.*

31 The three nuclides, U-233, U-235, and U-238, are isotopes of uranium because they have the same number of protons per atom and

(1) the same number of electrons per atom
(2) the same number of neutrons per atom
(3) a different number of electrons per atom
(4) a different number of neutrons per atom

32 Given the information in the table below:

Two Forms of Carbon

Form	Bonding	Hardness	Electrical Conductivity
diamond	Each carbon atom bonds to four other carbon atoms in a three-dimensional network.	very hard	no
graphite	Each carbon atom bonds to three other carbon atoms in two-dimensional sheets.	soft	yes

Diamond and graphite have different properties because they have different

(1) crystal structures
(2) electronegativities
(3) numbers of protons per atom
(4) numbers of valence electrons per atom

33 Given the equation representing a chemical reaction:

$$NaCl(aq) + AgNO_3(aq) \rightarrow NaNO_3(aq) + AgCl(s)$$

This reaction is classified as a

(1) synthesis reaction
(2) decomposition reaction
(3) single replacement reaction
(4) double replacement reaction

34 What is the formula for iron(II) oxide?

(1) FeO   (3) Fe_2O
(2) FeO_2 (4) Fe_2O_3

35 Given the reaction:

$$2KClO_3(s) \rightarrow 2KCl(s) + 3O_2(g)$$

How many moles of $KClO_3$ must completely react to produce 6 moles of O_2?

(1) 1 mole   (3) 6 moles
(2) 2 moles   (4) 4 moles

36 What is the number of moles of CO_2 in a 220.-gram sample of CO_2 (gram-formula mass = 44 g/mol)?

(1) 0.20 mol   (3) 15 mol
(2) 5.0 mol   (4) 44 mol

37 A solution contains 25 grams of KNO_3 dissolved in 200. grams of H_2O. Which numerical setup can be used to calculate the percent by mass of KNO_3 in this solution?

(1) $\dfrac{25\,g}{175\,g} \times 100$ (3) $\dfrac{25\,g}{225\,g} \times 100$

(2) $\dfrac{25\,g}{200.\,g} \times 100$ (4) $\dfrac{200.\,g}{225\,g} \times 100$

38 What is the molarity of 0.50 liter of an aqueous solution that contains 0.20 mole of NaOH (gram-formula mass = 40. g/mol)?

(1) 0.10 M   (3) 2.5 M
(2) 0.20 M   (4) 0.40 M

39 A mixture consists of ethanol and water. Some properties of ethanol and water are given in the table below.

Some Properties of Ethanol and Water

Property	Ethanol	Water
boiling point at standard pressure	78°C	100.°C
density at STP	0.80 g/cm³	1.00 g/cm³
flammability	flammable	nonflammable
melting point	−114°C	0.°C

Which statement describes a property of ethanol after being separated from the mixture?

(1) Ethanol is nonflammable.
(2) Ethanol has a melting point of 0.°C.
(3) Ethanol has a density of 0.80 g/cm³ at STP.
(4) Ethanol has a boiling point of 89°C at standard pressure.

40 A rigid cylinder with a movable piston contains a sample of hydrogen gas. At 330. K, this sample has a pressure of 150. kPa and a volume of 3.50 L. What is the volume of this sample at STP?

(1) 0.233 L   (3) 4.29 L
(2) 1.96 L   (4) 6.26 L

41 Which numerical setup can be used to calculate the heat energy required to completely melt 100. grams of $H_2O(s)$ at 0°C?

(1) (100. g)(334 J/g)
(2) (100. g)(2260 J/g)
(3) (100. g)(4.18 J/g•K)(0°C)
(4) (100. g)(4.18 J/g•K)(273 K)

42 During which phase change does the entropy of a sample of H_2O increase?

(1) $H_2O(g) \rightarrow H_2O(\ell)$
(2) $H_2O(g) \rightarrow H_2O(s)$
(3) $H_2O(\ell) \rightarrow H_2O(g)$
(4) $H_2O(\ell) \rightarrow H_2O(s)$

[6]

43 Given the formula for a compound:

$$H-\underset{\underset{H}{|}}{\overset{\overset{H}{|}}{C}}-\underset{\underset{H}{|}}{\overset{\overset{H}{|}}{C}}-\underset{\underset{H}{|}}{\overset{\overset{H}{|}}{C}}-\underset{\underset{H}{|}}{\overset{\overset{H}{|}}{C}}-N\overset{H}{\underset{H}{}}$$

What is a chemical name for this compound?

(1) 1-butanamide   (3) 1-butanamine
(2) 4-butanamide   (4) 4-butanamine

44 Given the equation for a reaction:

$$C_4H_{10} + Cl_2 \rightarrow C_4H_9Cl + HCl$$

Which type of reaction is represented by the equation?

(1) addition   (3) fermentation
(2) substitution   (4) polymerization

45 Which half-reaction equation represents reduction?

(1) $Cu \rightarrow Cu^{2+} + 2e^-$
(2) $Cu^{2+} + 2e^- \rightarrow Cu$
(3) $Ag + e^- \rightarrow Ag^+$
(4) $Ag^+ \rightarrow Ag + e^-$

46 Given the balanced ionic equation representing a reaction:

$$Zn(s) + Co^{2+}(aq) \rightarrow Zn^{2+}(aq) + Co(s)$$

Which statement describes the electrons involved in this reaction?

(1) Each Zn atom loses 2 electrons, and each Co^{2+} ion gains 2 electrons.
(2) Each Zn atom loses 2 electrons, and each Co^{2+} ion loses 2 electrons.
(3) Each Zn atom gains 2 electrons, and each Co^{2+} ion loses 2 electrons.
(4) Each Zn atom gains 2 electrons, and each Co^{2+} ion gains 2 electrons.

47 What are the two oxidation states of nitrogen in NH_4NO_2?

(1) +3 and +5   (3) −3 and +3
(2) +3 and −5   (4) −3 and −3

48 The table below shows the molar concentrations of hydronium ion, H_3O^+, in four different solutions.

Molar Concentration of H₃O⁺ Ions in Four Solutions

Solution	Molar Concentration of H₃O⁺ Ion (M)
A	0.1
B	0.01
C	0.001
D	0.0001

Which solution has the highest pH?

(1) A   (3) C
(2) B   (4) D

49 Given the equation:

$$^{235}_{92}U + {}^{1}_{0}n \rightarrow {}^{140}_{56}Ba + {}^{93}_{36}Kr + 3{}^{1}_{0}n + energy$$

Which type of nuclear reaction is represented by the equation?

(1) fission   (3) beta decay
(2) fusion   (4) alpha decay

50 Which nuclear emission has the *least* penetrating power and the greatest ionizing ability?

(1) alpha particle   (3) gamma ray
(2) beta particle   (4) positron

Part B–2

Answer all questions in this part.

Directions (51–65): Record your answers in the spaces provided in your answer booklet. Some questions may require the use of the *2011 Edition Reference Tables for Physical Setting/Chemistry.*

Base your answers to questions 51 through 54 on the information below and on your knowledge of chemistry.

The formulas and names of four chloride compounds are shown in the table below.

Formula	Name
CCl_4	carbon tetrachloride
RbCl	rubidium chloride
CsCl	cesium chloride
HCl	hydrogen chloride

51 Identify the noble gas that has atoms with the same electron configuration as the metal ions in rubidium chloride, when both the atoms and the ions are in the ground state.   [1]

52 Explain, in terms of atomic structure, why the radius of a cesium ion in cesium chloride is smaller than the radius of a cesium atom when both are in the ground state.   [1]

53 In the space *in your answer booklet*, draw a Lewis electron-dot diagram for a molecule of HCl.   [1]

54 Explain, in terms of charge distribution, why a molecule of carbon tetrachloride is a nonpolar molecule.   [1]

Base your answers to questions 55 through 57 on the information below and on your knowledge of chemistry.

Some isotopes of neon are Ne-19, Ne-20, Ne-21, Ne-22, and Ne-24. The neon-24 decays by beta emission. The atomic mass and natural abundance for the naturally occurring isotopes of neon are shown in the table below.

Naturally Occurring Isotopes of Neon

Isotope Notation	Atomic Mass (u)	Natural Abundance (%)
Ne-20	19.99	90.48
Ne-21	20.99	0.27
Ne-22	21.99	9.25

55 Identify the decay mode of Ne-19. [1]

56 State the number of neutrons in an atom of Ne-20 and the number of neutrons in an atom of Ne-22. [1]

57 Show a numerical setup for calculating the atomic mass of neon. [1]

Base your answers to questions 58 through 60 on the information below and on your knowledge of chemistry.

Periodic trends are observed in the properties of the elements in Period 3 on the Periodic Table. These elements vary in physical properties, such as phase, and in chemical properties, such as their ability to lose or gain electrons during a chemical reaction.

58 Identify the metals in Period 3 on the Periodic Table. [1]

59 Identify the element in Period 3 that requires the *least* amount of energy to remove the most loosely held electrons from a mole of gaseous atoms of the element in the ground state. [1]

60 State the general trend in atomic radius as the elements in Period 3 are considered in order of increasing atomic number. [1]

Base your answers to questions 61 through 63 on the information below and on your knowledge of chemistry.

A thiol is very similar to an alcohol, but a thiol has a sulfur atom instead of an oxygen atom in the functional group. The equation below represents a reaction of methanethiol and iodine, producing dimethyl disulfide and hydrogen iodide.

$$2 \left(\begin{array}{c} H \\ | \\ H-C-S-H \\ | \\ H \end{array} \right) + I_2 \longrightarrow \begin{array}{cc} H & H \\ | & | \\ H-C-S-S-C-H \\ | & | \\ H & H \end{array} + 2HI$$

Methanethiol   Dimethyl disulfide

61 State the number of electrons shared between the sulfur atoms in the dimethyl disulfide. [1]

62 Identify the polarity of an H–I bond and the polarity of an S–S bond. [1]

63 Explain, in terms of electron configuration, why sulfur atoms and oxygen atoms form compounds with similar molecular structures. [1]

Base your answers to questions 64 and 65 on the information below and on your knowledge of chemistry.

A student constructs an electrochemical cell. A diagram of the operating cell and the unbalanced ionic equation representing the reaction occurring in the cell are shown below.
The blue color of the solution in the copper half-cell indicates the presence of Cu^{2+} ions. The student observes that the blue color becomes less intense as the cell operates.

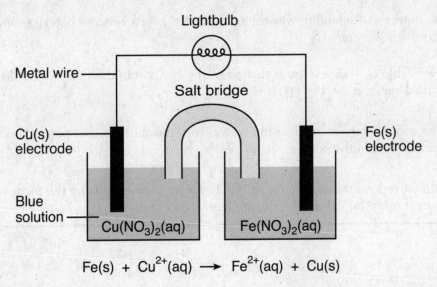

$$Fe(s) + Cu^{2+}(aq) \longrightarrow Fe^{2+}(aq) + Cu(s)$$

64 Identify the type of electrochemical cell represented by the diagram. [1]

65 State *one* inference that the student can make about the concentration of the Cu^{2+} ions based on the change in intensity of the color of the $Cu(NO_3)_2(aq)$ solution as the cell operates. [1]

Part C

Answer all questions in this part.

Directions (66–85): Record your answers in the spaces provided in your answer booklet. Some questions may require the use of the *2011 Edition Reference Tables for Physical Setting/Chemistry*.

Base your answers to questions 66 through 69 on the information below and on your knowledge of chemistry.

> In a laboratory investigation, a student is given a sample that is a mixture of 3.0 grams of NaCl(s) and 4.0 grams of sand, which is mostly SiO_2(s). The purpose of the investigation is to separate and recover the compounds in the sample. In the first step, the student places the sample in a 250-mL flask. Then, 50. grams of distilled water are added to the flask, and the contents are thoroughly stirred. The mixture in the flask is then filtered, using the equipment represented by the diagram below.

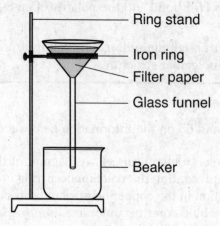

66 Explain, in terms of solubility, why the mixture in the flask remains heterogeneous even after thorough stirring. [1]

67 Based on Table G, state evidence that all of the NaCl(s) in the flask would dissolve in the distilled water at 20.°C. [1]

68 Describe a procedure to remove the water from the mixture that passes through the filter and collects in the beaker. [1]

69 The student reports that 3.4 grams of NaCl(s) were recovered from the mixture. Show a numerical setup for calculating the student's percent error. [1]

Base your answers to questions 70 through 73 on the information below and on your knowledge of chemistry.

In a laboratory activity, the volume of helium gas in a rigid cylinder with a movable piston is varied by changing the temperature of the gas. The activity is done at a constant pressure of 100. kPa. Data from the activity are plotted on the graph below.

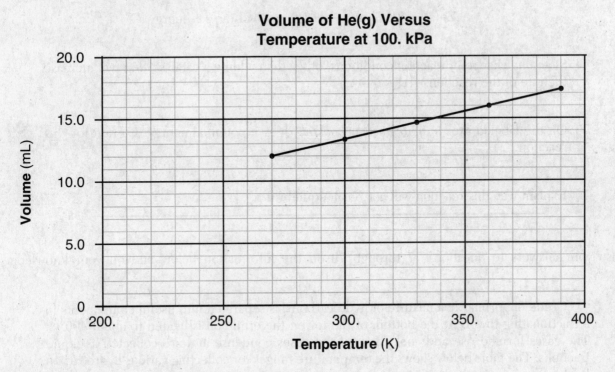

Volume of He(g) Versus Temperature at 100. kPa

70 Determine the temperature of the He(g) at a volume of 15.0 mL. [1]

71 Explain, in terms of particle volume, why the sample of helium can *not* be compressed by the piston to zero volume. [1]

72 State what happens to the average distance between the He atoms as the gas is heated. [1]

73 State a change in pressure that will cause the helium in the cylinder to behave more like an ideal gas. [1]

Base your answers to questions 74 through 76 on the information below and on your knowledge of chemistry.

The balanced equation below represents the reaction between a 5.0-gram sample of zinc metal and a 0.5 M solution of hydrochloric acid. The reaction takes place in an open test tube at 298 K and 1 atm in a laboratory activity.

$$Zn(s) + 2HCl(aq) \rightarrow H_2(g) + ZnCl_2(aq) + energy$$

74 State *one* change in reaction conditions, other than adding a catalyst, that will increase the rate of the reaction. [1]

75 On the labeled axes *in your answer booklet*, draw a potential energy diagram for this reaction. [1]

76 Explain why this reaction will *not* reach equilibrium. [1]

Base your answers to questions 77 through 79 on the information below and on your knowledge of chemistry.

Crude oil, primarily a mixture of hydrocarbons, is separated into useful components in a fractionating tower. At the bottom of the tower, the crude oil is heated to about 400°C. The gases formed rise and cool. Most of the gases condense and are collected as liquid fractions. The table below shows the temperature ranges for collecting various hydrocarbon fractions.

Hydrocarbon Fractions Collected

Number of Carbon Atoms per Molecule	Temperature Range (°C)
1-4	below 40
5-12	40-200
12-16	200-300
16-20	300-370
>20	above 370

77 Determine the number of carbon atoms in one molecule of an alkane that has 22 hydrogen atoms in the molecule. [1]

78 State the temperature range for the fraction collected that contains octane molecules. [1]

79 Draw a structural formula for 3-ethylhexane. [1]

[13]

[OVER]

Base your answers to questions 80 through 82 on the information below and on your knowledge of chemistry.

In a laboratory activity, a student titrates a 20.0-milliliter sample of HCl(aq) using 0.025 M NaOH(aq). In one of the titration trials, 17.6 milliliters of the base solution exactly neutralizes the acid sample.

80 Identify the positive ion in the sample of HCl(aq).   [1]

81 Show a numerical setup for calculating the concentration of the hydrochloric acid using the titration data.   [1]

82 The concentration of the base is expressed to what number of significant figures?   [1]

[14]

Base your answers to questions 83 through 85 on the information below and on your knowledge of chemistry.

In the past, some paints that glowed in the dark contained zinc sulfide and salts of Ra-226. As the radioisotope Ra-226 decayed, the energy released caused the zinc sulfide in these paints to emit light. The half-lives for Ra-226 and two other radioisotopes used in these paints are listed on the table below.

Radioisotopes in the Paints

Radioisotope	Half-Life (y)
Pm-147	2.6
Ra-226	1599
Ra-228	5.8

83 Explain, in terms of half-lives, why Ra-226 may have been used more often than the other isotopes in these paints. [1]

84 Complete the nuclear equation *in your answer booklet* for the beta decay of Pm-147 by writing an isotopic notation for the missing product. [1]

85 What fraction of an original Ra-228 sample remains unchanged after 17.4 years? [1]

[15]

The University of the State of New York

REGENTS HIGH SCHOOL EXAMINATION

PHYSICAL SETTING CHEMISTRY

————

ANSWER BOOKLET

Student..

Teacher..

School .... Grade ....

Record your answers for Part B–2 and Part C in this booklet.

Part B–2

51 _____

52 _____

_____

_____

53

54 _____

_____

_____

55 _____

56 Ne-20: _____

Ne-22: _____

57

58 _____

59 _____

60 _____

_____

_____

61 _____

62 H–I bond: _____

S–S bond: _____

63 _____

_____

_____

64 _____

65 _____

_____

_____

Part C

66 _____

_____

_____

67 _____

_____

_____

68 _____

_____

_____

69 _____

70 _____ K

71 _____

_____

_____

72 _____

_____

_____

73 _____

74 _____

_____

75

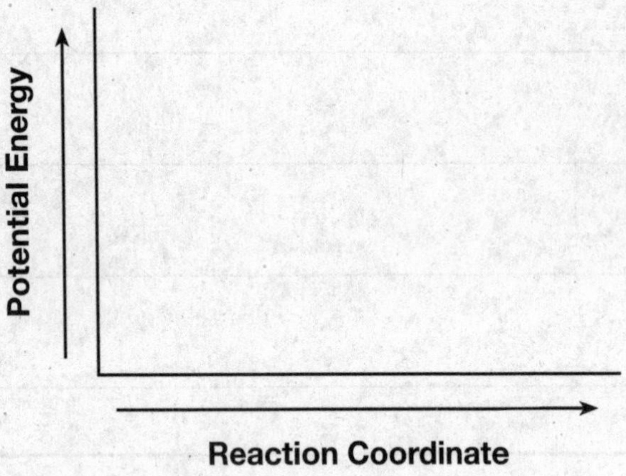

Potential Energy ↑

Reaction Coordinate →

76 _____

_____

_____

77 _____

78 _____ °C to _____ °C

79

80 _____

81

82 _____

83 _____

_____

_____

84 $^{147}_{61}\text{Pm} \rightarrow \ ^{0}_{-1}\text{e} +$ _____

85 _____

Part A

Answer all questions in this part.

Directions (1–30): For *each* statement or question, record on your separate answer sheet the *number* of the word or expression that, of those given, best completes the statement or answers the question. Some questions may require the use of the *2011 Edition Reference Tables for Physical Setting/Chemistry.*

1 According to the wave-mechanical model, an orbital is defined as the most probable location of

(1) a proton (3) a positron
(2) a neutron (4) an electron

2 The part of an atom that has an overall positive charge is called

(1) an electron (3) the first shell
(2) the nucleus (4) the valence shell

3 Which subatomic particles each have a mass of approximately 1 u?

(1) proton and electron
(2) proton and neutron
(3) neutron and electron
(4) neutron and positron

4 The discovery of the electron as a subatomic particle was a result of

(1) collision theory
(2) kinetic molecular theory
(3) the gold-foil experiment
(4) experiments with cathode ray tubes

5 The elements on the Periodic Table of the Elements are arranged in order of increasing

(1) atomic mass (3) atomic number
(2) formula mass (4) oxidation number

6 Which element is classified as a metalloid?

(1) Te (3) Hg
(2) S (4) I

7 At STP, $O_2(g)$ and $O_3(g)$ are two forms of the same element that have

(1) the same molecular structure and the same properties
(2) the same molecular structure and different properties
(3) different molecular structures and the same properties
(4) different molecular structures and different properties

8 Which substance can be broken down by chemical means?

(1) ammonia (3) antimony
(2) aluminum (4) argon

9 Which statement describes $H_2O(\ell)$ and $H_2O_2(\ell)$?

(1) Both are compounds that have the same properties.
(2) Both are compounds that have different properties.
(3) Both are mixtures that have the same properties.
(4) Both are mixtures that have different properties.

10 Which two terms represent major categories of compounds?

(1) ionic and nuclear
(2) ionic and molecular
(3) empirical and nuclear
(4) empirical and molecular

11 Which formula represents an asymmetrical molecule?

(1) CH_4 (3) N_2
(2) CO_2 (4) NH_3

[2]

12 Which statement describes the energy changes that occur as bonds are broken and formed during a chemical reaction?

(1) Energy is absorbed when bonds are both broken and formed.
(2) Energy is released when bonds are both broken and formed.
(3) Energy is absorbed when bonds are broken, and energy is released when bonds are formed.
(4) Energy is released when bonds are broken, and energy is absorbed when bonds are formed.

13 A solid sample of copper is an excellent conductor of electric current. Which type of chemical bonds are in the sample?

(1) ionic bonds
(2) metallic bonds
(3) nonpolar covalent bonds
(4) polar covalent bonds

14 Which list includes three forms of energy?

(1) thermal, nuclear, electronegativity
(2) thermal, chemical, electromagnetic
(3) temperature, nuclear, electromagnetic
(4) temperature, chemical, electronegativity

15 Based on Table S, an atom of which element has the strongest attraction for electrons in a chemical bond?

(1) chlorine   (3) oxygen
(2) nitrogen   (4) selenium

16 At which temperature and pressure would a sample of helium behave most like an ideal gas?

(1) 75 K and 500. kPa
(2) 150. K and 500. kPa
(3) 300. K and 50. kPa
(4) 600. K and 50. kPa

17 A cube of iron at 20.°C is placed in contact with a cube of copper at 60.°C. Which statement describes the initial flow of heat between the cubes?

(1) Heat flows from the copper cube to the iron cube.
(2) Heat flows from the iron cube to the copper cube.
(3) Heat flows in both directions between the cubes.
(4) Heat does not flow between the cubes.

18 Which sample at STP has the same number of atoms as 18 liters of $Ne(g)$ at STP?

(1) 18 moles of $Ar(g)$
(2) 18 liters of $Ar(g)$
(3) 18 grams of $H_2O(g)$
(4) 18 milliliters of $H_2O(g)$

19 Compared to H_2S, the higher boiling point of H_2O is due to the

(1) greater molecular size of water
(2) stronger hydrogen bonding in water
(3) higher molarity of water
(4) larger gram-formula mass of water

20 In terms of entropy and energy, systems in nature tend to undergo changes toward

(1) lower entropy and lower energy
(2) lower entropy and higher energy
(3) higher entropy and lower energy
(4) higher entropy and higher energy

21 Amines, amides, and amino acids are categories of

(1) isomers
(2) isotopes
(3) organic compounds
(4) inorganic compounds

22 A molecule of which compound has a multiple covalent bond?

(1) CH_4 (3) C_3H_8
(2) C_2H_4 (4) C_4H_{10}

[3]   [OVER]

23 Which type of reaction produces soap?

(1) polymerization   (3) fermentation
(2) combustion   (4) saponification

24 For a reaction system at equilibrium, LeChatelier's principle can be used to predict the

(1) activation energy for the system
(2) type of bonds in the reactants
(3) effect of a stress on the system
(4) polarity of the product molecules

25 Which value changes when a Cu atom becomes a Cu^{2+} ion?

(1) mass number
(2) oxidation number
(3) number of protons
(4) number of neutrons

26 Which reaction occurs at the anode in an electrochemical cell?

(1) oxidation   (3) combustion
(2) reduction   (4) substitution

27 What evidence indicates that the nuclei of strontium-90 atoms are unstable?

(1) Strontium-90 electrons are in the excited state.
(2) Strontium-90 electrons are in the ground state.
(3) Strontium-90 atoms spontaneously absorb beta particles.
(4) Strontium-90 atoms spontaneously emit beta particles.

28 Which nuclear emission is listed with its notation?

(1) gamma radiation, $_{0}^{0}\gamma$
(2) proton, $_{2}^{4}He$
(3) neutron, $_{-1}^{0}\beta$
(4) alpha particle, $_{1}^{1}H$

29 The energy released by a nuclear fusion reaction is produced when

(1) energy is converted to mass
(2) mass is converted to energy
(3) heat is converted to temperature
(4) temperature is converted to heat

30 Dating once-living organisms is an example of a beneficial use of

(1) redox reactions
(2) organic isomers
(3) radioactive isotopes
(4) neutralization reactions

Part B–1

Answer all questions in this part.

Directions (31–50): For *each* statement or question, record on your separate answer sheet the *number* of the word or expression that, of those given, best completes the statement or answers the question. Some questions may require the use of the *2011 Edition Reference Tables for Physical Setting/Chemistry*.

31 What is the net charge of an ion that has 11 protons, 10 electrons, and 12 neutrons?

(1) 1+   (3) 1–
(2) 2+   (4) 2–

32 Which electron configuration represents the electrons of an atom in an excited state?

(1) 2-5   (3) 2-5-1
(2) 2-8-5   (4) 2-6

33 Which element is a liquid at 1000. K?

(1) Ag   (3) Ca
(2) Al   (4) Ni

34 Which formula represents ammonium nitrate?

(1) NH_4NO_3 (3) $NH_4(NO_3)_2$
(2) NH_4NO_2 (4) $NH_4(NO_2)_2$

35 The empirical formula for butene is

(1) CH_2 (3) C_4H_6
(2) C_2H_4 (4) C_4H_8

36 Which equation represents a conservation of charge?

(1) $2Fe^{3+} + Al \rightarrow 2Fe^{2+} + Al^{3+}$
(2) $2Fe^{3+} + 2Al \rightarrow 3Fe^{2+} + 2Al^{3+}$
(3) $3Fe^{3+} + 2Al \rightarrow 2Fe^{2+} + 2Al^{3+}$
(4) $3Fe^{3+} + Al \rightarrow 3Fe^{2+} + Al^{3+}$

37 Given the balanced equation representing a reaction:

$$2H_2 + O_2 \rightarrow 2H_2O + energy$$

Which type of reaction is represented by this equation?

(1) decomposition
(2) double replacement
(3) single replacement
(4) synthesis

38 When a Mg^{2+} ion becomes a Mg atom, the radius increases because the Mg^{2+} ion

(1) gains 2 protons   (3) loses 2 protons
(2) gains 2 electrons   (4) loses 2 electrons

39 The *least* polar bond is found in a molecule of

(1) HI   (3) HCl
(2) HF   (4) HBr

40 A solution is prepared using 0.125 g of glucose, $C_6H_{12}O_6$, in enough water to make 250. g of total solution. The concentration of this solution, expressed in parts per million, is

(1) 5.00×10^1 ppm   (3) 5.00×10^3 ppm
(2) 5.00×10^2 ppm   (4) 5.00×10^4 ppm

41 What is the amount of heat, in joules, required to increase the temperature of a 49.5-gram sample of water from 22°C to 66°C?

(1) 2.2×10^3 J   (3) 9.1×10^3 J
(2) 4.6×10^3 J   (4) 1.4×10^4 J

42 A sample of a gas in a rigid cylinder with a movable piston has a volume of 11.2 liters at STP. What is the volume of this gas at 202.6 kPa and 300. K?

(1) 5.10 L   (3) 22.4 L
(2) 6.15 L   (4) 24.6 L

43 The equation below represents a reaction between two molecules, X_2 and Z_2. These molecules form an "activated complex," which then forms molecules of the product.

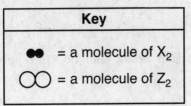

Key
• = a molecule of X_2
◯◯ = a molecule of Z_2

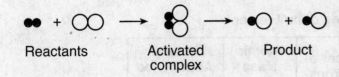

Reactants   Activated   Product
              complex

Which diagram represents the most likely orientation of X_2 and Z_2 when the molecules collide with proper energy, producing an activated complex?

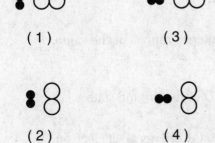

(1)   (3)

(2)   (4)

44 What is the chemical name for the compound $CH_3CH_2CH_2CH_3$?

(1) butane   (3) decane
(2) butene   (4) decene

45 In a laboratory activity, the density of a sample of vanadium is determined to be 6.9 g/cm³ at room temperature. What is the percent error for the determined value?

(1) 0.15%   (3) 13%
(2) 0.87%   (4) 15%

46 Given the equation representing a reaction:

$$Cd + NiO_2 + 2H_2O \rightarrow Cd(OH)_2 + Ni(OH)_2$$

Which half-reaction equation represents the oxidation in the reaction?

(1) $Ni^{4+} + 2e^- \rightarrow Ni^{2+}$
(2) $Ni^{4+} \rightarrow Ni^{2+} + 2e^-$
(3) $Cd \rightarrow Cd^{2+} + 2e^-$
(4) $Cd + 2e^- \rightarrow Cd^{2+}$

47 Which metal reacts spontaneously with $NiCl_2(aq)$?

(1) Au(s)   (3) Sn(s)
(2) Cu(s)   (4) Zn(s)

48 Which solution is the best conductor of an electric current?

(1) 0.001 mole of NaCl dissolved in 1000. mL of water
(2) 0.005 mole of NaCl dissolved in 1000. mL of water
(3) 0.1 mole of NaCl dissolved in 1000. mL of water
(4) 0.05 mole of NaCl dissolved in 1000. mL of water

49 Compared to a 1.0-liter aqueous solution with a pH of 7.0, a 1.0-liter aqueous solution with a pH of 5.0 contains

(1) 10 times more hydronium ions
(2) 100 times more hydronium ions
(3) 10 times more hydroxide ions
(4) 100 times more hydroxide ions

50 Given the equation representing a reaction:

$$^{208}_{82}Pb + ^{70}_{30}Zn \rightarrow ^{277}_{112}Cn + ^{1}_{0}n$$

Which type of reaction is represented by this equation?

(1) neutralization   (3) substitution
(2) polymerization   (4) transmutation

[6]

Part B–2

Answer all questions in this part.

Directions (51–65): Record your answers in the spaces provided in your answer booklet. Some questions may require the use of the *2011 Edition Reference Tables for Physical Setting/Chemistry*.

51 Show a numerical setup for calculating the percent composition by mass of oxygen in Al_2O_3 (gram-formula mass = 102 g/mol). [1]

52 Identify a laboratory process that can be used to separate a liquid mixture of methanol and water, based on the differences in their boiling points. [1]

Base your answers to questions 53 through 55 on the information below and on your knowledge of chemistry.

The table below shows data for three isotopes of the same element.

Data for Three Isotopes of an Element

Isotopes	Number of Protons	Number of Neutrons	Atomic Mass (u)	Natural Abundance (%)
Atom D	12	12	23.99	78.99
Atom E	12	13	24.99	10.00
Atom G	12	14	25.98	11.01

53 Explain, in terms of subatomic particles, why these three isotopes represent the same element. [1]

54 State the number of valence electrons in an atom of isotope *D* in the ground state. [1]

55 Compare the energy of an electron in the first electron shell to the energy of an electron in the second electron shell in an atom of isotope *E*. [1]

Base your answers to questions 56 through 58 on the information below and on your knowledge of chemistry.

The elements in Group 2 on the Periodic Table can be compared in terms of first ionization energy, electronegativity, and other general properties.

56 Describe the general trend in electronegativity as the metals in Group 2 on the Periodic Table are considered in order of increasing atomic number. [1]

57 Explain, in terms of electron configuration, why the elements in Group 2 have similar chemical properties. [1]

58 Explain, in terms of atomic structure, why barium has a lower first ionization energy than magnesium. [1]

_____

Base your answers to questions 59 through 61 on the information below and on your knowledge of chemistry.

A saturated solution of sulfur dioxide is prepared by dissolving $SO_2(g)$ in 100. g of water at 10.°C and standard pressure.

59 Determine the mass of SO_2 in this solution. [1]

60 Based on Table G, state the general relationship between solubility and temperature of an aqueous SO_2 solution at standard pressure. [1]

61 Describe what happens to the solubility of $SO_2(g)$ when the pressure is increased at constant temperature. [1]

_____

[8]

Base your answers to questions 62 through 65 on the information below and on your knowledge of chemistry.

Starting as a solid, a sample of a molecular substance is heated, until the entire sample of the substance is a gas. The graph below represents the relationship between the temperature of the sample and the elapsed time.

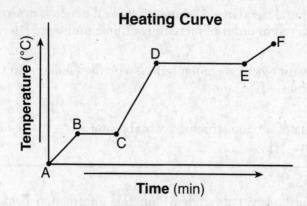

Heating Curve

62 Using the key *in your answer booklet*, draw a particle diagram to represent the sample during interval *AB*. Your response must include *at least six* molecules. [1]

63 Compare the average kinetic energy of the molecules of the sample during interval *BC* to the average kinetic energy of the molecules of the sample during interval *DE*. [1]

64 On the graph *in your answer booklet*, mark an **X** on the axis labeled "Temperature (°C)" to indicate the boiling point of the substance. [1]

65 State evidence that indicates the sample undergoes only physical changes during this heating. [1]

Part C

Answer all questions in this part.

Directions (66–85): Record your answers in the spaces provided in your answer booklet. Some questions may require the use of the *2011 Edition Reference Tables for Physical Setting/Chemistry*.

Base your answers to questions 66 through 68 on the information below and on your knowledge of chemistry.

"Water gas," a mixture of hydrogen and carbon monoxide, is an industrial fuel and source of commercial hydrogen. Water gas is produced by passing steam over hot carbon obtained from coal. The equation below represents this system at equilibrium:

$$C(s) + H_2O(g) + heat \rightleftharpoons CO(g) + H_2(g)$$

66 State, in terms of the rates of the forward and reverse reactions, what occurs when dynamic equilibrium is reached in this system. [1]

67 In the space *in your answer booklet*, draw a Lewis electron-dot diagram for a molecule of H_2O. [1]

68 Explain, in terms of collisions, why increasing the surface area of the hot carbon increases the rate of the forward reaction. [1]

Base your answers to questions 69 through 71 on the information below and on your knowledge of chemistry.

In a laboratory activity, each of four different masses of $KNO_3(s)$ is placed in a separate test tube that contains 10.0 grams of H_2O at 25°C.

When each sample is first placed in the water, the temperature of the mixture decreases. The mixture in each test tube is then stirred while it is heated in a hot water bath until all of the $KNO_3(s)$ is dissolved. The contents of each test tube are then cooled to the temperature at which KNO_3 crystals first reappear. The procedure is repeated until the recrystallization temperatures for each mixture are consistent, as shown in the table below.

Data Table for the Laboratory Activity

Mixture	Mass of KNO_3 (g)	Mass of H_2O (g)	Temperature of Recrystallization (°C)
1	4.0	10.0	24
2	5.0	10.0	32
3	7.5	10.0	45
4	10.0	10.0	58

69 Based on Table *I*, explain why there is a *decrease* in temperature when the $KNO_3(s)$ was first dissolved in the water. [1]

70 Determine the percent by mass concentration of KNO_3 in mixture 2 after heating. [1]

71 Compare the freezing point of mixture 4 at 1.0 atm to the freezing point of water at 1.0 atm. [1]

Base your answers to questions 72 through 74 on the information below and on your knowledge of chemistry.

The balanced equation below represents the reaction between carbon monoxide and oxygen to produce carbon dioxide.

$$2CO(g) + O_2(g) \rightarrow 2CO_2(g) + energy$$

72 On the potential energy diagram *in your answer booklet*, draw a double-headed arrow (↕) to indicate the interval that represents the heat of reaction. [1]

73 Determine the number of moles of $O_2(g)$ needed to completely react with 8.0 moles of $CO(g)$. [1]

74 On the potential energy diagram *in your answer booklet*, draw a dashed line to show how the potential energy diagram changes when the reaction is catalyzed. [1]

Base your answers to questions 75 through 77 on the information below and on your knowledge of chemistry.

The equation below represents an industrial preparation of diethyl ether.

Compound A   **Compound B**

75 Write the name of the class of organic compounds to which compound A belongs. [1]

76 Identify the element in compound B that makes it an organic compound. [1]

77 Explain, in terms of elements, why compound B is *not* a hydrocarbon. [1]

---

[12]

Base your answers to questions 78 through 81 on the information below and on your knowledge of chemistry.

A student is to determine the concentration of an NaOH(aq) solution by performing two different titrations. In a first titration, the student titrates 25.0 mL of 0.100 M H_2SO_4(aq) with NaOH(aq) of unknown concentration.

In a second titration, the student titrates 25.0 mL of 0.100 M HCl(aq) with a sample of the NaOH(aq). During this second titration, the volume of the NaOH(aq) added and the corresponding pH value of the reaction mixture is measured. The graph below represents the relationship between pH and the volume of the NaOH(aq) added for this second titration.

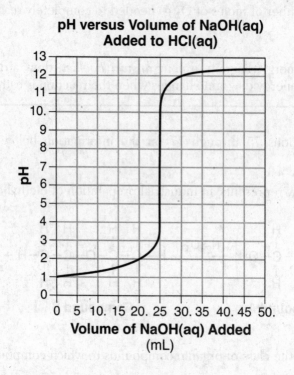

pH versus Volume of NaOH(aq) Added to HCl(aq)

Volume of NaOH(aq) Added (mL)

78 Identify the positive ion present in the H_2SO_4(aq) solution before the titration. [1]

79 Complete the equation *in your answer booklet* for the neutralization that occurs in the first titration by writing a formula of the missing product. [1]

80 Based on the graph, determine the volume of NaOH(aq) used to exactly neutralize the HCl(aq). [1]

81 State the color of phenolphthalein indicator if it were added after the HCl(aq) was titrated with 50. mL of NaOH(aq). [1]

Base your answers to questions 82 through 85 on the information below and on your knowledge of chemistry.

When uranium-235 nuclei are bombarded with neutrons, many different combinations of smaller nuclei can be produced. The production of neodymium-150 and germanium-81 in one of these reactions is represented by the equation below.

$$\ce{^{1}_{0}n} + \ce{^{235}_{92}U} \rightarrow \ce{^{150}_{60}Nd} + \ce{^{81}_{32}Ge} + 5\ce{^{1}_{0}n}$$

Germanium-81 and uranium-235 have different decay modes. Ge-81 emits beta particles and has a half-life of 7.6 seconds.

82 Explain, in terms of nuclides, why the reaction represented by the nuclear equation is a fission reaction. [1]

83 State the number of protons and number of neutrons in a neodymium-150 atom. [1]

84 Complete the equation *in your answer booklet* for the decay of Ge-81 by writing a notation for the missing nuclide. [1]

85 Determine the time required for a 16.00-gram sample of Ge-81 to decay until only 1.00 gram of the sample remains unchanged. [1]

PHYSICAL SETTING
CHEMISTRY

ANSWER BOOKLET

Student . . . .

Teacher . . . .

School . . . . Grade . . . .

Record your answers for Part B–2 and Part C in this booklet.

Part B–2
51
52 _____

53 _____

_____

_____

54 _____

55 _____

_____

_____

56 _____

_____

57 _____

_____

_____

58 _____

_____

_____

59 _____ g

60 _____

_____

_____

61 _____

_____

_____

62

Key
◯ = a molecule of the substance

[OVER]

63 _____

_____

_____

64

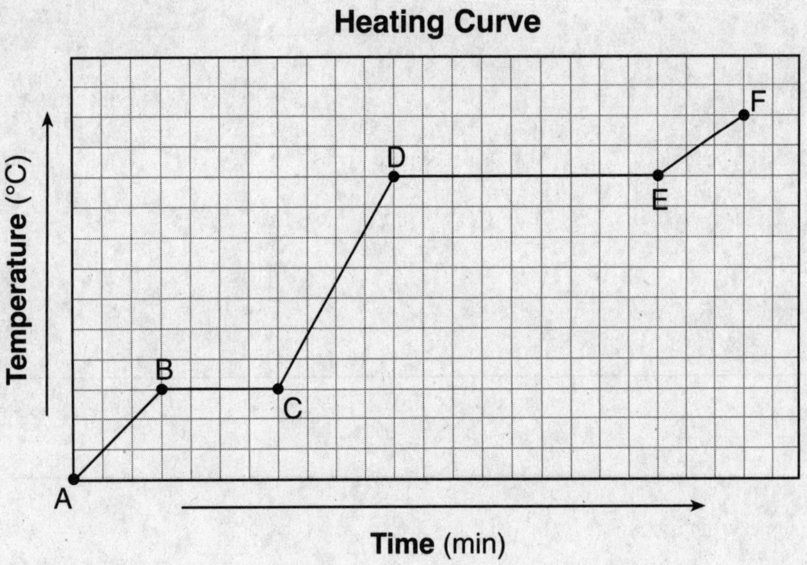

Heating Curve

(Graph with Temperature (°C) on vertical axis and Time (min) on horizontal axis, showing points A, B, C, D, E, F)

65 _____

_____

_____

Part C

66 _____

_____

_____

67

68 _____

_____

_____

69 _____

_____

_____

70 _____ %

71 _____

_____

_____

72

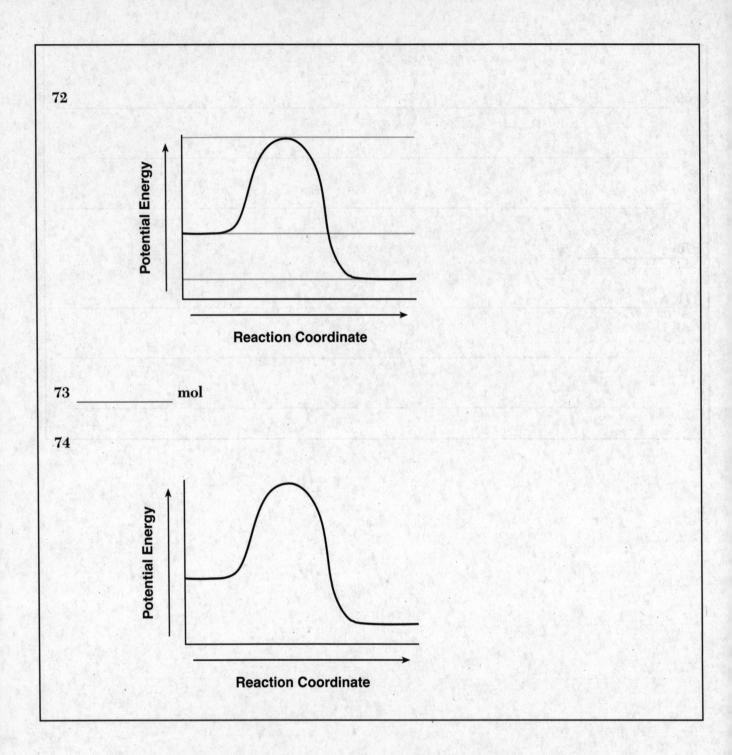

Reaction Coordinate

73 _____ mol

74

Reaction Coordinate

[OVER]

75 _____

76 _____

77 _____

_____

_____

78 _____

79 $2NaOH(aq) + H_2SO_4(aq) \rightarrow 2H_2O(\ell) + $ _____ (aq)

80 _____ **mL**

81 _____

82 _____

_____

_____

83 Protons: _____

Neutrons: _____

84 $^{81}_{32}Ge \rightarrow ^{0}_{-1}e + $ _____

85 _____ **s**

Part A

Answer all questions in this part.

Directions (1–30): For *each* statement or question, record on your separate answer sheet the *number* of the word or expression that, of those given, best completes the statement or answers the question. Some questions may require the use of the *2011 Edition Reference Tables for Physical Setting/Chemistry*.

1 Which statement describes the charge and location of an electron in an atom?

(1) An electron has a positive charge and is located outside the nucleus.

(2) An electron has a positive charge and is located in the nucleus.

(3) An electron has a negative charge and is located outside the nucleus.

(4) An electron has a negative charge and is located in the nucleus.

2 Which statement explains why a xenon atom is electrically neutral?

(1) The atom has fewer neutrons than electrons.

(2) The atom has more protons than electrons.

(3) The atom has the same number of neutrons and electrons.

(4) The atom has the same number of protons and electrons.

3 If two atoms are isotopes of the same element, the atoms must have

(1) the same number of protons and the same number of neutrons

(2) the same number of protons and a different number of neutrons

(3) a different number of protons and the same number of neutrons

(4) a different number of protons and a different number of neutrons

4 Which electrons in a calcium atom in the ground state have the greatest effect on the chemical properties of calcium?

(1) the two electrons in the first shell

(2) the two electrons in the fourth shell

(3) the eight electrons in the second shell

(4) the eight electrons in the third shell

5 The weighted average of the atomic masses of the naturally occuring isotopes of an element is the

(1) atomic mass of the element

(2) atomic number of the element

(3) mass number of each isotope

(4) formula mass of each isotope

6 Which element is classified as a metalloid?

(1) Cr   (3) Sc

(2) Cs   (4) Si

7 Which statement describes a chemical property of iron?

(1) Iron oxidizes.

(2) Iron is a solid at STP.

(3) Iron melts.

(4) Iron is attracted to a magnet.

8 Graphite and diamond are two forms of the same element in the solid phase that differ in their

(1) atomic numbers

(2) crystal structures

(3) electronegativities

(4) empirical formulas

9 Which ion has the largest radius?

(1) Br^- (3) F^-

(2) Cl^- (4) I^-

10 Carbon monoxide and carbon dioxide have

(1) the same chemical properties and the same physical properties

(2) the same chemical properties and different physical properties

(3) different chemical properties and the same physical properties

(4) different chemical properties and different physical properties

[2]

11 Based on Table S, which group on the Periodic Table has the element with the highest electronegativity?

(1) Group 1   (3) Group 17
(2) Group 2   (4) Group 18

12 What is represented by the chemical formula $PbCl_2(s)$?

(1) a substance
(2) a solution
(3) a homogeneous mixture
(4) a heterogeneous mixture

13 What is the vapor pressure of propanone at 50.°C?

(1) 37 kPa   (3) 83 kPa
(2) 50. kPa   (4) 101 kPa

14 Which statement describes the charge distribution and the polarity of a CH_4 molecule?

(1) The charge distribution is symmetrical and the molecule is nonpolar.
(2) The charge distribution is asymmetrical and the molecule is nonpolar.
(3) The charge distribution is symmetrical and the molecule is polar.
(4) The charge distribution is asymmetrical and the molecule is polar.

15 In a laboratory investigation, a student separates colored compounds obtained from a mixture of crushed spinach leaves and water by using paper chromatography. The colored compounds separate because of differences in

(1) molecular polarity
(2) malleability
(3) boiling point
(4) electrical conductivity

16 Which phrase describes the motion and attractive forces of ideal gas particles?

(1) random straight-line motion and no attractive forces
(2) random straight-line motion and strong attractive forces
(3) random curved-line motion and no attractive forces
(4) random curved-line motion and strong attractive forces

17 At which temperature will $Hg(\ell)$ and $Hg(s)$ reach equilibrium in a closed system at 1.0 atmosphere?

(1) 234 K   (3) 373 K
(2) 273 K   (4) 630. K

18 A molecule of any organic compound has at least one

(1) ionic bond   (3) oxygen atom
(2) double bond   (4) carbon atom

19 A chemical reaction occurs when reactant particles

(1) are separated by great distances
(2) have no attractive forces between them
(3) collide with proper energy and proper orientation
(4) convert chemical energy into nuclear energy

20 Systems in nature tend to undergo changes toward

(1) lower energy and lower entropy
(2) lower energy and higher entropy
(3) higher energy and lower entropy
(4) higher energy and higher entropy

21 Which formula can represent an alkyne?

(1) C_2H_4 (3) C_3H_4
(2) C_2H_6 (4) C_3H_6

[3]

[OVER]

22 Given the formula representing a compound:

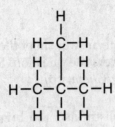

Which formula represents an isomer of this compound?

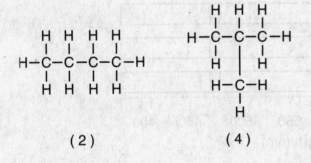

(1)   (3)

(2)   (4)

23 Which energy conversion occurs in an operating voltaic cell?

(1) chemical energy to electrical energy
(2) chemical energy to nuclear energy
(3) electrical energy to chemical energy
(4) electrical energy to nuclear energy

24 Which process requires energy to decompose a substance?

(1) electrolysis   (3) sublimation
(2) neutralization   (4) synthesis

25 The concentration of which ion is increased when LiOH is dissolved in water?

(1) hydroxide ion   (3) hydronium ion
(2) hydrogen ion   (4) halide ion

26 Which equation represents neutralization?

(1) $6Li(s) + N_2(g) \rightarrow 2Li_3N(s)$

(2) $2Mg(s) + O_2(g) \rightarrow 2MgO(s)$

(3) $2KOH(aq) + H_2SO_4(aq) \rightarrow$
$\quad K_2SO_4(aq) + 2H_2O(\ell)$

(4) $Pb(NO_3)_2(aq) + K_2CrO_4(aq) \rightarrow$
$\quad 2KNO_3(aq) + PbCrO_4(s)$

27 The stability of an isotope is related to its ratio of

(1) neutrons to positrons
(2) neutrons to protons
(3) electrons to positrons
(4) electrons to protons

28 Which particle has the *least* mass?

(1) alpha particle   (3) neutron
(2) beta particle   (4) proton

29 The energy released during a nuclear reaction is a result of

(1) breaking chemical bonds
(2) forming chemical bonds
(3) mass being converted to energy
(4) energy being converted to mass

30 The use of uranium-238 to determine the age of a geological formation is a beneficial use of

(1) nuclear fusion
(2) nuclear fission
(3) radioactive isomers
(4) radioactive isotopes

[4]

Part B–1

Answer all questions in this part.

Directions (31–50): For *each* statement or question, record on your separate answer sheet the *number* of the word or expression that, of those given, best completes the statement or answers the question. Some questions may require the use of the *2011 Edition Reference Tables for Physical Setting/Chemistry.*

Base your answers to questions 31 and 32 on your knowledge of chemistry and the bright-line spectra produced by four elements and the spectrum of a mixture of elements represented in the diagram below.

Bright-Line Spectra

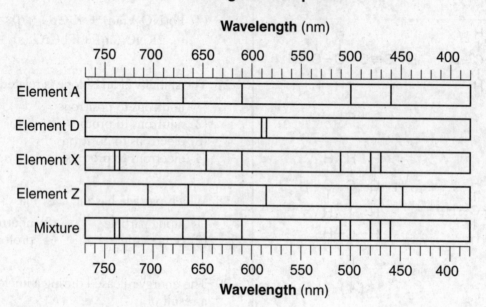

31 Which elements are present in this mixture?

(1) D and A
(3) X and A
(2) D and Z
(4) X and Z

32 Each line in the spectra represents the energy

(1) absorbed as an atom loses an electron
(2) absorbed as an atom gains an electron
(3) released as an electron moves from a lower energy state to a higher energy state
(4) released as an electron moves from a higher energy state to a lower energy state

33 The table below shows the number of protons, neutrons, and electrons in four ions.

Four Ions

Ion	Number of Protons	Number of Neutrons	Number of Electrons
A	8	10	10
E	9	10	10
G	11	12	10
J	12	12	10

Which ion has a charge of 2−?

(1) A   (3) G
(2) E   (4) J

34 What is the approximate mass of an atom that contains 26 protons, 26 electrons and 19 neutrons?

(1) 26 u   (3) 52 u
(2) 45 u   (4) 71 u

35 Which electron configuration represents a potassium atom in an excited state?

(1) 2-7-6   (3) 2-8-8-1
(2) 2-8-5   (4) 2-8-7-2

36 What is the total number of neutrons in an atom of K-42?

(1) 19   (3) 23
(2) 20   (4) 42

37 Given the equation representing a reaction:

$$2C + 3H_2 \rightarrow C_2H_6$$

What is the number of moles of C that must completely react to produce 2.0 moles of C_2H_6?

(1) 1.0 mol   (3) 3.0 mol
(2) 2.0 mol   (4) 4.0 mol

38 Given the equation representing a reaction:

$$Mg(s) + 2HCl(aq) \rightarrow MgCl_2(aq) + H_2(g)$$

Which type of chemical reaction is represented by the equation?

(1) synthesis
(2) decomposition
(3) single replacement
(4) double replacement

39 The table below lists properties of selected elements at room temperature.

Properties of Selected Elements at Room Temperature

Element	Density (g/cm³)	Malleability	Conductivity
sodium	0.97	yes	good
gold	19.3	yes	good
iodine	4.933	no	poor
tungsten	19.3	yes	good

Based on this table, which statement describes how two of these elements can be differentiated from each other?

(1) Gold can be differentiated from tungsten based on density.
(2) Gold can be differentiated from sodium based on malleability.
(3) Sodium can be differentiated from tungsten based on conductivity.
(4) Sodium can be differentiated from iodine based on malleability.

40 Which particle diagram represents a mixture?

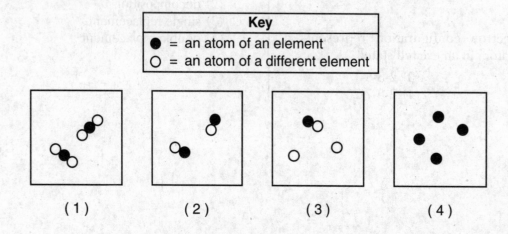

Key
● = an atom of an element
○ = an atom of a different element

(1)   (2)   (3)   (4)

41 An atom of which element reacts with an atom of hydrogen to form a bond with the greatest degree of polarity?

(1) carbon (3) nitrogen
(2) fluorine (4) oxygen

42 What is the concentration of an aqueous solution that contains 1.5 moles of NaCl in 500. milliliters of this solution?

(1) 0.30 M (3) 3.0 M
(2) 0.75 M (4) 7.5 M

43 The table below shows data for the temperature, pressure, and volume of four gas samples.

Data for Four Gases

Gas Sample	Temperature (K)	Pressure (atm)	Volume (L)
I	600.	2.0	5.0
II	300.	1.0	10.0
III	600.	3.0	5.0
IV	300.	1.0	10.0

Which two gas samples contain the same number of molecules?

(1) I and II (3) II and III
(2) I and III (4) II and IV

44 Based on Table I, what is the ΔH value for the production of 1.00 mole of $NO_2(g)$ from its elements at 101.3 kPa and 298 K?

(1) +33.2 kJ (3) +132.8 kJ
(2) −33.2 kJ (4) −132.8 kJ

45 Which equation represents an addition reaction?

(1) $C_3H_8 + Cl_2 \rightarrow C_3H_7Cl + HCl$
(2) $C_3H_6 + Cl_2 \rightarrow C_3H_6Cl_2$
(3) $CaCl_2 + Na_2CO_3 \rightarrow CaCO_3 + 2NaCl$
(4) $CaCO_3 \rightarrow CaO + CO_2$

46 Given the balanced equation representing a reaction:

$$Ni(s) + 2HCl(aq) \rightarrow NiCl_2(aq) + H_2(g)$$

In this reaction, each Ni atom

(1) loses 1 electron (3) gains 1 electron
(2) loses 2 electrons (4) gains 2 electrons

47 Which equation represents a reduction half-reaction?

(1) $Fe \rightarrow Fe^{3+} + 3e^-$ (3) $Fe^{3+} \rightarrow Fe + 3e^-$
(2) $Fe + 3e^- \rightarrow Fe^{3+}$ (4) $Fe^{3+} + 3e^- \rightarrow Fe$

48 Given the balanced ionic equation representing a reaction:

$$Cu(s) + 2Ag^+(aq) \rightarrow Cu^{2+}(aq) + 2Ag(s)$$

During this reaction, electrons are transferred from

(1) $Cu(s)$ to $Ag^+(aq)$
(2) $Cu^{2+}(aq)$ to $Ag(s)$
(3) $Ag(s)$ to $Cu^{2+}(aq)$
(4) $Ag^+(aq)$ to $Cu(s)$

49 Which metal reacts spontaneously with Sr^{2+} ions?

(1) Ca(s) (3) Cs(s)
(2) Co(s) (4) Cu(s)

50 Given the balanced equation representing a reaction:

$$HCl + H_2O \rightarrow H_3O^+ + Cl^-$$

The water molecule acts as a base because it

(1) donates an H^+ (3) donates an OH^-
(2) accepts an H^+ (4) accepts an OH^-

[8]

Part B–2

Answer all questions in this part.

Directions (51–65): Record your answers in the spaces provided in your answer booklet. Some questions may require the use of the *2011 Edition Reference Tables for Physical Setting/Chemistry.*

51 State the general trend in first ionization energy as the elements in Period 3 are considered from left to right. [1]

52 Identify a type of strong intermolecular force that exists between water molecules, but does *not* exist between carbon dioxide molecules. [1]

53 Draw a structural formula for 2-butanol. [1]

Base your answers to questions 54 through 56 on the information below and on your knowledge of chemistry.

Some compounds of silver are listed with their chemical formulas in the table below.

Silver Compounds

Name	Chemical Formula
silver carbonate	Ag_2CO_3
silver chlorate	$AgClO_3$
silver chloride	$AgCl$
silver sulfate	Ag_2SO_4

54 Explain, in terms of element classification, why silver chloride is an ionic compound. [1]

55 Show a numerical setup for calculating the percent composition by mass of silver in silver carbonate (gram-formula mass = 276 g/mol). [1]

56 Identify the silver compound in the table that is most soluble in water. [1]

Base your answers to questions 57 through 59 on the information below and on your knowledge of chemistry.

When a cobalt-59 atom is bombarded by a subatomic particle, a radioactive cobalt-60 atom is produced. After 21.084 years, 1.20 grams of an original sample of cobalt-60 produced remains unchanged.

57 Complete the nuclear equation by writing a notation for the missing particle. [1]

58 Based on Table *N*, identify the decay mode of cobalt-60. [1]

59 Determine the mass of the original sample of cobalt-60 produced. [1]

Base your answers to questions 60 through 62 on the information below and on your knowledge of chemistry.

A sample of a molecular substance starting as a gas at 206°C and 1 atm is allowed to cool for 16 minutes. This process is represented by the cooling curve below.

Cooling Curve for a Substance

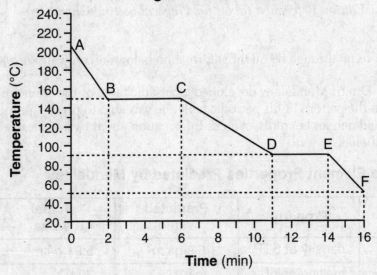

60 Determine the number of minutes that the substance was in the liquid phase, only. [1]

61 Compare the strength of the intermolecular forces within this substance at 180.°C to the strength of the intermolecular forces within this substance at 120.°C. [1]

62 Describe what happens to the potential energy and the average kinetic energy of the molecules in the sample during interval *DE*. [1]

Base your answers to questions 63 through 65 on the information below and on your knowledge of chemistry.

The diagram below represents a cylinder with a moveable piston containing 16.0 g of $O_2(g)$. At 298 K and 0.500 atm, the $O_2(g)$ has a volume of 24.5 liters.

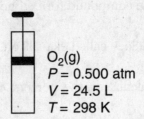

$O_2(g)$
$P = 0.500$ atm
$V = 24.5$ L
$T = 298$ K

63 Determine the number of moles of $O_2(g)$ in the cylinder. The gram-formula mass of $O_2(g)$ is 32.0 g/mol. [1]

64 State the changes in *both* pressure and temperature of the gas in the cylinder that would increase the frequency of collisions between the $O_2(g)$ molecules. [1]

65 Show a numerical setup for calculating the volume of $O_2(g)$ in the cylinder at 265 K and 1.00 atm. [1]

[10]

Part C

Answer all questions in this part.

Directions (66–85): Record your answers in the spaces provided in your answer booklet. Some questions may require the use of the *2011 Edition Reference Tables for Physical Setting/Chemistry*.

Base your answers to questions 66 through 69 on the information below and on your knowledge of chemistry.

In the late 1800s, Dmitri Mendeleev developed a periodic table of the elements known at that time. Based on the pattern in his periodic table, he was able to predict properties of some elements that had not yet been discovered. Information about two of these elements is shown in the table below.

Some Element Properties Predicted by Mendeleev

Predicted Elements	Property	Predicted Value	Actual Value
eka-aluminum (Ea)	density at STP	5.9 g/cm³	5.91 g/cm³
	melting point	low	30.°C
	oxide formula	Ea_2O_3	
	approximate molar mass	68 g/mol	
eka-silicon (Es)	density at STP	5.5 g/cm³	5.3234 g/cm³
	melting point	high	938°C
	oxide formula	EsO_2	
	approximate molar mass	72 g/mol	

66 Identify the phase of Ea at 310. K. [1]

67 Write a chemical formula for the compound formed between Ea and Cl. [1]

68 Identify the element that Mendeleev called eka-silicon, Es. [1]

69 Show a numerical setup for calculating the percent error of Mendeleev's predicted density of Es. [1]

Base your answers to questions 70 through 73 on the information below and your knowledge of chemistry.

Methanol can be manufactured by a reaction that is reversible. In the reaction, carbon monoxide gas and hydrogen gas react using a catalyst. The equation below represents this system at equilibrium.

$$CO(g) + 2H_2(g) \rightleftharpoons CH_3OH(g) + energy$$

70 State the class of organic compounds to which the product of the forward reaction belongs. [1]

71 Compare the rate of the forward reaction to the rate of the reverse reaction in this equilibrium system. [1]

72 Explain, in terms of collision theory, why increasing the concentration of $H_2(g)$ in this system will increase the concentration of $CH_3OH(g)$. [1]

73 State the effect on the rates of both the forward and reverse reactions if no catalyst is used in the system. [1]

Base your answers to questions 74 through 76 on the information below and on your knowledge of chemistry.

Fatty acids, a class of compounds found in living things, are organic acids with long hydrocarbon chains. Linoleic acid, an unsaturated fatty acid, is essential for human skin flexibility and smoothness. The formula below represents a molecule of linoleic acid.

74 Write the molecular formula of linoleic acid. [1]

75 Identify the type of chemical bond between the oxygen atom and the hydrogen atom in the linoleic acid molecule. [1]

76 On the diagram in your answer booklet, circle the organic acid functional group. [1]

[12]

Base your answers to questions 77 through 79 on the information below and on your knowledge of chemistry.

Fuel cells are voltaic cells. In one type of fuel cell, oxygen gas, $O_2(g)$, reacts with hydrogen gas, $H_2(g)$, producing water vapor, $H_2O(g)$, and electrical energy. The unbalanced equation for this redox reaction is shown below.

$$H_2(g) + O_2(g) \rightarrow H_2O(g) + energy$$

A diagram of the fuel cell is shown below. During operation of the fuel cell, hydrogen gas is pumped into one compartment and oxygen gas is pumped into the other compartment. Each compartment has an inner wall that is a porous carbon electrode through which ions flow. Aqueous potassium hydroxide, KOH(aq), and the porous electrodes serve as the salt bridge.

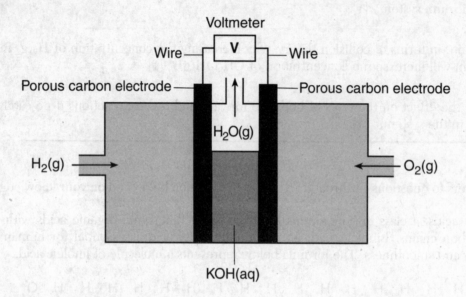

77 Balance the equation *in your answer booklet* for the reaction in this fuel cell, using the smallest whole-number coefficients. [1]

78 Determine the change in oxidation number for oxygen in this operating fuel cell. [1]

79 State the number of moles of electrons that are gained when 5.0 moles of electrons are lost in this reaction. [1]

[13]

[OVER]

Base your answers to questions 80 through 82 on the information below and on your knowledge of chemistry.

In a laboratory investigation, a student compares the concentration and pH value of each of four different solutions of hydrochloric acid, HCl(aq), as shown in the table below.

Data for HCl(aq) Solutions

Solution	Concentration of HCl(aq) (M)	pH Value
W	1.0	0
X	0.10	1
Y	0.010	2
Z	0.0010	3

80 State the number of significant figures used to express the concentration of solution Z. [1]

81 Determine the concentration of an HCl(aq) solution that has a pH value of 4. [1]

82 Determine the volume of 0.25 M NaOH(aq) that would exactly neutralize 75.0 milliliters of solution X. [1]

[14]

Base your answers to questions 83 through 85 on the information below and on your knowledge of chemistry.

Carbon dioxide is slightly soluble in seawater. As carbon dioxide levels in the atmosphere increase, more CO_2 dissolves in seawater, making the seawater more acidic because carbonic acid, $H_2CO_3(aq)$, is formed.

Seawater also contains aqueous calcium carbonate, $CaCO_3(aq)$, which is used by some marine organisms to make their hard exoskeletons. As the acidity of the sea water changes, the solubility of $CaCO_3$ also changes, as shown in the graph below.

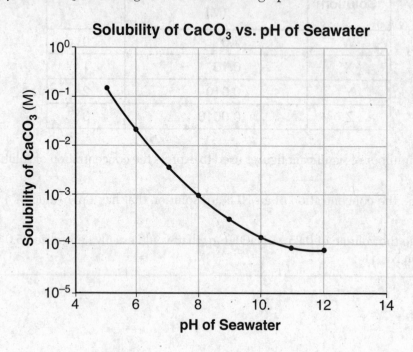

Solubility of CaCO₃ vs. pH of Seawater

83 State the trend in the solubility of $CaCO_3$ as seawater becomes more acidic. [1]

84 State the color of bromcresol green in a sample of seawater in which the $CaCO_3$ solubility is 10^{-2} M. [1]

85 A sample of seawater has a pH of 8. Determine the new pH of the sample if the hydrogen ion concentration is increased by a factor of 100. [1]

PHYSICAL SETTING
CHEMISTRY

———

ANSWER BOOKLET

Student . . . .

Teacher . . . .

School . . . . Grade . . . .

Record your answers for Part B–2 and Part C in this booklet.

Part B–2

51 _____

_____

_____

52 _____

53

54 _____

_____

_____

55

56 _____

57 $^{59}_{27}\text{Co} + $ _____ $\rightarrow ^{60}_{27}\text{Co}$

58 _____

59 _____ **g**

[2]

60 _____ **min**

61 _____

_____

_____

62 Potential energy: _____

Average kinetic energy: _____

63 _____ **mol**

64 Change in pressure: _____

Change in temperature: _____

65

Part C

66 _____

67 _____

68 _____

69

70 _____

71 _____

_____

_____

72 _____

_____

_____

73 Rate of forward reaction: _____

Rate of reverse reaction: _____

[4]

74 _____

75 _____

76

H—C—C—C—C—C—C=C—C—C=C—C—C—C—C—C—C—C—C—O—H

with the corresponding H atoms above and below each carbon and =O on the terminal carbon

77 _____ $H_2(g)$ + _____ $O_2(g) \rightarrow$ _____ $H_2O(g)$ + energy

78 From _____ to _____

79 _____ **mol**

80 _____

81 _____ M

82 _____ mL

83

_____

_____

84 _____

85 _____